Hairdressing

The Foundations | 6th Edition

SCOTT SMURTHWAITE@CREAM

Hairdressing

Student textbooks

Begin Hairdressing: The Official Guide to Level 1 1e *Martin Green*

Hairdressing – The Foundations: The Official Guide to Level 2 6e *Leo Palladino and Martin Green*

Professional Hairdressing: The Official Guide to Level 3 5e *Martin Green and Leo Palladino*

The Official Guide to the City & Guilds Certificate in Salon Service 1e *John Armstrong with Anita Crosland, Martin Green and Lorraine Nordmann*

The Colour Book: The Official Guide to Colour for NVQ Levels 2 & 3 1e *Tracey Lloyd with Christine McMillan-Bodell*

eXtensions: The Official Guide to Hair Extensions 1e *Theresa Bullock*

Salon Management *Martin Green*

Men's Hairdressing: Traditional and Modern Barbering 2e *Maurice Lister*

African-Caribbean Hairdressing 2e *Sandra Gittens*

The World of Hair Colour 1e *John Gray*

The Cutting Book: The Official Guide to Cutting at S/NVQ Levels 2 and 3 *Jane Goldsbro and Elaine White*

Professional Hairdressing titles

Trevor Sorbie: The Bridal Hair Book 1e *Trevor Sorbie and Jacki Wadeson*

The Art of Dressing Long Hair 1e *Guy Kremer and Jacki Wadeson*

Patrick Cameron: Dressing Long Hair 1e *Patrick Cameron and Jacki Wadeson*

Patrick Cameron: Dressing Long Hair 2 1e *Patrick Cameron and Jacki Wadeson*

Bridal Hair 1e *Pat Dixon and Jacki Wadeson*

Professional Men's Hairdressing: The art of cutting and styling 1e *Guy Kremer and Jacki Wadeson*

Essensuals, the Next Generation Toni and Guy: Step by Step 1e *Sacha Mascolo, Christian Mascolo and Stuart Wesson*

Mahogany Hairdressing: Step to Cutting, Colouring and Finishing Hair 1e *Martin Gannon and Richard Thompson*

Mahogany Hairdressing: Advanced Looks 1e *Martin Gannon and Richard Thompson*

The Total Look: The Style Guide for Hair and Make-up Professional 1e *Ian Mistlin*

Trevor Sorbie: Visions in Hair 1e *Trevor Sorbie, Kris Sorbie and Jacki Wadeson*

The Art of Hair Colouring 1e *David Adams and Jacki Wadeson*

Beauty therapy

Beauty Basics: The Official Guide to Level 1 1e *Lorraine Nordmann*

Beauty Therapy – The Foundations: The Official Guide to Level 2 3e *Lorraine Nordmann*

Professional Beauty Therapy–The Official Guide to Level 3 2e *Lorraine Nordmann*

The Official Guide to the City & Guilds Certificate in Salon Services 1e *John Armstrong with Anita Crosland, Martin Green and Lorraine Nordmann*

The Complete Guide to Make-Up 1e *Suzanne Le Quesne*

The Encyclopedia of Nails 1e *Jacqui Jefford and Anne Swain*

The Art of Nails: A Comprehensive Style Guide to Nail Treatments and Nail Art 1e *Jacqui Jefford*

Nail Artistry 1e *Jacqui Jefford*

The Complete Nail Technician 2e *Marian Newman*

Manicure, Pedicure and Advanced Nail Techniques 1e *Elaine Almond*

The Official Guide to Body Massage 2e *Adele O'Keefe*

An Holistic Guide to Massage 1e *Tina Parsons*

Indian Head Massage 2e *Muriel Burnham-Airey and Adele O'Keefe*

Aromatherapy for the Beauty Therapist 1e *Valerie Worwood*

An Holistic Guide to Reflexology 1e *Tina Parsons*

An Holistic Guide to Anatomy and Physiology 1e *Tina Parsons*

The Essential Guide to Holistic and Complementary Therapy 1e *Helen Beckmann and Suzanne Le Quesne*

The Spa Book 1e *Jane Crebbin-Bailey, Dr John Harcup, and John Harrington*

SPA: The Official Guide to Spa Therapy at Levels 2 and 3, *Joan Scott and Andrea Harrison*

Nutrition: A Practical Approach 1e *Suzanne Le Quesne*

Hands on Sports Therapy 1e *Keith Ward*

Encyclopedia of Hair Removal: A Complete Reference to Methods, Techniques and Career Opportunities, *Gill Morris and Janice Brown*

The Anatomy and Physiology Workbook: For Beauty and Holistic Therapies Levels 1–3. *Tina Parsons*

The Anatomy and Physiology CD-Rom. Beautiful Selling: The Complete Guide to Sales Success in the Salon *Rath Langley*

THE **OFFICIAL** GUIDE TO S/NVQ LEVEL 2

Hairdressing

The Foundations | **6th Edition**

Leo Palladino and Martin Green

SCOTT SMURTHWAITE@CREAM

DELMAR
CENGAGE Learning·

Australia • Brazil • Japan • Korea • Mexico • Singapore • Spain • United Kingdom • United States

**Hairdressing - The Foundations:
The Official Guide to Hairdressing
at S/NVQ Level 2, Sixth Edition**
Leo Palladino and Martin Green

Publisher: Melody Dawes

Development Editor: Lucy Mills

Content Project Editor: Jamina Ward

Manufacturing Manager: Helen Mason

Senior Production Controller: Maeve Healy

Marketing Manager: Rachel Doyle

Typesetter: ICC Macmillan Inc.

Cover design: HCT Creative

Text design: Design Deluxe, Bath, UK

Illustrators: Oxford Designers and
Illustrators unless otherwise stated

For product information and technology assistance, contact
emea.info@cengage.com
For permission to use material from this text or product,
and for permission queries,
email **clsuk.permissions@cengage.com**

The Author has asserted the right under the Copyright, Designs and Patents Act 1988 to be identified as Author of this Work.

This work is adapted from Hairdressing-The Foundations, 5th Edition, published by Delmar, a division of Cengage Learning, Inc. ©2006.

Cover image kindly supplied by Schwarzkopf Professional Essential Looks - Eclectic Collection - Autumn/Winter 08/09.

British Library Cataloguing-in-Publication Data A catalogue record for this book is available from the British Library.

ISBN: 978-1-4080-1154-6

Cengage Learning EMEA
Cheriton House, North way, Andover
Hampshire, SP10 5BE, UK

Cengage Learning products are represented in Canada by Nelson Education Ltd.

For your lifelong learning solutions, visit

www.cengage.co.uk

Printed in Italy by G. Canale & C. S.p.A.
1 2 3 4 5 6 7 8 9 10 – 11 10 09

Contents

Part**one**

Generic Salon Skills

Chapter**one**

Chapter**two**

TRACEY DEVINE@ANGELS

Chapter**three**

Chapter**four**

Part**two**

Customer Centered Services

Chapter**five**

Chapter**six**

Part**three**

Hairdressing Technical Services

Chapter**seven**

Chapter**eight**

Chapter**nine**

Chapter**ten**

Chapter**seventeen**

Foreword

When Habia first began to promote the NVQ Level 2 qualification in hairdressing, back in 1989, no one envisaged the phenomenal success that would be achieved. Within five years the NVQ established itself as the accepted qualification throughout the hairdressing industry. Fundamental to this achievement was the success of *Hairdressing – The Foundations*. 20 years later, Leo Palladino and Martin Green's book *Hairdressing – The Foundations* is still the book to follow.

Ever since my first meeting with Leo and our publishers in 1989, Habia has been an integral part of *Hairdressing – The Foundations*. So much so that we are now publishing the sixth edition. I am delighted that Leo has actively and consistently updated his original book in keeping with changes to the qualification and to changes within the industry. This edition has the added bonus of a contribution from the respected author Martin Green. Both authors have a great ability to cater to learners at all levels. Martin is the author of *Begin Hairdressing: The Official Guide for Level 1* and *co-author* with *Leo Palladino for Professional Hairdressing: The Official Guide for Level 3*.

Alan Goldsbro, Habia CEO

Acknowledgements

TRACEY DEVINE@ANGELS

The authors and publishers would like to thank the following:

For providing the cover image
Schwarzkhopf Professional Essential Looks – Eclectic
    Collection – Autumn/Winter 08/09

For providing pictures for the book
Adam Harris @ MG Martin Gold, Stanmore
Alamy
Andrew O'Toole (Photographer)
Dr Andrew Wright
Andy Lych (photographer) www.andylynch.org
Anne McGuigan @ Anne McGuigan Hair and Beauty,
    Leighton Buzzard
The Artistic Team @ Jacks of London
The Artistic Team @ TPL Hairdressing
BaByliss Pro
Balmain
Beauty Express
Ben White and the Eleven Hair Art Team
Cinderella Hair www.cinderellahair.co.uk
Christopher Appleton @ George's Hair Salon, Leicester
Chubb
Clynol
Connect-2-Hair Ltd
CREAM Artistic Team
Damien Carney for Joico
Daniele Cipriani (Photographer)
Denman
Dome Cosmetics
Ellisons
Errol Douglas
Essence PR
Fellowship for British Hairdressing F.A.M.E. Team 2008
www.gebetterton.co.uk
Gloss Communications
Goldwell UK
Gorgeous PR
Great Lengths (www.greatlengths.net)
Habia
Hama Sanders (Photographer)
HMSO
i-stock photography
IT&LY
Jemico
Dr John Gray
John Rawson
The John Rawson partnership

Karen Scantlebury @ Ciente, Berkhamsted
Karine Jackson
Ken Picton @ Ken Picton
Kyoko Homma (Photographer)
Lee Moran @ Sanrizz
Leonardo Rizzo @ Sanrizz
Lewis Moore @ Francesco Group, Streetly
L'Oreal Professionnel
Lynne Welsh @ Mosko, Wishaw
M. Balfre
Dr M H Beck
Mahogany Hairdressing Salons and Academy
    (www.mahoganyhair.co.uk)
Mark Woolley (hair stylist), Pete Webb (photographer)
Matrix
Mediscan
Melanie Tudor @ En Route Hair and Beauty,
    Wakefield
Michael Barnes for Goldwell
MK Hair Studio & Academy (www.mkhsa.co.uk)
NHF Inspire, Photography: Simon Powell
Ozzie Rizzo (Photography)
Patrick Cameron
Paul Falltrick for Matrix
Paul Hawes @ Review, Petersfield and
    Waterlooville, Hants
Richard Ward
Rae Palmer for Schwarzkopf
Redken
REM
Rush London
Saks (www.saks.co.uk)
SANRIZZ Artistic Team
Scott Smurthwaite @ Cream
Sharon Cox @ Sanrizz
Sorisa
Susan Hall @ Reds Hair and Beauty, Sunderland
Terry Calvert and the Clipso Artistic Team
Theresa Bullock
Tim Lawton @ TPL Hairdressing, Nantwich
Tracey Devine @ Angels, Aberdeen
UK Skills
Vicky Turner @ Goldsworthy's
Wahl (UK) Ltd
Wella
Wellcome images

Acknowledgements

For their help with the photoshoot

Photoshoot location:

HQ Hair

71 High Street and 25 Cambray Place, Cheltenham, Glos

Models:

Alex Bilak
Caroline Palmer
Dale Carney
Dawn Stanley
Elisabeth Crabbe
Es John
Gareth Dazely
Holly Batin
Jamie Horder
Laura Paoletti
Lucia Parry
Lucy Dix

Sara Horder
Sean O'Riley
Sian Jennings
Teyah Lee
Tom O'Shea

Stylists:

Becci Fincham
HQ Hair Cheltenham
Jodi Green
Martin Green

Make up:

Holly Batin

Photography:

Fi Deane

Special Thank You:

Goldwell for all their help and support in providing the products and technical assistance within the photo shoot.

Every effort has been made to trace the copyright holders, but if any have been inadvertently overlooked the publisher will be pleased to make the necessary arrangements at the first opportunity. Please contact the publisher directly.

Introduction

Welcome to the craft: A career in creativity

A career in hairdressing or barbering has never been as popular as it is now; competition is fierce and the standards are high. So you too must aim high, particularly if you see our craft as your opportunity for a lifelong career. A job for life is a rare thing, but with the skills that you are learning now, and the knowledge that you acquire over time, you will be better prepared for the challenges ahead.

You are learning an NVQ at a very special and unique time and that is because our industry is going through a major transformation. You may have wanted to do hairdressing or barbering for a long time and have really been itching to get started, but right now and for the first time ever, the opportunity to gain experience is going to be available to many other young students too.

The new Diploma curriculum is a breakthrough for all those people who want to find out *how* and want to find out *now*. Having the opportunity to sample the industry and learn more about it before starting a job qualification is a fantastic step forward from what has been available before. So whichever route you have taken to get you to where you are now, good luck and all the best for the future.

Martin Green

SCOTT SMURTHWAITE@CREAM

Hairdressing NVQ/SVQ Level 2

As our customers' expectations rise, our standards must rise too. This means that our hairdressing industry will need better-trained staff who are more flexible and highly motivated. Over recent years the NVQ/SVQ Level 2 has provided the definitive minimum standard for occupational competence and a foundation level forming the basis of professional excellence.

Many jobs have a similar work focus since all companies need customers in order to exist. You will notice this particularly if you think about those practices that are similar across many different industries or professions. For instance, many of the day-to-day duties performed by a receptionist in a hairdressing salon are similar to the tasks performed by a receptionist in a leisure centre. There is a common denominator and this is primarily concerned with communication. The communication may be carried out in many different ways: on the telephone, face to face, by e-mail or through other electronic means. Similarly if you think about the tasks in retail – stock control, product rotation, the restocking of shelves and till operation – you can see that there are many ways in which people working in different occupations do similar things.

So, bearing these factors in mind, the modern standards have been devised to be far more flexible in their approach. It is now common for one industry sector to use another sector's standards. This principle of standalone, reusable material is now widely used. Our Hairdressing Level 2 units have been designed this way and in the next section you will find an outline of the units and the main outcomes that make up the qualification.

NVQ/SVQ – an introduction

National vocational qualifications (NVQs) and Scottish vocational qualifications (SVQs) have a common structure and design. That is to say, they all follow a particular format for all occupations and vocational sectors. Each vocational qualification is structured the same way and is made up from a number of grouped components.

Each grouping or unit will address a specific task or area of work e.g. reception. When a staff member is asked to 'do reception' the work involves many different tasks: handling payments, making appointments, receiving clients and restocking products and stationery materials. These individual tasks are referred to in NVQ/SVQ terms as the 'main outcomes'.

Hairdressing Level 2 NVQ/SVQ structure

Nine units must be completed for the full NVQ/SVQ.

Each candidate must complete the eight mandatory units plus one optional unit from the option group overleaf.

Unit code	Unit title	Chapter
G20	Make sure your own actions reduce risks to health and safety	1
	ENTO (HSS 1)	
G17	Give clients a positive impression of yourself and your organisation (ICS Unit 9)	3
G7	Advise and consult with clients	5
GH8	Shampoo, condition and treat the hair and scalp	7
GH9	Change hair colour	16
GH10	Style and finish hair	8
GH11	Set and dress hair	10
GH12	Cut hair using basic techniques	12

Optional units (one of these units must also be completed)

Unit code	Unit title	Chapter
G4	Fulfil salon reception duties	4
G18	Promote additional services or products to clients (ICS Unit 10)	6
G8	Develop and maintain your effectiveness at work	2
GH13	Plait and twist hair	10
GH14	Perm and neutralise hair	17
GH15	Attach hair to enhance a style	11

Barbering Level 2 NVQ/SVQ structure

Eight units must be completed for the full NVQ/SVQ.

Each candidate must complete the six mandatory units plus one from each of the two optional groups below.

Mandatory units (all of these must be completed)

Unit code	Unit title	Chapter
G20	Make sure your own actions reduce risks to health and safety	1
	ENTO (HSS 1)	
G7	Advise and consult with clients	5
GH8	Shampoo, condition and treat the hair and scalp	7
GB3	Cut hair using basic barbering techniques	13
GB4	Cut facial hair to shape using basic techniques	14
GB5	Dry and finish men's hair	9

Plus 1 of the following optional units

Unit code	Unit title	Chapter
AH21	Create basic patterns in hair	15
GH14	Perm and neutralise hair	17
GB2	Change men's hair colour	16

Plus 1 of the following optional units

Unit code	Unit title	Chapter
G4	Fulfil salon reception duties	4
G8	Develop and maintain your effectiveness at work	2
G17	Give clients a positive impression of yourself and your organisation (ICS Unit 9)	3
G18	Promote additional services or products to clients (ICS Unit 10)	6

Units and main outcomes

The units listed above denote the smallest components of the NVQ/SVQ that can be credited by certificate: they are the smallest parts of a full NVQ/SVQ that can be awarded to a candidate. Each unit comprises a unit title and one or more individual main outcomes, and these main outcomes, are the smallest meaningful activities in NVQ/SVQs.

Unit code, title and main outcomes (example: health and safety)

Unit code	Unit title	Main outcomes
G20	Make sure your own actions reduce risks to health and safety	G20.1 Identify the hazards and evaluate the risks in your workplace
		G20.2 Reduce the risks to health and safety in your workplace

The main outcomes

Main outcomes are brief statements that outline the tasks in hand. Their titles are always expressed in 'do this' language, e.g. 'Identify the hazards and evaluate the risks in your workplace'. However, while giving you an idea of what needs to be done, it doesn't say how it's to be done.

The National Occupational Standards cover this in greater detail. Not only do they specify how each task is to be performed (i.e. 'performance criteria'), they also give the circumstances or situations in which these actions must be done (the 'range').

Performance criteria

The performance criteria are a list of the essential actions. Although these may not be necessarily in the order in which they should be done, they do provide a definitive checklist of what needs to be done. During training these performance criteria form the smallest components of method.

Example of performance criteria showing how the task must be done

Main outcome	Performance criteria
GH8.1 Maintain effective and safe methods of working when shampooing, conditioning and treating the hair and scalp	**1** Ensuring your client's clothing is effectively protected throughout the service **2** Wearing personal protective equipment, if required **3** Positioning your client to meet the needs of the service without causing them discomfort **4** Ensuring your own posture and position whilst working minimises fatigue and the risk of injury

Range

The range statements provide a number of conditions or applications in which the main outcomes must be performed. Quite simply, they state under what particular circumstances, and on what occasions, or in which special situations, the activity must take place.

Example of range statements – identifying which situations or circumstances need to be included when doing the task

Main outcome	Range
GH8.1 Maintain effective and safe methods of working when shampooing, conditioning and treating the hair and scalp	**Look to identify any contra-indications such as:** skin and scalp disorders and diseases **Look to identify any contra-indications such as:** cuts and abrasions **Ask questions to identify any contra-indications such as:** product allergies

Knowledge and understanding (referred to as EKU in this book)

NVQs and SVQs are not only about doing. If you do your work properly, you need to understand what you are doing and why you are doing it. The terms 'theory', 'learning' and 'principles' generally refer to essential knowledge and understanding.

Typical knowledge statements covering what you need to know

Main outcome	Essential knowledge and understanding
GH8.1 Maintain effective and safe methods of working when shampooing, conditioning and treating the hair and scalp	**You should know:** when and how to complete client records **You should know:** the range of protective clothing that should be available for clients **You should know:** why it is important to use personal protective equipment

At the point where a task's performance criteria and range have been covered and knowledge has been learnt, the task is carried out competently and a skill has been acquired.

Shared knowledge

Units and main outcomes often share similar components. For example, some of the performance criteria used within the main outcomes are the same, e.g. GH12.1, Maintain effective and safe methods of working when cutting hair, and GH10.1, Maintain effective and safe methods of working when styling and finishing hair. Similarly, knowledge that is essential and underpins one main outcome will often occur in another. This duplication may at first seem unnecessary, but it occurs because of the modular, standalone design of NVQ/SVQs. This can be useful in terms of speeding up the learning process as sometimes knowledge or skills learnt in one activity are then directly applicable to other tasks. Recording and documenting these learnt experiences are then made even simpler; knowledge learnt in one situation can be quickly cross-referenced to similar activities in your portfolio or work log.

Under assessment

Your competence, your ability to carry out a task to a standard, is measured during assessment. Your ability to carry out the task – 'performance evidence' – will be observed and measured against the performance criteria. Therefore your assessor will be watching to see how you carry out your work. Sometimes, when it is not possible to cover all the situations that might crop up, your assessor might ask you questions about what you have done and how you might apply that in a different situation. To help you get used to this, the activities that appear throughout the book contain lots of the types of questions that you might be asked.

Your understanding and background knowledge of work tasks is also measured through questions asked by your assessor. Sometimes you might be asked to give a personal account of what you have learned. This could take the form of writing a sequence of events that need to be done to complete the task satisfactorily. Other questions may ask you specifically about particular tasks; more often than not, these types of questions take the form of short-answer questions. Again, the activities covered within this book give plenty of examples and practice.

About this book

ADAM HARRIS@
MG MARTIN GOLD

The common structure and design that exist within NVQ/SVQs are mirrored in many ways within this text. For the first time in the hairdressing NVQ/SVQ official series, revisions and updates have been totally reworked to provide:

A) the fastest possible navigation to the things that you want to find out about
B) a book that covers all the aspects of the NVQ for both hairdressing and barbering standards
C) a chapter structure that now mirrors the NVQ standards in unit as well as outcome format.

You will be able to navigate standards; getting faster access to the information and the unique EKU referencing system directs you straight to the information that you need to know.

All of these features and illustrations have been redesigned and reorganised in order to help you accelerate through your Level 2 programme.

How to use this book

You can use this book in a number of differing ways:

1 You can use the EKU reference map to quickly find text that covers the things that you want to know without having to *wade* through pages of text.
2 You can use the revised chapter structure to cover complete units as you get to them within your training.
3 You can use the book as a quick guide and overview to the things that you will be doing and the things that you will learn.
4 You can use it as your standalone course guide covering the A–Z of hairdressing at NVQ Level 2.

This new format will help you to use and read this book more easily. Each chapter addresses specific units from the NVQ/SVQ Level 2. At the beginning of each chapter a referencing system provides a quick signposting to the information you want, providing a variety of starting and finishing points. In this next example, you can see the variety of features and icons used within the text.

e-teaching website

A new **e-teaching website** for trainers accompaines this text book.

This resource includes **handouts**, **PowerPoint™ slides**, **interactive quizzes**, an **image bank** and **videoclips** – all carefully designed to help trainers make classroom delivery more interactive and to provide extra materials for lesson planning.

Please visit www.eteachhairdressing.co.uk for more information or contact your Cengage Learning sales representative at emea.info@cengage.com

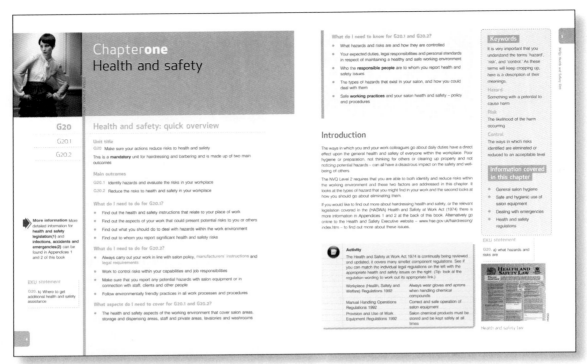

NVQ/SVQ reference, unit title and main outcome An at-a-glance overview of the unit and main outcomes covered in the chapter.

What aspect do I need to do? A brief overview of the activities involved in the unit and customised information telling you what you need to do about practical tasks.

What aspects do I need to cover? A quick guide that covers the range of things that are included and the contexts in which things will need to be done.

What do I need to know? Customised information on what you need to learn and understand in order to complete a task satisfactorily.

Information covered in this chapter A list of information covered within the chapter.

Key words Special or technical terms.

Step-by-steps Photo sequences to illustrate procedures.

Hair science Other technical information relevant to the chapter.

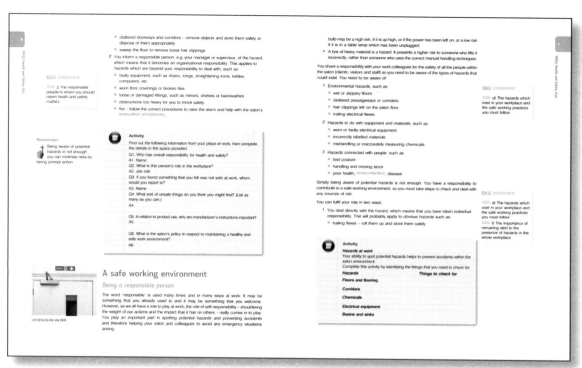

Remember boxes Tips or hints on points to remember.

EKU reference points These map the essential knowledge required in the standards directly to paragraphs covering this information.

Activities Placed throughout the book to give you practical experience of things that you need to learn.

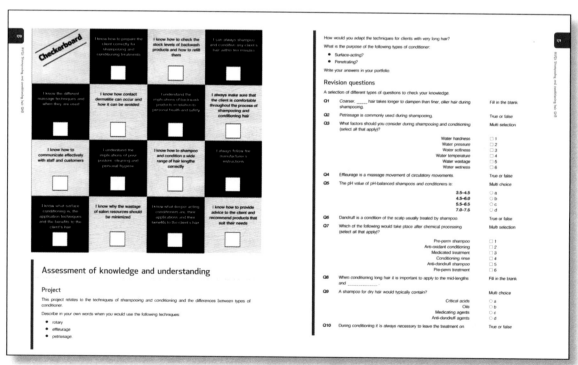

Checkerboard A self-check system and means of recording progress towards achievement.

Tests A variety of self-assessment tests are available at the end of the chapter with answers at the back of the book.

Essential Knowledge mapping grid

To use this essential knowledge mapping grid simply find the EKU statement in the standards that you want to learn more about. Then using this grid match the number to it's corresponding page.

For example, say that you want to look up the information about **G17.5 how to recognise when a client is angry or confused** from within **Unit G17 Give clients a positive impression of yourself and your organisation**, just look in the table G17 below and look at the corresponding page for EKU number 5.

Green units are applicable to both Barbering and Hairdressing		Blue units are applicable to Barbering at Level 2		Orange units are applicable to Hairdressing at Level 2

G20 Make sure your own actions reduce risks to health and safety

EKU	a	b	c	d	e	f	g	h	i	j	k	l	m	n	o	p	q	
Page	5	11	9	7	9	7	9	19	9	8	4	11	16	14	17	18	12	

G17 Give clients a positive impression of yourself and your organisation

EKU	1	2	3	4	5													
Page	46	49	50	47	58													

G7 Advise and consult with clients

EKU	1	2	3	4	5	6	7	8	9	10	11	12	13	14	15	16	17	18	19
Page	129	141	111	111	124	124	128	112	120	104	111	111	104	104	104	105	115	98	129
EKU	20	21	22	23	24														
Page	99	99	100	100	102														

GH8 Shampoo, condition and treat the hair and scalp

EKU	1	2	3	4	5	6	7	8	9	10	11	12	13	14	15	16	17	18	19
Page	148	157	148	153	151	149	146	146	160	150	149	150	150	150	149	149	153	150	165
EKU	20	21	22	23	24	25	26	27	28	29	30	31	32	33	34	35	36	37	38
Page	158	146	167	167	167	168	153	167	161	161	151	151	151	165	153	166	152	149	151
EKU	39	40	41	42	43	44	45	46	47	48	49	50	51	52					
Page	152	152	165	158	166	164	163	158	168	151	168	168	168	169					

GH9 Change hair colour and **GB2** Change men's hair colour

EKU	1	2	3	4	5	6	7	8	9	10	11	12	13	14	15	16	17	18	19
Page	389	390	397	390	389	397	372	372	372	390	390	389	389	390	390	389	384	386	383
EKU	20	21	22	23	24	25	26	27	28	29	30	31	32	33	34	35	36	37	38
Page	389	390	390	390	390	397	397	397	395	395	395	396	396	396	396	376	382	383	382
EKU	39	40	41	42	43	44	45	46	47	48	49	50	51	52	53	54	55	56	57
Page	400	392	400	383	400	400	384	400	392	378	378	394	394	393	393	390	398	398	405
EKU	58	59	60	61	62	63	64	65	66	67	68								
Page	383	398	411	411	411	411	413	413	413	413	413								

GH10 Style and finish hair

EKU	1	2	3	4	5	6	7	8	9	10	11	12	13	14	15	16	17	18	19
Page	176	177	185	178	175	176	176	176	176	175	177	177	177	177	178	173	177	192	184
EKU	20	21	22	23	24	25	26	27	28	29	30	31	32	33	34	35	36	37	38
Page	184	187	188	175	192	182	185	182	187	179	187	188	187	187	178	188	195	191	191
EKU	39	40	41																
Page	191	180	191																

GH11 Set and dress hair

EKU	1	2	3	4	5	6	7	8	9	10	11	12	13	14	15	16	17	18	19
Page	218	224	219	219	219	218	219	219	219	219	219	219	219	219	217	219	240	217	226
EKU	20	21	22	23	24	25	26	27	28	29	30	31	32	33	34	35	36	37	38
Page	230	224	224	242	220	220	220	223	220	227	227	227	227	231	227	231	233	247	248
EKU	39	40	41	42															
Page	248	247	248	247															

GH12 Cut hair using basic techniques

EKU	1	2	3	4	5	6	7	8	9	10	11	12	13	14	15	16	17	18	19
Page	273	277	275	273	273	277	273	276	277	277	276	277	282	274	279	279	280	278	274
EKU	20	21	22	23	24	25	26	27	28	29	30	31	32						
Page	278	286	286	286	288	289	295	279	289	289	300	300	300						

G4 Fulfil salon reception duties

EKU	1	2	3	4	5	6	7	8	9	10	11	12	13	14	15	16	17	18	19
Page	63	67	71	74	63	86	63	68	70	79	70	66	69	71	74	74	68	68	68
EKU	20	21	22	23	24	25	26	27	28	29									
Page	79	79	79	79	79	79	79	79	73	73									

G18 Promote additional services or products to clients

EKU	1	2	3	4	5	6													
Page	134	134	134	134	135	139													

G8 Develop and maintain your effectiveness at work

EKU	1	2	3	4	5	6	7	8	9	10	11	12	13	14	15	16	17	18	19
Page	27	27	27	27	28	29	39	32	34	34	34	29	29	27	28	28	26	28	36
EKU	20	21	22	23	24	25													
Page	31	36	37	39	38	25													

GH13 Plait and twist hair

EKU	1	2	3	4	5	6	7	8	9	10	11	12	13	14	15	16	17	18	19
Page	218	219	219	218	219	219	219	219	219	219	219	219	243	240	240	240	240	241	242
EKU	20	21	22	23	24	25	26	27	28	29	30	31	32						
Page	242	242	242	242	234	244	244	244	239	247	247	242	247						

GH14 Perm and neutralise hair

EKU	1	2	3	4	5	6	7	8	9	10	11	12	13	14	15	16	17	18	19
Page	421	421	429	422	441	441	418	422	418	423	421	421	421	421	421	438	421	421	421
EKU	20	21	22	23	24	25	26	27	28	29	30	31	32	33	34	35	36	37	38
Page	421	421	425	429	429	428	428	428	428	428	429	420	437	436	438	438	423	426	423
EKU	39	40	41	42	43	44	45	46	47	48	49	50	51	52	53	54	55		
Page	423	429	423	429	422	433	430	437	430	441	441	444	444	444	444	444	444		

GH15 Attach hair to enhance a style

EKU	1	2	3	4	5	6	7	8	9	10	11	12	13	14	15	16	17	18	19
Page	255	256	255	252	255	255	255	255	255	255	256	255	255	256	256	260	255	258	259
EKU	20	21	22	23	24	25	26	27	28	29	30	31	32	33	34	35	36	37	38
Page	259	259	259	259	259	259	258	258	259	257	265	259	258	258	260	260	257	256	257
EKU	39	40	41	42	43	44	45	46	47	48	49	50	51	52	53	54	55		
Page	260	256	260	261	261	264	265	265	265	267	267	267	267	267	265	266	261		

Barbering units

GB3 Cut hair using basic barbering techniques

EKU	1	2	3	4	5	6	7	8	9	10	11	12	13	14	15	16	17	18	19
Page	308	309	310	305	309	309	309	309	310	309	309	310	309	317	309	314	313	313	315
EKU	20	21	22	23	24	25	26	27	28	29	30	31	32	33	34	35	36	37	38
Page	314	314	313	317	315	313	321	319	321	322	322	322	320	323	323	323	318	321	330
EKU	39	40	41	42															
Page	331	331	331	331															

GB4 Cut facial hair to shape using basic techniques

EKU	1	2	3	4	5	6	7	8	9	10	11	12	13	14	15	16	17	18	19
Page	337	338	339	335	337	347	337	337	336	338	338	338	338	337	344	342	344	344	340
EKU	20	21	22	23	24	25	26	27	28	29	30	31	32	33	34	35			
Page	340	345	348	339	345	345	345	345	345	345	350	350	349	350	350	339			

GB5 Dry and finish men's hair

EKU	1	2	3	4	5	6	7	8	9	10	11	12	13	14	15	16	17	18	19
Page	204	204	205	205	205	204	204	204	204	204	204	204	205	205	205	205	204	204	211
EKU	20	21	22	23	24	25	26	27	28	29	30	31	32	33	34	35	36	37	38
Page	211	211	211	211	211	205	205	207	209	209	208	212	211	212	212	212	212	212	212

AH21 Create basic patterns in hair

EKU	1	2	3	4	5	6	7	8	9	10	11	12	13	14	15	16	17	18	19
Page	356	356	356	354	356	356	356	356	356	356	356	356	357	356	356	363	358	364	359
EKU	20	21	22	23	24	25	26	27	28	29	30	31	32	33	34	35	36	37	38
Page	359	359	360	360	362	368	368	368	364	364	365	366	364	364	362	364	367	368	366
EKU	39	40	41	42			45												
Page	363	360	366	368			356												

Part**one**
Generic salon skills

1 Vicky Turner@Goldsworthy's 2 Paul Hawes@Review, Petersfield, Waterlooville, Hants 3 Ken Picton@Ken Picton 4 Vicky Turner@Goldsworthy's 5 Hair: Richard Ward, Photography: Daniele Cipriani 6 Hair: NHF Inspire, Photography: Simon Powell Left Hair: Reds Hair and Beauty Sunderland, Photography: John Rawson@trp

TRACEY DEVINE @ ANGELS

Chapter**one**
Health and safety

Health and safety: quick overview

Unit title

G20 Make sure your actions reduce risks to health and safety

This is a **mandatory** unit for hairdressing *and* barbering and is made up of two main outcomes

Main outcomes

G20.1 Identify hazards and evaluate the risks in your workplace

G20.2 Reduce the risks to health and safety in your workplace

What do I need to do for G20.1?

● Find out the health and safety instructions that relate to your place of work

● Find out the aspects of your work that could present potential risks to you or others

● Find out what you should do to deal with hazards within the work environment

● Find out to whom you report significant health and safety risks

What do I need to do for G20.2?

● Always carry out your work in line with salon policy, manufacturers' instructions and legal requirements

● Work to control risks within your capabilities and job responsibilities

● Make sure that you report any potential hazards with salon equipment or in connection with staff, clients and other people

● Follow environmentally friendly practices in all work processes and procedures

What aspects do I need to cover for G20.1 and G20.2?

● The health and safety aspects of the working environment that cover salon areas, storage and dispensing areas, staff and private areas, lavatories and washrooms

More information More detailed information for **health and safety legislation(1) and infections, accidents and emergencies(2)** can be found in Appendices 1 and 2 of this book

EKU *statement*

G20.k) Where to get additional health and safety assistance

What do I need to know for G20.1 and G20.2?

- What hazards and risks are and how they are controlled

- Your expected duties, legal responsibilities and personal standards in respect of maintaining a healthy and safe working environment

- Who the responsible people are to whom you report health and safety issues

- The types of hazards that exist in your salon, and how you could deal with them

- Safe working practices and your salon health and safety – policy and procedures

Introduction

The ways in which you and your work colleagues go about daily duties have a direct effect upon the general health and safety of everyone within the workplace. Poor hygiene or preparation, not thinking for others or clearing up properly and not noticing potential hazards – can all have a disastrous impact on the safety and well-being of others.

The NVQ Level 2 requires that you are able to both identify and reduce risks within the working environment and these two factors are addressed in this chapter. It looks at the types of hazard that you might find in your work and the second looks at how you should go about eliminating them.

If you would like to find out more about hairdressing health and safety, or the relevant legislation covered in the (HASWA) Health and Safety at Work Act (1974) there is more information in Appendices 1 and 2 at the back of this book. Alternatively go online to the Health and Safety Executive website – www.hse.gov.uk/hairdressing/index.htm – to find out more about these issues.

Keywords

It is very important that you understand the terms 'hazard', 'risk', and 'control.' As these terms will keep cropping up, here is a description of their meanings.

Hazard
Something with a potential to cause harm

Risk
The likelihood of the harm occurring

Control
The ways in which risks identified are eliminated or reduced to an acceptable level

Information covered in this chapter

- General salon hygiene
- Safe and hygienic use of salon equipment
- Dealing with emergencies
- Health and safety regulations

EKU *statement*

G20.a) what hazards and risks are

Activity

The Health and Safety at Work Act 1974 is continually being reviewed and updated, it covers many smaller component regulations. See if you can match the individual legal regulations on the left with the appropriate health and safety issues on the right. (Tip: look at the regulation wording to work out its appropriate link.)

Workplace (Health, Safety and Welfare) Regulations 1992	Always wear gloves and aprons when handling chemical compounds
Manual Handling Operations Regulations 1992	Correct and safe operation of salon equipment
Provision and Use of Work Equipment Regulations 1992	Salon chemical products must be stored and be kept safely at all times

Health and safety law

An introduction to health and safety

Health and safety in small businesses

HSE

HMSO   What you should know about – where to get more information

Health and safety law

Personal Protective Equipment at Work Regulations 1992	Dermatitis a notifiable skin condition that results from sensitivity to chemicals
Control of Substances Hazardous to Health Regulations 2002 (COSHH)	Monitoring and maintenance of workplace hygiene and cleanliness
Electricity at Work Regulations 1989	Always keep well stocked, just in case of accidents occurring at work
Reporting of Injuries, Diseases and Dangerous Occurrences Regulations 1995	Manufacturer information relating to the use of chemical products
Cosmetic Products (Safety) Regulations 1989	The movement and handling of objects needs to be done safely and properly
Health and Safety (First Aid) Regulations 1981	Items of salon electrical equipment must be checked and tested each year

G20.1   Identify hazards and evaluate the risks in your workplace

Hazard and risk

Almost anything may be a hazard, but may or may not become a risk. For example:

- A trailing electric cable from a piece of equipment is a hazard if it is trailing across a passageway as there is a high risk of someone tripping over it, but if it lies along a wall out of the way, the risk is much less.

- Poisonous or flammable chemicals are hazards and may present a high risk. However, if they are kept in a properly designed secure store and handled by properly trained and equipped people, the risk is much less than if they are left about for anyone to use.

- A failed light bulb is a hazard. If it is just one of many in a room it presents very little risk, but if it is the only light on a stairwell, it is a very high risk. Changing the bulb may be a high risk, if it is up high, or if the power has been left on, or a low risk if it is in a table lamp which has been unplugged.

- A box of heavy material is a hazard. It presents a higher risk to someone who lifts it incorrectly, rather than someone who uses the correct manual handling techniques.

You share a responsibility with your work colleagues for the safety of all the people within the salon (clients, visitors and staff) so you need to be aware of the types of hazards that could exist. You need to be aware of:

1 Environmental hazards, such as:

- wet or slippery floors
- cluttered passageways or corridors
- hair clippings left on the salon floor
- trailing electrical flexes.

2 Hazards to do with equipment and materials, such as:

- worn or faulty electrical equipment
- incorrectly labelled materials
- mishandling or inaccurately measuring chemicals.

3 Hazards connected with people, such as:

- bad posture
- handling and moving stock
- poor health, cross-infection, disease.

EKU *statement*

G20.d) The hazards which exist in your workplace and the safe working practices you must follow

Simply being aware of potential hazards is not enough. You have a responsibility to contribute to a safe working environment, so you must take steps to check and deal with any sources of risk.

You can fulfil your role in two ways:

1 You deal directly with the hazard, which means that you have taken individual responsibility. This will probably apply to obvious hazards such as:

- trailing flexes – roll them up and store them safely

EKU *statement*

G20.d) The hazards which exist in your workplace and the safe working practices you must follow

G20.f) The importance of remaining alert to the presence of hazards in the whole workplace

Activity

Hazards at work

Your ability to spot potential hazards helps to prevent accidents within the salon environment.

Complete this activity by identifying the things that you need to check for.

Hazards	Things to check for
Floors and flooring	
Corridors	
Chemicals	
Electrical equipment	
Basins and sinks	

- cluttered doorways and corridors – remove objects and store them safely or dispose of them appropriately
- sweep the floor to remove loose hair clippings

2 You inform a responsible person, e.g. your manager or supervisor, of the hazard, which means that it becomes an organisational responsibility. This applies to hazards which are beyond your responsibility to deal with, such as:

- faulty equipment, such as dryers, tongs, straightening irons, kettles, computers, etc.
- worn floor coverings or broken tiles
- loose or damaged fittings, such as mirrors, shelves or backwashes
- obstructions too heavy for you to move safely
- fire – follow the correct procedures to raise the alarm and help with the salon's evacuation procedures.

EKU *statement*

G20.j) The responsible people to whom you should report heath and safety matters

Remember

Being aware of potential hazards is not enough: you can minimise risks by taking prompt action.

Activity

Find out the following information from your place of work, then complete the details in the space provided.

Q1. Who has overall responsibility for health and safety?

A1. Name

Q2. What is this person's role in the workplace?

A2. Job role

Q3. If you found something that you felt was not safe at work, whom would you report to?

A3. Name

Q4. What sort of unsafe things do you think you might find? (List as many as you can.)

A4.

Q5. In relation to product use, why are manufacturer's instructions important?

A5.

Q6. What is the salon's policy in respect to maintaining a healthy and safe work environment?

A6.

i-STOCK/©LISA VALDER

A safe working environment

Being a responsible person

The word 'responsible' is used many times and in many ways at work. It may be something that you already used to and it may be something that you welcome. However, as we all have a role to play at work, the role of self-responsibility – shouldering the weight of our actions and the impact that it has on others – really comes in to play. You play an important part in spotting potential hazards and preventing accidents and therefore helping your salon and colleagues to avoid any emergency situations arising.

So how can I make a difference?

Suppose, for example, that someone had carelessly blocked a fire door with recently delivered stock. You could take the initiative and move the stock items to a safe and secure location.

However, there are occasions where being responsible requires that you make a quick judgement of what you have found and tell someone else about it. When you notice a potential hazard that you cannot easily rectify yourself, tell your supervisor immediately.

Imagine, for instance, that the lower, adjustable cutting blade on a pair of clippers became loose. If this was unnoticed by one of the stylists they might pick the clippers up and use them on a client!

In this situation your swift action might save a client from a serious injury. You see the hazard and understand the risk, but the essential readjustment of the blades should only be undertaken by a suitably trained person.

Salon/workplace policy

Salons will vary in size, layout and organisational structure and because of this each salon has their own set of rules relating to safe and healthy practices, processes and procedures. This information is made available to you at the point of joining an organisation, usually within an induction process.

The induction training sets out the basic rules of your employment: what's expected of you and what you can expect from the company. During your induction you may be given a number of documents that you should keep for future information and later use. Amongst these will be the salon's policy in relation to the following health and safety issues:

- fire and emergency evacuation procedures
- people to whom you should report to in the event of emergency or significant risk to people's safety
- the things that you *may* undertake yourself to control risks to the health, safety and welfare of others
- the things that you *may not* undertake yourself to control risks to the health, safety and welfare of others
- health and safety training information.

In addition to the above, you will find the following prominently placed health and safety notices/records available on display:

- health and safety rules and regulations poster
- COSHH information booklet
- salon risk assessments
- Public Liability Insurance certificate
- fire safety evacuation procedures
- accident book (records of injuries and treatments provided)
- (where necessary) written health and safety policy.

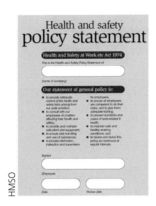

An example health and safety policy statement

Activity

Salon layout

Draw a floor plan of your salon. Within your sketch you need to show where the following can be found:

1 Fire extinguisher(s)

2 Storage for products/equipment

3 Disposal of waste and sharps.

4 Sterilising equipment

5 Personal protective equipment

6 Accident book

7 Fire exit(s)

8 First–aid box/kit

9 Health and safety information

G20.2   Reduce the risks to health and safety in your workplace

People are exposed to all kinds of hazardous substances at work. These can include chemicals that people make or work with directly, and also dust, fumes and bacteria which can be present in the workplace. Exposure can happen by breathing them in, contact with the skin, splashing them into the eyes or swallowing them. If exposure is not prevented or properly controlled, it can cause serious illness, including cancer, asthma and dermatitis, and sometimes even death.

The health and safety laws are designed to protect you, the clients and your fellow staff members. So your personal health and safety and safe methods of work are absolutely essential. This chapter will explain how you can help reduce risks to health and safety within the working environment for everyone's benefit.

The **Health and Safety at Work Act 1974** is the main, overarching legislation, made by parliament, relating to business premises, under which, all other regulations exist. Although the Act contains many individual regulations the responsibility for maintaining these falls upon you and your employer. In short: *employers have a legal duty under the HASAWA (1974) to ensure that:*

- The premises are safe to work within.
- All equipment and salon systems are safe to use.
- Employees have access to personal protective equipment.
- Contractors and self-employed staff working on the premises benefit from the same health and safety policy.
- Health and safety systems are appropriately reviewed and updated.

Employees have duties too. They should:

- follow appropriate systems of work laid down for their safety;
- make proper use of equipment provided for their safety;
- cooperate with their employer on health and safety matters;
- inform the employer if they identify hazardous activities/situations;
- take care to ensure that their activities do not put others at risk.

Both employers and employees have a joint responsibility for:

- the safety of the working environment
- taking reasonable care of themselves or others who may be affected by their working practices and must support their employer in fulfilling their obligations in the compliance of current health and safety requirements.

For more specific information on the health and safety regulations see Appendix 1, pages 448–452.

Obstructions

Passageways and corridors are dangerous, regardless of whether the obstruction is in doorways or a corridor, on stairs or in a fire exit. In an emergency, people might have to leave the salon in a hurry – perhaps even in the dark if the electricity has gone off. It could be disastrous if someone injured themselves or fell. So:

- always be on the lookout for any obstruction in these areas;
- if you see something that could present a risk, tell your work supervisor.

Spillage and breakages

You do need to act quickly in the event of a spillage or breakage but stop and think before doing anything.

- First of all, what has been spilled or dropped?
- Do you know what it is?
- Is this something that needs special care and attention when handling?
- Should you report the situation to someone else, or can you handle the situation yourself?

Activity

Find out your salon's policy in respect of the following procedures and write your responses in your portfolio.

Briefly describe what safe working practices are.

How should hazardous substances be stored, dispensed and used?

What are the salon's rules regarding smoking, consuming food and drink on the premises and policy in respect to alcohol and other drugs?

What is the salon's policy in the event of an emergency occurring?

What are the salon's expectations in respect to personal presentation and hygiene?

ISTOCKPHOTO.COM/JEFF CHEVRIER

- If you can, should you be wearing gloves?
- What else do you need to get to rectify the situation safely without creating another hazard?

Disposal of waste

EKU *statement*

G20.q) The risks to the environment which may be present in your workplace and/or in your own job

General salon waste

Everyday items of salon waste should be placed in an enclosed waste bin fitted with a suitably resistant polyethylene bin liner. When the bin is full, the liner can be sealed using a wire tie and placed ready for refuse collection. If for any reason the bin liner punctures, put the damaged liner and waste inside a second bin liner. Wash out the inside of the bin itself with hot water and detergent.

Being environmentally aware requires us to be more responsible in the ways in which we dispose of our waste items. Take particular care in following the salon's procedures for the safe disposal of:

- aluminium foil and cans, glass bottles and plastic waste, packaging etc.
- paper, cardboard and other biodegradables
- chemical hairdressing products (not down drains and sinks)
- aerosols and other pressurised items.

(All of these items can be recycled or have local authority guidance on how they are safely disposed of.)

Disposal of sharp items

COURTESY OF ELLISONS

Used razor blades and similar items should be placed into a safe container (sharps box). When the container is full it can be disposed of safely. This type of salon waste should be kept away from general salon waste as special arrangements may be provided by your local authority. Contact your local council office's environmental health department for more information.

Lifting and handling large objects

(A list of health and safety regulations can be found in the appendices section of this book.)

As manual handling is an everyday part of salon processes, it is also covered here, as a range of skeletal and muscular disorders can occur if safe lifting procedures are not observed.

Bad posture resulting from the incorrect handling of large and/or heavy items can result in low back pain/problems, repetitive strain injuries and strain disorders.

Think about the situations that can occur in a salon environment i.e.

COURTESY OF BEAUTY EXPRESS

Sharps box

- moving stock into storage
- unpacking heavy or awkward items
- lifting equipment and moving salon furniture
- working heights – chairs, trolleys, dryers etc.

The health and safety regulations require employers to:

- *avoid* the need for hazardous manual handling, so far as is reasonably practicable;

- *assess* the risk of injury from any hazardous manual handling that can't be avoided; and

- *reduce* the risk of injury from hazardous manual handling, so far as is reasonably practicable.

EKU *statement*

G20.i) The safe working practices for your own job

Think before lifting/handling

Adopt a stable position with feet apart and one leg slightly forward to maintian balance

Start in a good posture

Keep the head up when handling

Put down, then adjust

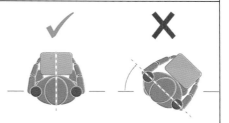

Avoid twisting the back or learning sideways, especially while the back is bent

HMSO

Activity

Risks in the salon environment

From the list below tick the risks that could apply to you within the salon and then make brief notes on how they can be avoided.

1 Inhaling fumes from chemicals

2 Chemical burns

3 Cutting yourself

4 Tripping over boxes of stock

5 Slipping on hair clippings

6 Falling down the stairs

7 Developing dermatitis

8 Injury due to unsafe practices

9 Electric shock from equipment

10 Food poisoning

11 Slipping on wet floor

EKU *statement*

G20.i) The safe working practices for your own job

HMSO

Avoid dermatitis

Cut out dermatitis: many trainee hairdressers have to give up hairdressing because of this common occupational health hazard. You can avoid this condition by making sure that you always use disposable non-latex gloves. Always dry your hands thoroughly after washing and moisturise them to keep them healthy.

What does dermatitis look like?

Five steps to prevent dermatitis

HMSO

Step 1. Wear disposable non-latex gloves when rinsing, shampooing, colouring, bleaching, etc.

Step 2. Dry your hands thoroughly with a soft cotton or paper towel.

Step 3. Moisturise after washing your hands, as well as at the start and end of each day. It's easy to miss fingertips, finger webs and wrists.

Step 4. Change gloves between clients. Make sure you don't contaminate your hands when you take them off.

Step 5. Check your skin regularly for early signs of dermatitis.

What do you do if you think you have it?

If you think you are suffering from dermatitis, then you should visit your doctor for advice and treatment. If you believe it has been caused or made worse by your work as a hairdresser, then you should mention this to your doctor and you must also tell your employer; as they are required by law to report a case of work-related dermatitis amongst their staff.

Handling chemicals

Many of the hairdressing services involve some contact with chemicals and salons have safe ways of dealing with this. Employers have a legal obligation to control the exposure of hazardous substances in the workplace and you are protected by the Control Of Substances Hazardous to Health Regulations (2002) COSHH. Most hairdressing chemicals are safe and only propose a risk to health at the point when they are handled and used.

COSHH precautions

Risk assessments made by your employer will indicate the types of chemicals available within the salon and the safe ways in which they may be handled or used. These chemical products will vary from cleaning items – such as washing materials, bleach and polish – to the more typical salon specific items such as colours, lighteners, hydrogen peroxide and general styling materials.

Make sure that you use the lists provided by your employer, these will indicate the level of risk that each of the chemical products presents to you. They will give a hazard rating and details on how they can be handled safely with the personal protective equipment provided by your employer.

EKU statement

G20.e) The particular health and safety hazards which may be present in your own job role

EKU statement

G20.n) Suppliers' and manufacturers' instructions for the safe use of equipment, materials and products which you must follow

EKU statement

G20.e) The particular health and safety hazards which may be present in your own job role

For more information see Personal Protective Equipment at Work Regulations 1992 in Appendix 1 page 450.

Keep floors clear and clean

The most common cause of injuries at work is the slip or trip. Resulting falls can be serious and a busy salon means lots of people: the more clients there are, the more hair clippings there will be. Loose clippings left on the salon floor present a hazard to staff and clients alike.

Both wet and dry hair clippings are easily slipped on, so make sure that you sweep the working areas regularly. Don't wait for stylists to finish; get rid of clippings before they build up. Clear them away from areas where people are working or walking and then brush them into a dustpan and put them into the waste bin.

Working with computers

Using a computer for long periods of time can give rise to back problems, repetitive strain injury or other musculoskeletal disorders. These health problems may become serious if no action is taken. They can be caused by poor design of workstations (and associated equipment such as chairs), insufficient space, lack of training or not taking breaks from display screen work.

Work with a screen does not cause eye damage, but many users experience temporary eye strain or stress. This can lead to reduced work efficiency or taking time off work.

Working with electricity

Electricity can kill. Although deaths from electric shocks are very rare in hairdressing salons, even a non-fatal shock can cause severe and permanent injury. An electric shock from faulty or damaged electrical equipment may lead to a fall (e.g. down a stairwell.)

Those using electricity may not be the only ones at risk. Poor electrical installations and faulty electrical appliances can lead to fires which can also result in death or injury to others.

Get into the habit of looking for loose cables and plugs on tongs, straighteners and hand driers *before* plugging them in for use. If you think that a piece of electrical equipment is faulty or damaged, tell your supervisor immediately. Make sure that no one else tries to use it.

For more information see Electricity at Work Regulations 1989 in Appendix 1 page 451.

COSHH: A brief guide to the Regulations
What you need to know about the Control of Substances Hazardous to Health Regulations 2002 (COSHH)

COSHH leaflet

 HIGHLY FLAMMABLE
 TOXIC
 HARMFUL
 CORROSIVE
 EXPLOSIVE
 OXIDIZING

Symbols showing types of hazardous substances

How and where you can get more help

Preventing slips and trips at work INDG225(rev1)
FREE (available in packs of 15
ISBN 0 7176 2760 8 £5.00)

Workplace health, safety and welfare INDG244(rev1)
FREE (available in packs of 10
ISBN 0 7176 6192 X £5.00)

Slips and trips: Guidance for employers on identifying hazards and controlling risks
HSG155
ISBN 0 7176 1145 0 £7.50

Slips and trips website: www.hse.gov.uk/slips

Remember

Hazards	Check for
Floors	✔ Are they slippery or wet?
Doorways	✔ Are they clear of obstacles?
Electrical flexes	✔ Are they loose or trailing?
Chemicals	✔ Are they labelled and stored correctly?
Equipment	✔ Is it worn or in need of attention?

EKU *statement*

G20.l) Your scope and responsibility for controlling risks

i-STOCK/© GEOTRAC

G20.m) Workplace instructions for managing risks which you are unable to deal with

Remember

Don't attempt to carry out any electrical repairs at work!

Only those with appropriate technical knowledge and experience are allowed to do this.

Stress at work

Many people argue about the definition and sometimes even the existence of 'stress'. However, research has shown that whatever you choose to call it, there is a clear link between poor work organisation and subsequent ill health. HSE has chosen to use the word stress and define it as:

 the adverse reaction people have to excessive pressure or other types of demand placed on them.

Stress at work can be tackled in the same way as any other risk to health, hazards can include:

- lack of control over the way you do your work, work overload (or underload)
- lack of support from your managers/supervisors
- conflicting or ambiguous roles
- poor relationships with colleagues (including bullying) or
- poor management of organisational change.

HSE related information

- Management of Health and Safety at Work Regulations 1999

Stress website: www.hse.gov/uk/stress

Working together to reduce stress at work: A guide for employees MISC686
**Free (available in packs of 15
ISBN 0 7176 6122 9   £ 5.00)**

Activity

1. List the things that the staff uses within the salon that could be potentially unsafe if they are not used the right way.

2. Find out what sorts of things that could be a danger in the staff room.

3. What sorts of waste are generated during normal daily routines in the salon?

Did you know?

- All employers and self-employed people have to assess risks at work?
- Employers with five or more employees should have a written health and safety policy?
- Employers with five or more employees have to record the significant findings of their risk assessment?
- Employers have a duty to involve their employees or their employees' safety representatives on health and safety matters?
- Employers have to provide free health and safety training or protective equipment for employees where needed?

Personal health and hygiene

Hairdressing, beauty therapy and nail craft are all personal services, and as such are very different to trades such as retail, joinery or engineering in the way that practitioners communicate with and handle their clients. Salon staff and their clients can have quite a close relationship, which has both advantages and disadvantages. Your clients will judge your personal and professional standards by your personal presentation, the way in which you present yourself. Remember, hairdressing is an image-conscious industry. We strive to provide a high-quality service that gives clients well-cut, well-styled and well-groomed hair, so that they feel pleased and confident and have greater self-esteem. Would you give clients confidence if you turned up for appointments with stained overalls, unkempt hair and dirty hands and nails?

Hands and nails

Your hands should always be perfectly clean. Dirt on your hands and under your nails will harbour bacteria, and by spreading germs you could infect other people. Your hands need washing not only before going to work, but several times throughout the day. When you are shampooing and conditioning, your hands could lose moisture and become dry and cracked. Broken skin allows germs to enter and infection may follow. To prevent this from happening, you should always wear disposable non-latex gloves.

Disposable non-latex gloves

Working together
to reduce stress at work
A guide for employees

   HMSO

EKU *statement*

G20.o) The importance of personal presentation in maintaining health and safety in your workplace

Remember

Always wear disposable non-latex gloves.

When? On any occasion where you come into contact with chemicals.

Why? Because gloves are a protective barrier against infection.

Always wash your hands.

When? Before work, after eating, after using the toilet and after coughing, sneezing or blowing your nose.

Why? Because your hands are one of the main sources for spreading infection.

Always wear protective clothing/ equipment.

When? Always wear a plastic apron for any salon procedure involving chemicals.

Why? This will prevent spillages onto your clothes, particularly when colouring and perming.

Activity

General salon hygiene

Complete this table by listing how you would maintain a clean, hygienic salon.

Jobs to do:	How is this cleaned and maintained?
Work surfaces	
Floors	
Salon tools and equipment	
Towels and gowns	
Salon seating	

i-STOCK/©IRYNA KURHAN

Your body

Human skin contains sweat glands that secrete waste in the form of sweat. Skin in areas such as the armpits, feet and genitals have more sweat glands than elsewhere and the warm, moist conditions provide an ideal breeding ground for bacteria.

Decaying bacteria causes body odour (BO), so it is essential to take a shower/bath on a daily basis to remove the build-up of sweat, dead skin cells and surface bacteria.

Mouth Frequent tooth-brushing will help to eliminate bad breath and maintains good, personal oral hygiene by removing the particles of food from between the teeth that can cause a build-up of plaque and even start tooth decay!

Safe posture

It is important that you adopt the correct posture whilst working, as bad posture can lead to clinical fatigue – symptoms include impaired coordination – aches, pains, an accident, or even longer-term skeletal injury. An incorrect standing position will put undue strain on your back, shoulders and neck muscles.

Professional posture is derived from standing correctly. Professionals' shoulders are level, their head upright and their body weight distributed evenly over their legs with their feet slightly apart. Any other standing position – dropped shoulder, hip pushed forwards or sideways – looks unprofessional. Slouching is not only uncomfortable; it is dangerous and is an example of poor body language: it communicates to customers and colleagues an uncaring attitude.

Personal behaviour

EKU *statement*

G20.p) The importance of personal behaviour in maintaining the health and safety of others

Work should be enjoyable but knowing the difference between general friendly banter between colleagues and taking things too far is vitally important. Treat your fellow workers with respect. Courtesy amongst staff is just as important as it is with client communications. Behave sensibly at all times within the salon; it's one thing acting quickly to avert mishaps, such as spillages or breakages, but rushing about the salon could cause an accident.

Always use the equipment in the way it was intended. If you're not sure how something works or is handled, ask first! Remember, always use the manufacturer's instructions: that is what they are there for.

Activity

Match the information on the left with the relevant statements on the right.

Regular washing	Occurs when food particles are left between teeth
Bad breath (halitosis)	Catch on the client's scalp and hair
Personal cleanliness and a smart appearance	Can lead to fatigue or longer-term injury
Bracelets, necklaces and rings	Will prevent build-up of sweat and BO
Bad posture	Reflects your pride in your work

Good salon hygiene

It is important you develop an awareness of health and safety risks and that you are always aware of any risks in any situation. Quite simply, a tidy salon is easier to clean so get into the habit of clearing up your work as you go.

19

EKU *statement*

G20.c) Your responsibilities for health and safety as required by law covering your job role

G20.h) The responsibilities for health and safety in your job description

Activity

Now find out what the expected standards at your place of work are in relation to the following aspects.

Aspect to consider: Salon's expected standards:

Your personal hygiene

Your jewellery

Your work shoes

Your work clothing

What is your company's policy if you fail to meet these standards?

Floors and seating

Floors should be kept clean at all times. This means that they will need regular mopping, sweeping or vacuuming. When working areas are damp-mopped during normal working hours, make sure that adequate warning signs are provided close to the wet areas. The salon's seating will be made of material that is easily cleaned. It should be washed regularly with hot water and detergent. After they have dried, the seats can be made hygienically clean by wiping over with disinfectant or an antiseptic lotion.

Floors need regular sweeping

Working surfaces

All surfaces within the salon, including the reception, staff and stock preparation areas, should be washed down at least once each day. Most salons now use easily maintained wipe-clean surfaces, usually some form of plastic laminate. They can be cleaned with hot water and detergent, and after the surfaces are dry they can be wiped over with a hygienic, spirit-based antiseptic which will not smear. Don't use scourers or abrasives as these will scratch plastic surfaces. Scratched surfaces look dull and unattractive as well as containing minute crevices in which bacteria will develop.

Mirrors

Glass mirrors should be cleaned every morning before clients arrive. Never try to style a client's hair while they sit in front of a murky, dusty or smeary mirror. Glass surfaces should be cleaned and polished using either hot water and detergent or a spirit-based lotion that evaporates quickly without smearing.

Remember

 Take all precautions to avoid occupational contact dermatitis – always use protective disposable non-latex gloves where possible.

Towels and gowns

Each client must have a fresh, clean towel and gown. These should be washed on a suitable (washing machine) wash programme at 60°C to remove any soiling or staining and to prevent the spread of infection by killing any bacteria. Fabric conditioners may be used to provide a luxurious softness and freshness.

COURTESY OF ELLISONS

GOLDWELL

IMAGE COURTESY OF GOLDWELL

Cape

Activity

See if you can answer these questions in your portfolio

Q1a What type of container is liquid or crème hydrogen peroxide kept in?

Q1b Why is hydrogen peroxide hazardous to health?

Q2a Permanent colours (hair dyes) are packaged in what sort of container?

Q2b What chemicals are found in permanent hair colours?

Q3a How should hair bleaching powder be stored?

Q3b Why is hair bleaching powder hazardous to health?

Q4a How are shampoos and conditioners stored ready for use at the backwash?

Q4b How are they dispensed when they are used on clients?

Q5a What type of container is perm solution kept in?

Q5b What hazard to health does perm solution present?

Styling tools

Most pieces of salon equipment, such as combs, brushes and curlers, are made from plastics. These materials are relatively easy to keep hygienically safe, if they are used and cleaned properly.

Combs should be washed daily. When not in use they should be immersed into an antibacterial solution. When they are then needed they can be rinsed and dried and are then ready for use.

If any styling tools are accidentally dropped on to the floor, do not use them until they have been adequately cleaned. Don't put contaminated items onto work surfaces as they could spread infection and disease.

Handle non-plastic items, such as scissors and clipper blades, with care. When they need cleaning, the flat edges can be wiped over after spraying with a disinfectant or surgical spirit. Then wipe carefully with a cotton wool swab. Although most of these items are made of special steels, don't immerse them in sterilising fluids. These fluids contain chemicals that will corrode the precision-made surfaces of the blades.

(More information relating to sterilising hairdressing equipment can be found in Unit GH12 Cut hair using basic techniques, Ultraviolet and chemical methods page 276)

Regularly used clippers in the hairdressing salon will require frequent routine checks for both safety and efficiency. Hair will get trapped between the blades; this reduces cutting performance and constant vibration may loosen the cutting edges. The tiny, cut fragments of hair between the blades will increase friction between the cutting surfaces and reduce the amount of movement of the upper, cutting edge. This will need routine checking and lubricating.

Activity

General health and safety checklist

	Yes	No
Who is in charge of health and safety in your salon?		
Has your salon got a written health and safety policy?		
Has your salon done risk assessments?		
Do you know what COSHH means?		
Do you know where the first aid kit is?		
Do you know where the accident book is?		
Do you know the salon's emergency procedures?		

Activity

Personal protective equipment

The column on the left lists items of personal protective equipment (PPE) that your salon provides for staff and client safety. Complete the information in the space provided.

PPE	When is it used	Why it is used
Disposable (non-latex) gloves		
Gowns and towels		
Stylists waterproof apron		
Barrier cream		
Cotton 'neck' wool		

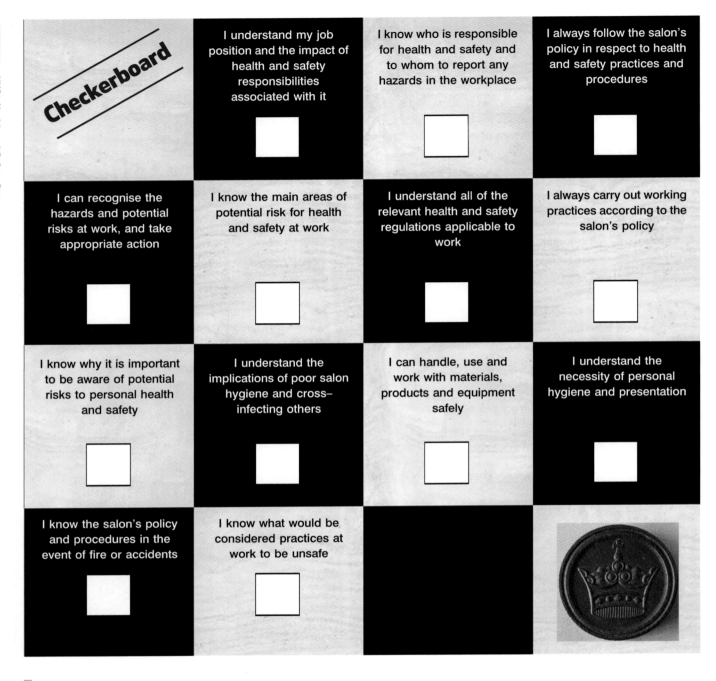

Checkerboard

I understand my job position and the impact of health and safety responsibilities associated with it	I know who is responsible for health and safety and to whom to report any hazards in the workplace
I always follow the salon's policy in respect to health and safety practices and procedures	

I can recognise the hazards and potential risks at work, and take appropriate action

I know the main areas of potential risk for health and safety at work

I understand all of the relevant health and safety regulations applicable to work

I always carry out working practices according to the salon's policy

I know why it is important to be aware of potential risks to personal health and safety

I understand the implications of poor salon hygiene and cross-infecting others

I can handle, use and work with materials, products and equipment safely

I understand the necessity of personal hygiene and presentation

I know the salon's policy and procedures in the event of fire or accidents

I know what would be considered practices at work to be unsafe

Assessment of knowledge and understanding

Project

For this project you will need to use the information from the salon's risk assessments and the COSHH salon information booklet.

For each of the following:

- one cold wave perming lotion
- one tube of permanent colour
- one powder bleaching product

find out:

- the chemical composition
- how it is used safely
- how it should be stored safely
- how it is handled
- any other special conditions that apply to it.

Revision questions

A selection of different types of questions to check your health and safety knowledge. (Also see Appendix 2.)

Q1 A _____ is something with potential to cause harm. Fill in the blank

Q2 Risk assessment is a process of evaluation to develop safe working practices. True or false

Q3 Which of the following are environmental hazards (select all that apply)? Multi selection

Boxes of stock left in the reception area	☐ 1
Stock upon shelves in the store room	☐ 2
Wet or slippery floors	☐ 3
Shampoo backwash positions	☐ 4
Salon work stations	☐ 5
Trailing flexes from electrical equipment	☐ 6

Q4 First–aid boxes should contain paracetamol tablets. True or false

Q5 Which of the following regulations relates to the safe handling of chemicals? Multi choice

PPE	○ a
RIDDOR	○ b
COSHH	○ c
OSRPA	○ d

Q6 All salons must have a written health and safety policy. True or false

Q7 Which of the following records must a salon keep up to date by law? Multi selection

Telephone book	☐ 1
Accident book	☐ 2
Appointment book	☐ 3
Electrical equipment annual test records	☐ 4
Health and safety at work checklist	☐ 5
Fire drill records	☐ 6

Q8 The _____ regulations require employers to provide adequate equipment Fill in the blank
and facilities in case of an accident occurring.

Q9 What colour is the label on a dry powder filled fire extinguisher? Multi choice

Red	○ a
Cream	○ b
Black	○ c
Blue	○ d

Q10 A dry powder filled fire extinguisher can be used on all classes of fire. True or false

Preparing for assessment checklist

Remember to:

✔	work safely and hygienically in the salon at all times
✔	prepare clients correctly for the services you are going to carry out
✔	put on your personal protective wear when it is appropriate
✔	get the clients to put on protective wear when it is appropriate
✔	look out for potential hazards and know what action you should take in rectifying them
✔	keep the work areas clean, hygienic and free from hazards
✔	clean and sterilise the tools and equipment before they are used
✔	dispose of waste items safely and correctly
✔	adhere to the safety factors when working on clients' hair
✔	adhere to the salon's emergency procedures at all times
✔	be aware of the salon's first-aid procedures
✔	work within the limits of your own authority in the all of the above.

Chapter**two**
Personal effectiveness

More Information
Questioning and listening skills (see Unit G17 pages 52)

EKU *statement*

G8.25) The questioning and listening skills you need in order to find out information

G8

G8.1

G8.2

Personal effectiveness: quick overview

Unit title

G8 Develop and maintain your effectiveness at work

This is an **optional** unit and is made up of two main outcomes

Main outcomes

G8.1 Improve your personal performance at work

G8.2 Work effectively as part of a team

What do I need to do for G8.1?

● Be able to identify your own strengths and weaknesses.

● Discuss development and review progress against targets with relevant people

● Seek assistance from relevant people

● Take opportunities to learn new things

● Listen and respond to the needs of your fellow staff members

What do I need to do for G8.2?

● Work together productively as a team

● Make effective use of your time

● Communicate with fellow staff in a polite and courteous way

● Avoid conflicts by resolving issues and problems as they arise

What aspects do I need to cover for G8.1 and G8.2?

● The learning opportunities arising from salon training and working with other staff

● The achievement of personal and productivity targets

● Providing assistance to others by individual and team efforts

Appraisal

The system of reviewing your past and planning your future work objectives

Strengths and weaknesses

The difference between personal skill areas that you excel in and those that you need to work on

Harmony

Maintaining a good working relationship and atmosphere with your fellow staff

Personal development

Recognising the opportunities that arise at work when you get the chance to learn new things

Information covered in this chapter

- Identifying personal strengths and weaknesses
- Job descriptions
- Appraisals and setting targets
- Working together effectively as a team

EKU statement

G8.17) How to maintain awareness of current and emerging trends and developments within the industry and why this is important

What do I need to know for G8.1 and G8.2?

- The salon's expectations in relation to your job role; i.e. targets, responsibilities and performance
- The limits of your authority and your responsibilities
- The salon's work expectations and personal targets
- Ways of continually updating your personal development plan
- How to respond to others in a professional work setting
- Where to find help or information with problems, issues or training related aspects

Introduction

This unit is about you taking the responsibility at work to improve your performance, achieve personal targets and get along with your colleagues. Doing well in your job really makes a difference to the whole team; as the staff in any salon situation is an integral part of the formula for success. No salon can afford to carry *dead weight*; everyone must shoulder their responsibilities as a valued member of the team. So your work input is vital and equally as important as anyone else's in maintaining the smooth running of the business.

Working towards known targets is the baseline or benchmark in the world of work; without them we wouldn't know if we got things right. Sometimes these targets will be set by others, perhaps following appraisals or training reviews. This type of planning provides a clear route to occupational competence, recognition by others and a

COURTESY OF SAKS HAIR & BEAUTY, WWW.SAKS.CO.UK

better self-esteem. But the most effective hairdressers are those that are self-motivated, they are keen to learn and find any opportunity to learn themselves by watching others, keeping in touch with fashions and eager in providing assistance to fellow team members. So what could you achieve if you learn to set your own goals and managed to work independently of others?

Every salon needs a well trained core of senior, capable and respected staff. You have already set out on your particular time-line to achieve that aim. *How long do you want it to take?*

Remember

The National Occupational Standards (NOS) can be obtained from the Hairdressing and Beauty Therapy Industry Authority (HABIA).

Remember

'Continuing professional development' (CPD) is the term used by professionals who continually update their skills. Your trainer and assessor will undertake CPD activities.

G8.1   Improve your personal performance at work

You should have a clear understanding of what you should be doing and what you are aiming to achieve at work. If you don't know this how can you tell whether you are getting it right?

The tried and tested system for looking at personal effectiveness is the performance appraisal process, it is conducted on a periodic basis with your supervisor, to mutually review progress to date and agree suitable courses for action in the future. The way in which you work and the impact that has on the team and salon is vital to the success of the business as a whole. What you do and say affects others; the positive and helpful way that you assist colleagues in their work and the way in which you relate to them is called teamwork.

Your ability to meet the expected standards at work is referred to as 'personal effectiveness' and this is the result of care, interest, respect and ongoing training.

You should be able to:

- make use of opportunities to learn
- work towards the industry recognised National Occupational Standards (NOS)
- identify your own strengths and weaknesses
- work to achievable, mutually agreed personal and salon targets
- review your progress towards targets.

EKU *statement*

G8.1) Your job role and responsibilities and how this relates to the role of other team members

G8.2) How to get information about your job, your work responsibilities and the standards expected of you

G8.3) How to find out relevant information about other people's areas of responsibility

G8.4) The limits of your own authority and that of others in relation to giving assistance

Make use of opportunities to learn

In order to make use of opportunities to learn you have to be able to spot them. So what sort of things are learning opportunities?

Everything that you do in the salon provides a learning opportunity. Each task that you haven't been able to carry out yourself before provides you with a target for the future. It's never a case of: 'I'll never be able to do that'. Or 'It's OK for you; you've been doing it for ages'. It's also about continual improvement. In order to learn something, it has to be

EKU *statement*

G8.14) who can help you identify and obtain opportunities for your development/training

COURTESY OF SAKS HAIR & BEAUTY, WWW.SAKS.CO.UK

practised and that means several times in different situations before it can be done every time to the correct standard.

Watch how the senior staff tackles difficult or complex tasks. Stand by them and offer your help, you can learn a lot more if you are able to see closely how procedures are completed. Ask questions, sometimes things are far more complex than they seem.

If you are wandering around aimlessly at work it is probably because you don't know what you should be doing. Just think how your colleagues will see this; they might view you as lazy or deliberately trying to avoid working as a team player. If you are unclear about what you should be doing at work, ask your manager or a senior member of staff.

EKU statement

G8.18) The importance of continually using and updating your own personal development plan

G8.14) Who can help you identify and obtain opportunities for your development/training

EKU statement

G8.15) How using the National Occupational Standards for Hairdressing can help you identify your development needs

G8.16) How to access Information on National Occupational Standards and qualifications, relevant to hairdressing

EKU statement

G8.5) Why it is important to work within your job responsibilities and what might happen if you do not do so

Work towards the industry-recognised National Occupational Standards (NOS)

The standards set down by HABIA provide the minimum requirements for anyone working competently. At NVQ Level 2, the NOS encompass all the jobs that you will be doing as a junior stylist in work. As you work through the units you will find that some tasks are easier than others and you shouldn't be worried as there can be many reasons for that. Everyone is different and, in training, people have different learning styles.

Some trainees handle visual tasks easier than others, they watch closely looking at details and methods. Others find that practice makes perfect; the continual repetition of practical processes is the only way that they can master the skill. Yet others can be told something once and it is indelibly etched into their minds.

When trainees start work in a salon, much of what goes on can seem quite alien. This can seem overwhelming; the large majority of people who come into the craft wanting to be hairdressers are shocked by the amount of things that they need to learn. The NOS comprise of many units and each one can have several component parts. When the units are broken down into the smaller, more manageable bits, they don't seem quite so bad. In fact much of what is learned in one unit can be applied to others as well.

The NOS provides a specification, a template, for the correct methods of working. It highlights the techniques that you need to use when working and the order or sequence in which hairdressing tasks are done. If you don't follow these pre-set procedures and try to do things your own way, these things will happen:

1 The result of what you are attempting to do will be wrong.

2 You will be not only letting yourself down, but all your other colleagues with whom you work too.

3 You will find yourself in the manager's office explaining why you thought your way was a better idea.

In many hairdressing procedures there are other ways of doing things, but you must know what the expected result is, before you can work out other ways of doing tasks. This is why the National Occupational Standards exist: they provide you with the simplest correct ways of doing things so that you know you are doing things right.

Identifying your own strengths and weaknesses

The periodical process of evaluation and review is called 'appraisal'. It can be undertaken in two ways: by yourself, that is self-appraisal (you measure your own strengths and weaknesses against set standards) or in conjunction with your manager on a more formal basis.

Being able to spot your own mistakes is a starting point. We all know that if we do things the right way, we gain the personal satisfaction of getting it right. Conversely, if we keep making mistakes and get it wrong more times than right, we feel wretched and that will inevitably lose the salon's clients. This low self-esteem needs to be avoided; it is negative and does nothing for our self-motivation.

EKU *statement*

G8.12) How to identify your strengths and weaknesses

G8.13) The importance of continuous professional development and how it affects your job role

EKU *statement*

G8.6) The standards of behaviour that are expected of you when working in the salon

Activity

Fill in the middle column with the letters A, B, C, etc. for the statements that best apply to you (here is an example):

Level of ability	Employee fills in this column	Supervisor fills in this column
I can do this very well		
I can do this OK		
I think I'm getting there		
I find this a bit tricky		
I can't do this at all		
I can do this very well	A, G, H, P	

A *I neutralise perms on short to medium-length hair*

B *I neutralise perms on long hair*

C *I handle payments by cards at reception*

D *I make appointments for all services*

E *I help, assist and communicate with clients on a routine basis*

F *I prepare the chemicals carefully for the stylists*

G *I recommend products to clients, encouraging them to buy*

H *I recommend treatments to clients, encouraging them to buy*

I *I conduct salon business over the phone*

J *I blow-dry clients' hair to help out the stylists*

K *I apply colour for stylists*

L *I am always punctual for work*

M *I am particular about my appearance*

N *I thoroughly clean and prepare the working surfaces*

O *I monitor the usage of stock and materials*

P *I notice when things need doing*

Q *I recognise situations where there may be a potential hazard*

After you have completed the activity of putting the letters A–Q in the appropriate box, you may have other additional statements that you want to add to your list. Does your supervisor agree with your responses? Hand this to your supervisor and ask to have your responses checked. Lastly, your supervisor can fill in the last column in the same way. Now see if both columns match.

The important aspect of self-appraisal is having the ability to make an honest evaluation and review of your own progress. Try the activity below as an example of how you could do this for yourself.

Work to achievable, mutually agreed personal and salon targets

In many work settings you will be asked to complete some form of self-evaluation before the performance appraisal. The self-evaluation (if completed honestly) will provide a discussion document which can be used to *shape* the appraisal process and identify the areas where you now meet expectations or alternatively, have further room for improvements.

The appraisal process

At the beginning of the appraisal period, the manager and the employee jointly discuss, develop and mutually agree the objectives and performance measures (targets) for that period. An individual learning plan will then be drafted, outlining the expected outcomes over the next review period.

During the appraisal period, should there be any significant changes in factors such as objectives or performance measures, these will be discussed between the manager and employee and any amendments will be added to the action plan/individual learning plan.

At the end of the appraisal period, the results are discussed by the employee and the manager, and both manager and employee sign the appraisal. A copy is prepared for the employee and the original is kept on file.

An appraisal of performance will contain the following information:

- appraisee's name
- appraisal period

- appraiser's name and title
- performance objectives
- job title
- work location
- results achieved
- identified areas of strengths and weaknesses
- an ongoing action plan (individual learning plan)
- an (optional) overall performance grading.

Activity

Self-Appraisal   Name . . . .

This self-appraisal is designed to help you reflect on your job performance. After completion this will be used as a discussion document within your appraisal

1   In what aspects of your job do you feel that you have performed well?

2   In what aspects of your job do you think that you could do better?

3   What aspects of your job do you particularly like?

4   What aspects of your job do you dislike?

5   What things have you encountered within your work that you have found difficult?

Remember

The appraisal is a positive and forward-looking process, including:

- positive feedback for the things that are going well
- constructive and fair criticism where there are weaknesses
- positive suggestions
- setting of specific targets
- follow-up after appraisal.

EKU *statement*

G8.18) The importance of continually using and updating your own personal development plan

G8.20) How to react positively to reviews and feedback and why this is important

Remember

Preparing for appraisal
- Think about each statement on the form.
- Think about the things you are good at.
- Think about any issues you have.
- Write some notes to remind you about what you want to talk about during the meeting. These may include things that are not covered by the form. (Don't forget to take your notes with you to the meeting.)

For you, the appraisal is a good way to air any problems in the workplace and to make points about training needs and the future. For your supervisor, it is a good way to identify possible problems in the workplace, training needs and to contribute towards effective management.

EKU *statement*

G8.8) The commercially viable range of times for the performance of hairdressing services offered

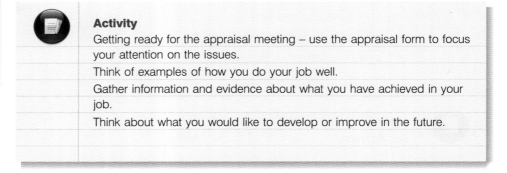

Activity

Getting ready for the appraisal meeting – use the appraisal form to focus your attention on the issues.

Think of examples of how you do your job well.

Gather information and evidence about what you have achieved in your job.

Think about what you would like to develop or improve in the future.

At the meeting

Refer to your appraisal form and your notes to remind yourself of what you want to say.

- Be positive, express yourself clearly.
- Ask questions.
- Discuss and agree your next steps with your manager.
- Make sure the appraisal form is filled in with details of what is agreed.

After the meeting

- Remind your manager about how he or she agreed to help you.
- Make sure you keep to the agreements you made.

Review your progress towards targets

The joint review process of appraisal would fulfil no purpose at all unless it looks at your current situation, your feelings and work performances. It should then measure that against the mutually agreed targets and then finally, create an ongoing development plan/individual learning plan, which can be reviewed at some future date.

EKU *statement*

G8.18) The importance of continually using and updating your own personal development plan

Ask for help

However, you should not wait for a formal review or appraisal. If you are having problems with any aspect of your training or your job you should ask for support or assistance from a senior stylist, your trainer or manager. If you have completed the objectives set out in your training or appraisal before the due target date, ask for more objectives to be set. This will help to keep you more motivated by completing your training earlier and increasing your knowledge of the job, enabling you to do higher-skilled work.

Performance appraisal

Name:	*Kira Kortova*
Job title:	*Trainee stylist*
Date of previous appraisal	*N/A*
Review of prior targets and objectives	*New employee (started 5/1/2009)*
Date of this appraisal:	*5/6/2009*
Objectives:	*To obtain competence within:* • *cutting hair layering techniques across the range.* • *blow-drying hair on a variety of hair types and lengths.*
Notes on achievement:	*Competence has been achieved across the range for all the cutting requirements.*
	Competence has been achieved for most blow-drying range requirements.
Training requirements:	*Further training and practice is needed within the area of blow-drying longer length effects.*
Any other comments on performance by appraiser:	*Kira has achieved most of the objectives set out during the last appraisal.*
Any comments on the appraisal by the staff member appraised:	*I feel that this has been a fair appraisal of my progress although I did not achieve all of my performance targets.* *K.Kortova*
Action plan:	*To achieve occupational competence across the range for blow-drying (i.e. longer length hair).*
	To undergo training and practice in perming methods and techniques.
	To take assessment for perming.
Date of next appraisal:	*4/12/2009*

An appraisal form

SMART objectives

Well-defined objectives will fit the SMART principle. This is a common target setting system that ensures that expected outcomes are:

- **Specific** – The target(s) should be unambiguous; providing clear objectives.
- **Measurable** – Set in a context that is objective; e.g. 'Must achieve 100 per cent of sales targets'.
- **Achievable** – Within the bounds of the appraisee's capabilities.
- **Realistic** – Appropriate to the needs of the appraisee in relation to the appraisee's abilities.
- **Timed** – Set with an agreed time-line from the outset.

EKU *statement*

G8.2) How to get information about your job, your work responsibilities and the standards expected of you

G8.3) How to find out relevant information about other people's areas of responsibility

Activity
Strengths and weaknesses chart
This activity provides a way for you to study and assess your strengths and weaknesses at work.

COURTESY OF SAKS HAIR & BEAUTY, WWW.SAKS.CO.UK

EKU statement

G8.6) The standards of behaviour that are expected of you when working in the salon

G8.9) Your productivity targets and time-scales

G8.10) Your personal development targets and time-scales

G8.11) The importance *of* meeting your work targets

When you have filled in the table below ask your trainer to check your responses.

Personal skill	My strengths	My weaknesses
Dealing with clients		
Communicating with work colleagues		
Organising my own work		
Helping others in their work		
Sorting out things myself		

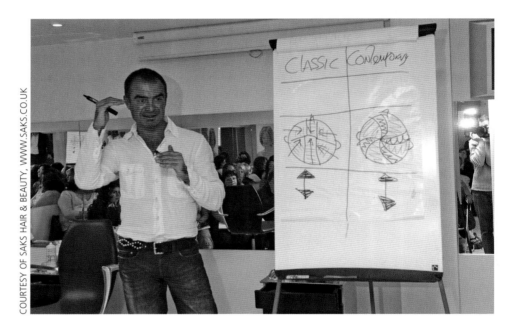

Measuring effectiveness

To be able to measure progress towards training targets as well as overall work contributions, there needs to be clear, stated expectations of the performance required of you. For both training and work activities, this is the standard to which you will need to demonstrate competence.

In training situations, your personal programme will state the:

- training activities that will take place
- tasks which need to be performed
- standards and the levels of performance expected
- types of assessment that should be expected
- review of your progress towards these agreed targets and when it is to take place.

In normal work situations, performance appraisal will be based on the following factors:

- results achieved against set objectives and job requirements
- any additional accomplishments and contributions

- contributions made by the individual as compared with those of other staff members.

The job requirements will be outlined in your employee's job description. A job description is a list of the functions and roles expected within the job. The job descriptions should include details of the following:

- the job title
- the work location(s)
- responsibility (to whom and for what)
- the job purpose
- main functions (listed)
- standards expected
- any other special conditions.

The standards expected from the job holder will often be produced in the staff handbook. They would normally include:

- standards of behaviour and appearance
- the salon's code of conduct
- Job description
- the grievance procedure
- employee legal entitlements and responsibilities
- health and safety requirements.

EKU *statement*

G8.1) Your job role and responsibilities and how this relates to the role of other team members

Remember

 Whether it is called appraisal, evaluation, assessment or review, a meeting or interview with your manager can help you to think about:

- how you feel about your job
- how your training is going
- what you would like to do in the future.

Job description – Stylist	
Location:	Based at salon as advised
Main purpose of job:	To ensure customer care is provided at all times
	To maintain a good standard of technical and client care, ensuring that up-to-date methods and techniques are used following the salon training practices and procedures
Responsible to:	Salon manager
Requirements:	To maintain the company's standards in respect of hairdressing/beauty services
	To ensure that all clients receive service of the best possible quality
	To advise clients on services and treatments
	To advise clients on products and after-care
	To achieve designated performance targets
	To participate in self-development or to assist with the development of others
	To maintain company policy in respect of:
	• personal standards of health/hygiene
	• personal standards of appearance/conduct
	• operating safely whilst at work
	• timekeeping and service provision
	• brand image and public promotion
	as laid out in employee handbook
	To carry out client consultation in accordance with company policy
	To maintain company security practices and procedures
	To assist your manager in the provision of salon services
	To undertake additional tasks and duties required by your manager from time to time.

If these have been stated from the outset, at least the employee knows what is expected. If you do not have a job description ask your employer or manager if you can have one, so that you know precisely what is expected of you and how your job role fits into or alongside those of your colleagues. You will have a clear guide on your *limits of authority*. Some large salons will have a staff structure chart that explains everyone's role in the salon and the reporting structure.

EKU *statement*

G8.19) Why harmonious working relationships are important

G8.21) Support cooperative ways of working (e.g. anticipate the needs of others for information and support, avoid actions that discriminate against others or offend others, act assertively when needed to protect your rights, show that you are willing to help resolve disagreements)

Activity

Look at the statements on the left and match them up with the corresponding statement on the right.

Relationships at work are based upon	personal preferences and choice
Friendships outside work are based upon	effective communication takes place
Customer care is built on	mutual respect and teamwork
Good customer relations occur when	professionalism and personal service
Teamwork takes place when	making the best of personal strengths and working to improve weaknesses
Self-development in the job role means	all the staff do their jobs efficiently

G8.2 Work effectively as part of a team

Creating and maintaining good working relationships with your fellow staff members is essential. Only a harmonious working team can be productive and effective. The relationships that must be built and maintained at work are very different to those that exist outside of that environment. Hairdressing businesses rely solely upon providing a repeat service to its customers at a price that is profitable for the firm and that its clients are happy to pay.

The formula may seem simple: unfortunately it isn't. There are so many factors that affect this delicate balance. Unlike other businesses, personal services rely solely upon people and the communication between them.

Hairdressing is not just about selling. Why is that? Well, when a product is sold, more often than not, the purchaser has made a conscious decision to buy. The standard or quality is defined by the product's composition. The only factors affecting the sale are competing products and their price, availability, features and benefits.

Remember

There is a huge difference between the friendships that you build out of choice and the others that you have to accept and work with in the professional world.

Be an effective team member

When you work in a salon, regardless of whether it is a large company chain or a small independent salon, you will be an important part of their team. You will be working with other people whom you don't know, yet you will have to get on with them. As a team member you will need to know:

- the other members of the team
- who is responsible for different things
- to whom you need to go if you need any help.

Teamwork is about making an active contribution, seeking to assist others even if it is only holding brushes whilst the stylist is blow-drying. Don't expect to be asked to do things all the time; think ahead and see if you can anticipate what others will need.

Anticipating the needs of others is a follow-on from providing support by cleaning and preparing the work areas ready for use, locating and preparing products as and when they are required.

ISTOCKPHOTO.COM/PIDJOE

Respond to requests willingly

Cooperate with your colleagues. Make a positive contribution to your team. When a colleague asks you for help you should respond willingly and politely to the request. Remember, working in a public place is like being on show all the time. Clients will see, hear and *feel* any tension within the salon. How others see you in your work role will have a huge impact on your professionalism: you would rather be thought of as a willing, helpful trainee than a quiet, moody one!

Maintain harmony and always try to minimise conflicts. Most good working relationships develop easily; others, however, will need to be worked at. People at work are different, so in order for you to work as a team player you must develop a mutual respect for others, even if they would *never* get on your personal friends list.

EKU *statement*

G8.3) How to find out relevant information about other people's areas of responsibility

G8.22) How to manage your time *effectively*

Make effective use of your working day

Always make good use of your time. In a busy salon there is always something that needs doing, so sometimes you will have to juggle between two or three things at the same time!

- Keep a list of the different tasks you have been asked to do (that way you won't get into trouble for trying to remember them all).
- Find out which ones take priority. Some jobs are more important or urgent and they will need to be done first.
- If you don't understand what has been asked of you, ask someone before it's too late!
- Remember, if you do have to leave something halfway through, make sure that you get back to complete it at the earliest convenient moment.

ISTOCKPHOTO.COM/ STEPHAN ZABEL

Remember

 Treat other people as you would wish to be treated yourself.

EKU *statement*

G8.24) How to deal with relationship difficulties and conflicts when working with others

EKU *statement*

G8.22) How to manage your time *effectively*

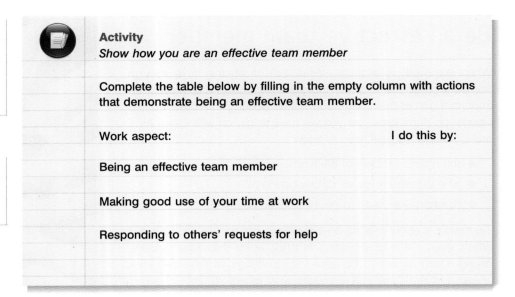

Activity
Show how you are an effective team member

Complete the table below by filling in the empty column with actions that demonstrate being an effective team member.

Work aspect:	I do this by:
Being an effective team member	
Making good use of your time at work	
Responding to others' requests for help	

Report problems to relevant people

Within any organisational structure there is a hierarchy and this is important for you to know to whom you should go if you need any help or have any grievances.

Remember

- Treat others with respect.
- Be sensitive and responsive to the needs of others.
- Show concern and care for others.
- Avoid actions that may offend others.

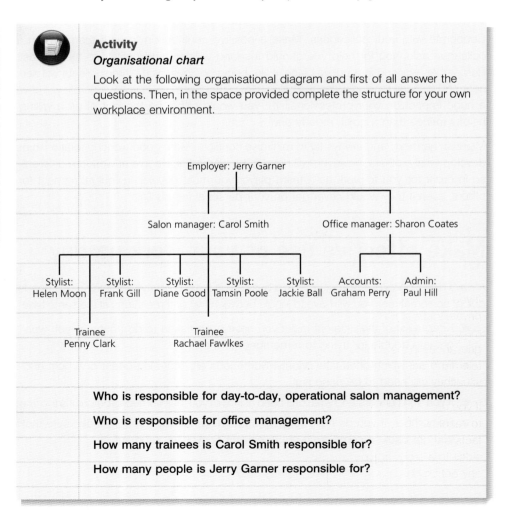

Activity
Organisational chart

Look at the following organisational diagram and first of all answer the questions. Then, in the space provided complete the structure for your own workplace environment.

Who is responsible for day-to-day, operational salon management?

Who is responsible for office management?

How many trainees is Carol Smith responsible for?

How many people is Jerry Garner responsible for?

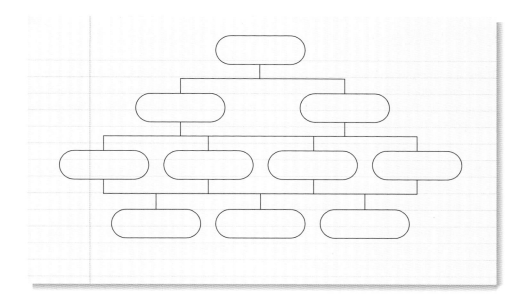

As you can see from the example above, different people do different jobs. For example, you would need to know whom to contact if you were ill and couldn't get into work. Conversely, if you had a query about your wages you might need to contact somebody else.

In another situation, imagine that a client has returned to the salon with a complaint about her hair and she is demanding her money back. You won't have the authority to deal with this; you will have to get someone to handle the complaint.

EKU *statement*

G8.23) Whom to report to when you have difficulties in working with others

Activity

What is your salon's policy in respect to handling client complaints? Write your answer in your portfolio.

Resolving problems with other members of the team

EKU *statement*

G8.7) Your salon's appeal and grievance procedure

If you do have a problem with another member of the team, you need to approach them privately about it first. You should think carefully about what you are going to say and make sure that your time and place is suitable. It is highly unprofessional to air your grievances in the public salon area; any backchat or arguing in front of clients will not be tolerated. So save it, count to ten and choose a more appropriate time to tackle the situation.

If you cannot sort it out yourselves, you should report it to your manager who will want to resolve the situation quickly and fairly. Make sure that you cover all the relevant facts and provide any other supporting information. Remember there are always two sides to a story, so your manager will want to hear the other side as well before taking any action.

Remember

 Never carry out any task at work if you are unsure what has been asked of you. Ask a senior colleague to explain what the task involves.

Grievance and disciplinary procedures

There are times when disputes cannot be sorted out easily. In these situations a formal salon procedure comes into play. Your salon will have its own way of implementing grievance or disciplinary procedures, and you should receive this information during your induction. The procedure will cover the following issues:

- conflict at work between staff
- unfair or presumed unfair treatment at work (e.g. being asked to do tasks beyond your abilities or unsafe practices)
- discrimination in any situation or scenario.

Where staff members fail to meet the required standards, they can expect disciplinary action to be taken against them. This can vary between salons. Up until now the following formal steps were involved:

Step 1   Verbal warning
Step 2   Written warning
Step 3   Dismissal

Though salons can still choose to follow this disciplinary procedure, there is now no legal requirement to do so, to allow greater flexibility between you and your employer when resolving disputes.

Acts of gross misconduct/gross incompetence

Your salon will have its own standards and expectations relating to conduct and behaviour and the team are happier in their work if they know what is expected of them.

The following list provides examples of acts of gross misconduct:

- carrying or taking illicit drugs on the work premises
- thieving from the salon or fellow staff members
- drinking alcohol on the premises
- wilfully damaging company property
- endangering yourself, fellow staff members or salon clients and visitors
- disclosing private company information and data.

Acts of gross incompetence will have the same summary dismissal as gross misconduct. These actions of negligence can occur during normal work activities and will put the salon's good name and reputation in jeopardy. Typical examples of this would be:

- careless or improper use of chemicals on clients, e.g. spillages causing bodily harm incurring hospitalisation
- careless timing of chemical treatments, e.g. causing scalp burns, hair damage or loss
- careless or improper use of equipment, e.g. tampering with electrical items causing harm to others, incorrect timings of processes causing harm or damage.

Remember

There are a number of actions that fall outside of this disciplinary procedure.

Acts of gross misconduct if proven will always incur summary dismissal.

EKU *statement*

G8.6) The standards of behaviour that are expected of you when working in the salon

Remember

If you are unsure of what constitutes an act of gross misconduct or an act of gross incompetence/ negligence, ask your supervisor.

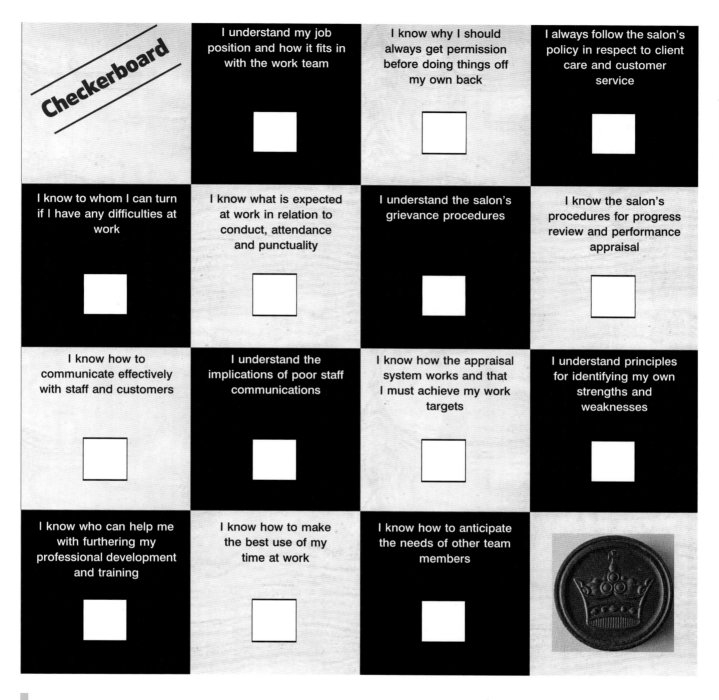

Checkerboard

Checkerboard	I understand my job position and how it fits in with the work team	I know why I should always get permission before doing things off my own back	I always follow the salon's policy in respect to client care and customer service
I know to whom I can turn if I have any difficulties at work	I know what is expected at work in relation to conduct, attendance and punctuality	I understand the salon's grievance procedures	I know the salon's procedures for progress review and performance appraisal
I know how to communicate effectively with staff and customers	I understand the implications of poor staff communications	I know how the appraisal system works and that I must achieve my work targets	I understand principles for identifying my own strengths and weaknesses
I know who can help me with furthering my professional development and training	I know how to make the best use of my time at work	I know how to anticipate the needs of other team members	

Assessment of knowledge and understanding

Project

For this project you will need to gather information from other people with whom you work.

There is a simple tried-and-tested method for self-assessing one's own current position: the SWOT analysis. This helps you think through your:

- strengths
- weaknesses

- opportunities
- threats

in relation to where you are now and where you need to be.

For each of the titles – strengths, weaknesses, opportunities and threats – write a small summary of your attributes, and then show this to your supervisor to see if they agree.

The completed SWOT analysis can be recorded in your portfolio and will provide a basis for your future action plan.

Activity
SWOT analysis

After completing your SWOT analysis, look a little more closely at the positive and negative aspects.

Choosing the positive aspects first. How can you develop these attributes further?

Now select the negative aspects. What do you need to do in order to change these into positives too?

This exercise will help you form the basis of your next action plan: discuss your SWOT analysis and your suggested routes for further development with your trainer.

Keep copies of all the information for use in your portfolio.

Revision questions

A selection of different types of questions to check your personal effectiveness knowledge.

Q1 Working in _____ minimises conflict between staff members.

Fill in the blank

Q2 Relationships at work are different to those outside of work.

True or false

Q3 Which of the following are examples of good team work?

Multi selection

Sitting in the staff room exchanging jokes	☐ 1
Preparing trolleys with curlers	☐ 2
Sitting at the reception desk	☐ 3
Recognising the needs of others	☐ 4
Collecting cakes at break time	☐ 5
Passing up materials to the stylists	☐ 6

Q4 Personal development is about getting your own way.

True or false

Q5 Which of the following is part of SWOT analysis?

Multi choice

Diluting peroxide strengths	○ a
Identifying personal opportunities	○ b
Threatening others	○ c
Feeling weak	○ d

Q6 Talking and listening to your seniors is an important part of good team communications.　　　　　　　True or false

Q7 What takes place in an appraisal?　　　　　　　Multi selection

A review of your aspirations	☐ 1
A review of your current position	☐ 2
A review of your future conduct	☐ 3
A review of your past conduct	☐ 4
A review of clients treatment history	☐ 5
An informal chat about your fellow staff	☐ 6

Q8 Your non-verbal communication will say more about what you are _____ than your mouth.　　　　　　　Fill in the blank

Q9 Which of the following is contained in a job description?　　　　　　　Multi choice

Records of your conduct	○ a
Terms and conditions of employment	○ b
Roles and responsibilities	○ c
Records of your training	○ d

Q10 Your effectiveness at work is also linked to your efficiency.　　　　　　　True or false

Preparing for assessment checklist

Remember to:

✔	communicate positively and effectively in the salon at all times
✔	develop yourself in those activities that provide further progress in your career
✔	work together harmoniously with others as a team player
✔	recognise the occasions when others need assistance
✔	work at maintaining professional relationships with fellow staff members
✔	use your time efficiently and effectively
✔	work towards personal targets and know why they should be achieved.

Chapter**three**
Personal presentation

G17

G17.1

G17.2

G17.3

Customer communication: quick overview

Unit title

G17 Give clients a positive impression of yourself and your organisation

This is a **mandatory** unit for hairdressing and an **optional** unit for barbering and is made up of three main outcomes

Main outcomes

G17.1 Establish effective rapport with clients

G17.2 Respond appropriately to clients

G17.3 Communicate information to clients

What do I need to do for G17.1?

- Always make sure your appearance is suitable for personal service

- Make clients feel valued, communicate in a professional, respectful and friendly way

- Listen and respond to clients' needs

- Keep clients informed, be reassuring and positive during their visit

What do I need to do for G17.2?

- Respond promptly to client requests for assistance

- Modify your communication with clients to suit the purpose or event

- Confirm with clients that you have understood their requests

- Respond to clients' in an appropriate way

- Give time for clients to consider your offers of service

What do I need to do for G17.3?

- Respond promptly to clients' requests for information

- Provide accurate information about salon services

- Provide explanations for information that clients may find confusing or complicated

- Be clear with your explanation when clients' needs or requests can not be met

What aspects do I need to cover for G17.1, G17.2 and G17.3?

- All aspects and references to good customer service whenever you communicate to the salon's clientele

What do I need to know for G17.1, G17.2, and G17.3?

- The salon's policy in regard to expected behaviour and appearance

- The salon's policy in regard to customer contact/communication

- The salon's policy in respect to responding to client requests

- How to recognise when clients are angry, confused or dissatisfied

Keywords

Communication
Listening, hearing and responding to the client

Body language
The *visual* communication of feelings, emotions and views

Client care
Maintaining goodwill whilst developing a regular, repeated business

Information covered in this chapter

- Personal appearance and behaviour
- Good customer service
- Client communication
- Verbal and written communication
- Non-verbal communication (body language and mood recognition)

Introduction

If there were a motto that you needed to learn for this chapter it is this one.

You don't get a second chance to make a good first impression.

Good customer communication is an essential part of any successful business. Get it right and many positive attributes are inferred; a professional, good service, respect for others, care and control. All these things are perceived to be the indicators of a quality service. Poor customer communication is none of these!

All of us enjoy the experience of good service if we feel that the person serving us really wants to create the right impression; i.e. by responding to our needs and giving us useful, accurate information. So as hairdressers we are always on show, every detail of our behaviour when we deal with clients is plain to see. How we conduct ourselves affects the impression that the clients form of the service they receive. *Excellent client service can only be provided by people who are good with people* and the key word here is communication, in particular professional communication.

G17.1 Establish effective rapport with clients

Presenting yourself

The introduction to this section referred to creating a positive impression as being the first part of good customer communication. Unfortunately, it is human nature to

EKU *statement*

G17.1) Your salon's requirements for appearance and behaviour

be judgemental and that means that we all tend to try to quantify and *catalogue* everything that we come into contact with. We observe it and our minds quickly give it a label. In other words, we see something and we quickly search through our memories to see if it resembles something that we have already encountered. If we have, we catalogue it and give it a label with that reference. The whole process takes a few seconds!

Lazy, reticent, eager, professional, scary, attractive.

There are a few labels that we attach to others. So how do you want to be viewed?

Personal standards

Appearance

Your personal appearance is as important as your personal cleanliness. The effort you put into getting ready for work reflects your pride in the job. Your own individual look is OK as long as you appreciate and accept that there are professional standards of dress and appearance that must be followed.

Clothes

It's far easier to wear a uniform at work than your own clothes. Uniforms are created specifically with work in mind; they are an easy option for cleaning, maintenance and eliminating difficult 'what to wear' choices.

If you do wear your own clothes they should be clean, well ironed and made from fabrics that are suitable not only for your intended work, but also for the time of year. Also, clothes revealing too much of your body will be considered unprofessional and possibly provocative!

Remember

 A good hairdresser considers others, adapts to situations and is respectful to clients at all times.

Shoes

Hairdressing involves a lot of standing and your feet can get tired, hot, sweaty and even sore, so wear sensible shoes with low heels and make sure the shoe will protect your feet from any falling objects.

It is also better to wear shoes that allow your feet to 'breathe', as ventilated feet remain cool and comfortable throughout the working day. Many modern materials can combine comfort with contemporary style. Trainers are great but check that your workplace permits them before turning up at work in them.

Your hair

When working in a salon, it is important to maintain a professional appearance and your hair needs to be clean and well presented. Long hair should be kept away from your face to allow eye contact with clients and display positive body language.

Jewellery

It is better not to wear too much jewellery because it harbours germs. Rings, bracelets and long necklaces can get in the way of everyday tasks such as washing hair. Moisture and shampooing products may get trapped under rings and this can cause dermatitis. Jewellery will also cause discomfort to clients if it gets caught in their hair.

Greeting and meeting clients

Your greeting of the client is the next way, beyond the first impression, on how you will be judged. Get this right and any previous invisible barriers or uncertainties will disappear.

New customers entering into the salon need to be made to feel welcome; don't forget, they are walking into an alien environment. They don't know what to expect and may not know anyone who works within the salon. Similarly, the regular client needs to feel part of the business too, they expect the familiar faces whom they see on a regular basis to recognise them and to welcome them too.

This is the difference between being a customer at a shop and a valued client in a salon. We can show people that we remember them by the way that we greet them.

- Stop what you are doing.
- Make eye to eye contact.
- Say 'Good morning (or afternoon) Mrs XXXX'.
- Ask 'How can I help you?'

Remember

There are three main reasons for talking to clients and colleagues; to:

1 welcome people

2 pass on information and

3 get information.

EKU *statement*

G17.1) Your salon's requirements for appearance and behaviour

G17.4) Your salon's rules and procedures regarding the methods of communication you use

G17.2   Respond appropriately to clients

What is good customer service?

Good customer service means making the client your number one priority. Quite simply, it is looking after their individual needs and making sure that their visit to the salon is both a pleasurable and enjoyable experience. This begins from the point that the client makes contact with or enters into the salon, and continues until they leave. Helping the client to manage their own hair between visits extends the service they receive from you further. Initially, aftercare advice is provided by the stylist, but you can help too. If you have any tips or have found that certain equipment or accessories work well, tell them how they can get the results they are looking for.

How can I respond appropriately to clients?

✔	Be respectful and polite in the way that you speak to them.
✔	Listen to what they have to say and *hear* their requests.
✔	Identify their needs and understand their requests.
✔	Avoid talking about contentious or controversial issues.
✔	Provide feedback on progress and keep clients informed.

Remember

 Good customer relationships are built to L.A.S.T.

L = Listen

- Concentrate on what the client is saying.
- Show the client that you are listening properly through open body language.
- Ask for further information or for details to be repeated, if required.
- Check the information – repeat details back to the client.

A = Apologise

- Empathise with the client.
- Always remain calm, polite and professional.
- Use appropriate language, tone and body language.
- Don't make excuses or blame others.

S = Solve

- Follow company guidelines or procedures.
- Deal with problems as quickly as possible.
- Tell the client what you are going to do and by when.
- Follow up any problems you passed on to someone else.

T = Thank

- Thank the client for bringing the problem to your attention.
- Use a sincere tone of voice.

Activity

Customer care and communication

Complete this table by writing in the space on the right the sorts of things that you could do that would demonstrate good customer care in relation to the word(s) on the left.

Items:	How could you demonstrate good customer care?
Magazines	
Tea or coffee	
Towel and gown	
Products and services	

Paying respect

We are familiar with being told that you can't demand respect you have to earn it, but it's different for customers: they can expect it.

So why is that? Well, unlike us, who have to earn respect from others, the valued business customer is *paying* for it and that's how service industries work.

Listening and hearing

See Communication (page 51).

Identify needs

There are two ways to identify and establish the needs of the client:

1 by examination and analysis
2 by asking questions.

The methods of examination and analysis are covered elsewhere in this book (see Consultation and Advice, Chapter 5).

Questioning If we don't ask, we won't know; we want the client to feel valued and properly served during their visit. We just can't assume the needs of others, guessing what they want; in nine cases out of ten we would be way off the mark. Good customer service is finding out what the client wants by questioning and then doing something about it with a prompt, accurate and respectful response.

Contentious and controversial issues

Generally speaking, people like to talk and the hairdressing salon is one of those places where conversation is not only expected, but good fun too. However, beware: you must be a professional at all times. Be careful what you say and to whom you are saying it to!

Never get drawn into conversations that lead to gossip. It's OK to talk about TV programmes, music interests, celebrities and the reported things that they have done, but it's quite another to discuss stories about people that you or the client knows!

There are other taboos too: keep away from politics and religion. It's OK for you to have your opinions, as long as you don't end up *haranguing* other people about them. Remember, what you believe in is personal and important to you, but you can't and must not expect everyone else to hold the same views.

Provide feedback on progress

Keep clients informed. Many of the salon's services and treatments involve lengthy processes and procedures, and that can mean plenty of waiting around. Well,

EKU *statement*

G17.2) Your salon's guidelines for how to recognise what your client wants and respond appropriately

G17.4) Your salon's timeliness in responding to client questions and requests for information

I-STOCK/©ANA ABEJON

Remember

When talking to clients
What you believe in is personal and important to you, but you can't and mustn't expect everyone else to hold the same views.

that's how it can seem to a client when they are waiting for a perm or treatment to develop.

For example: if a client is waiting in reception, tell them what is happening and why they haven't been attended to yet. Similarly, if a client has had a colouring service, then the colour needs a certain amount of time to develop. Explain what is happening and give an indication of how long it will take. (And if you don't know, find out from the stylist first.)

Good service checklist

The client's trust and goodwill are enhanced by clear communication and in the ways that you communicate with them. Leaving misunderstandings unexplained can undermine a great deal of hard work. So, while you are working, make sure that you:

- Tell the client the reasons for any delays or disruptions in services. Give them reassurance in what is taking place, particularly if it involves a new service or a different look.
- Learn to recognise the needs of your clients. Everyone is different with differing requirements.
- Remember your clients and things about them; even the simplest of things can make all the difference – whether a client prefers coffee to tea, or if they take sugar in hot drinks. Little things like this show that you have listened and learned and, what's more, you have taken an interest in them.
- Tell your client about the services that your salon provides, the special techniques and promotions that are currently on offer.
- Get help from your team. If there is something that you are not sure about or something unexpected is happening, get a senior's opinion and avoid something going wrong.

EKU *statement*

G17.3) Your salon's rules and procedures regarding the methods of communication you use

Remember

 The language you use depends on to whom you are talking, why you are talking and where you are.

With colleagues

Your language may be quite informal (but not in front of clients). You may also use some technical terms.

With clients

Your language will generally be more formal but you will need to simplify or explain technical terms.

Activity
In your own words, write down what these words mean to you:

Goodwill

Client care

Positive communication

Body language

Good service

Activity

Barriers to communication

Certain situations like those listed below can get in the way of effective communication. Discuss ways in which these potential barriers can be overcome.

1　Physical barriers

2　Time constraints

3　Assumptions

4　Moods and attitudes

5　Language barriers

6　Personality clashes

7　Background noise

Remember

 Speech volume
A loud voice is often thought of as aggressive or overbearing.

A quiet or soft voice is often thought of as timid or polite.

G17.3　Communicate information to clients

Communication

Good communicators use a mixture of skills in their daily routines. They have:

- *Excellent listening skills* – This is the ability to hear and understand what the client is saying. This can be particularly useful as sometimes the person prompting the change may not be the client in the chair! Other people can have a strong influence on our clients, so you need to find out if the proposed changes are realistic, suitable, practical or even possible.

- *Good speaking skills* – Long silences can often be uncomfortable. Knowing when it is right to speak or when to keep quiet is an invaluable interpersonal skill. During a normal consultation you, the hairdresser, will be taking the lead. You will be asking questions, i.e. trying to elicit enough information in the time span available to make the right judgements. You will be weighing up what the client wants and balancing it against the limitations arising from the analysis. You will be getting the client to agree on the various possible options and planning the necessary course of action.

- In day-to-day, routine communication with a client the balance can change. More often than not, the client will have plenty to say, particularly when you ask them about what has happened since their last visit.

- *'Reading' skills* – The ability to read situations, to understand what has been said or not said, is exceptionally useful. There are times when your client will take

EKU *statement*

G17.3) Your salon's rules and procedures regarding the methods of communication you use

I-STOCK/©SANDRA GLIGORIJEVIC

MICHAEL BARNES FOR GOLDWELL

Remember

It's not what you say it's how you say it.
Vocal (voice)

Volume (how loud or quiet)

Pace (how fast or slow)

Pitch (how high or low)

Tone (the manner of speaking)

Feedback sounds ('mmm', 'ah-ha', 'errr').

Remember

Tone of voice

You can often tell what mood someone is in from the tone they use.

on a certain facial expression, or say something that makes you think. In these situations, your ability to read the situation, your perceptiveness in picking this up and responding appropriately may have a crucial impact on your long-term relationship.

Activity

Communication

Good communication with clients is essential. Without it, a stylist will not make the right decisions or take the correct courses of action.

Write down what you think are the advantages or disadvantages for the following communication techniques.

Communication technique	Advantages	Disadvantages
Example: Hand gestures	Helps to direct people – shows them the way	Can appear rude if it isn't backed up with helpful advice
Other body language		
Oral communication		
Written communication		

We communicate to one another in the following ways:

- verbal communication
- non-verbal communication
- written communication.

Verbal communication

Verbal communication is what you say and what others hear, it should always be:

- clear to the listener
- brief and to the point
- uncomplicated – easy to understand, avoiding the use of technical terms
- friendly and courteous.

Speech is used to pass on information and to ask questions. We have already covered the professional ways of passing on information to clients and staff. But we also need to gain information from others too, and that's done by questioning:

- *Closed questions* – This type of question should be avoided. Closed questions lead the client to give only simple yes or no responses and yield very little information. Examples are: 'Have you washed your hair with anything different lately?' 'Do you find the colour application at home is easy?' 'Have you always had a centre parting?' 'Did you have your highlights done recently?'

- *Open questions* – These are a better type of question to use when you want the client to give you information. Examples are: 'What products do you use when you wash your hair at home?' 'How do you apply the colour when you do it at home?' 'Which way do you style the front of your hair?' 'When was the last time that you had a full set of highlights?' You will have informal conversations chatting with your client during the service and more formal, structured conversations greeting your client and in a consultation situation.

HOB SALONS

Talking and listening to your client is one of the most important parts of the hairdressing service. It will enable you to find out what the client wants and if they have any problems with their hair. You need to listen closely to what they are saying and ask questions to clarify any areas you are not sure about. You also need to ask open questions about their hair to ensure that you get enough information to make a choice explore ideas and give opinions, such as:

- Would you like to change anything about your hairstyle?
- What products do you use on your hair?
- How much time do you have to style your hair?

Activity

With a colleague, practice asking different types of questions. Ask your supervisor to explain the difference between open and closed questions. Notice the difference in the amount of information offered when you do ask open questions.

Activity

How would you change the wording of these closed questions to turn them into open questions and find out more about the client's hair?

Is this a permanent colour on your hair?

Would you consider a different hairstyle?

Did you find that the new conditioner helped you manage your hair?

Do you like styling products on your hair?

Non-verbal communication

Non-verbal communication is commonly referred to as 'body language' and this type of communication is an effective way of letting others know what we really mean.

We express ourselves with body language through:

- posture
- gestures
- facial expression

Body language

As well as using words we show our interest, attitude and feelings by bodily expressions. Non-verbal communication (NVC) or body language to put it more simply, is especially important. It can truly show what we are feeling, even if our mouths are saying something quite different!

In the animal world the main form of communication and interaction from one creature to another is through body language. The cat that is alarmed when it is confronted by a dog on the street turns sideways on and hunches up. This makes him look larger than he actually is. Size means everything. You pull away sharply and when you get home the dog sulks; he gets right in your view and turns his back to you. Animals' positioning, posturing and mannerisms all mean something; they all convey a very clear and strong message.

We too, express our interest and attitudes via non-verbal communication through eye contact, posture and general body positioning. So it is very important that we send the right message, particularly when dealing with clients and potential customers.

Eye contact

The first rule of good communication is always maintaining eye contact when talking to the client. Where possible, maintain eye level as well. For example if you are carrying out a consultation, sit down with your client; never stand over them or talk to them through the mirror. Standing over or above your client and looking down conveys a feeling of authority, as if you were trying to assert control.

I love you

The eyes give away our innermost feelings too; this is particularly obvious when we show attraction to someone. When we are attracted to someone, the dark centres of the eye, i.e. the pupils, grow wider and dilate. Look into them and you'll soon know if attraction is mutual, eye contact lasts longer with attraction and the eyes form a more intense gaze. The reason people's pupils dilate is adrenaline which is released when you are excited or afraid. So, whether you fancy someone, think you're about to win a poker hand or are telling lies, they will dilate.

Body zones – space invaders!

People have a comfort zone. This is the space around the body within which they feel at ease. Obviously the extent of this space varies from person to person. Within a close, intimate relationship, shared proximity may be welcome, but an uninvited invasion of this space is at best, very uncomfortable, and at worst – menacing or threatening!

Physical contact

Most people are embarrassed by physical contact from someone they do not know well.

Posture, body position and gestures

Much has been written on the subject of body language and the psychological effects that it has on those reading it. It is far too complex a subject to address in a few simple paragraphs.

COURTESY OF SAKS, WWW.SAKS.CO.UK

Posture, or composure of the body, is a form of body language in this context. Reading the message of this form of communication is a skill that develops over time and once learnt is never forgotten. However, there are few obvious rules that can help to convey the right message and create a right impression.

- Slouching in the salon or at reception looks very unprofessional.
- Folded arms and the crossing of arms on the chest is a protective gesture that portrays a closed mind or shows defensiveness.
- Open palms, as a gesture supporting explanation or information, with hands at waist height and palms upward, indicates that the person has nothing to hide. This is interpreted as openness or honesty.
- Scratching behind the ear or the back of the neck whilst listening indicates that the listener is uncertain or doesn't understand. Rubbing the nose whilst listening can indicates that you don't believe what you are hearing.
- Inspecting fingernails or looking at a watch is a plain and simple indication of boredom or vanity.
- Talking with your hand in front your mouth may lead the listener to believe you are not being honest. You're hiding yourself by your gestures.
- Shifting from foot to foot shows that you're worrying about getting found out! It also says that you would rather be somewhere else; to get away so that no guilty expressions are spotted.

These forms of communication are only an indication of feelings and emotions. In isolation they may not mean anything at all. However, taken together they can convey a very clear message. Make sure that

Remember

Body zones–proxemics
Do not crowd or appear over-familiar with your client. Imagine how you would feel if someone came up to you and got a little too close. What do you do? Immediately back off and go onto the defensive.

Centrally through head	Through lobe of ear
Shoulders level	Through shoulder joint
Centrally through trunk	
Hips level	Through or slightly behind hip so hip joint 'locks' on standing
Arms equal length	
Legs equal length	Slightly in front of knee joint so knee 'locks' when standing
	Through arch of foot closer to heel than toes
Weight equally distributed on feet	
Lateral line of gravity	Dorsiventral line of gravity

Good posture

you send the appropriate signals and look interested, keen, ready to help and positive. And above all show that you can listen.

Mirroring posture

If you're in tune with the person you're speaking to you will often find you unconsciously mirror each other's body postures. So, if you rest your hand on your chin, the other person will follow you. If he or she leans forwards you'll find yourself making the same move and so on.

This technique is often used in interviews by helping to make the candidates feel at ease. Conversely, the technique is used as a subconscious sales tool, when sales representatives want us to part with our money.

You're a liar!

- Sweating
- excessive hand movements
- biting of fingernails
- chewing of the inside of the mouth
- drying up of the mouth and
- lack of eye contact.

The list above provides a general indication that shows that we are telling 'porky pies'. Some people are very good at masking these indicators, but in most cases they are obvious and a plain indication that someone is not telling the truth.

Activity

Which of the examples of non-verbal communication below would be considered to be positive expressions of communication when listening to a client explaining what she wants?

Non-verbal communication	Tick which ones ✔
Yawning	
Looking at the ceiling	
Shaking the head	
Sitting with arms and legs crossed	
Making eye contact	
Nodding	
Putting your arm around the client	
Frowning	
Smiling	

Confidential information

Throughout all of your dealings with your clients you must remain professional. This is particularly true when it comes to handling confidential information. There are more clients lost by stylists through careless talk than through poor hair-dressing!

- Make sure that your discussions with clients remain discreet. Private information should remain private.
- You should never repeat to another person what has been said to you in confidence. Even if it is true!
- Recorded or documented information is personal to the clients. The Data Protection Act protects you and your clients from unlawful disclosure of information to others.

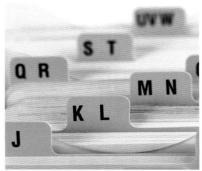

I-STOCK/©IVAN BAJIC

Written communication

Most day-to-day communication between staff or clients is spoken. However, there are times when information has to be recorded. Client records, taking messages and stock procedures are typical examples of this.

Client records can be manual or computerised; in either event they will contain similar information:

- client name and title
- address and contact information
- previous service, treatment, tests and product information
- date, costs and timings of previous visits
- stylist/operator details and any other additional memos.

The client record is normally used during consultation; this will give you detailed background information relating to their previous visits and allows you a more informed basis for planning a suitable course of action. The information needn't be too long; as long as you have covered the essential aspects that will do.

Taking messages

A memo (memorandum) is a quick and easy way of recording information rather than trying to remember and pass on messages later. In most cases we don't remember or if we do it's too late to do anything about it.

An effective memo is clear and includes the following:

✔	for whom it is intended
✔	who took the message
✔	the date and time
✔	its purpose
✔	clear details or instructions.

Remember

 Always make sure that your written records are accurate. Incorrect or incomplete client information could result in a future disaster.

Remember

Always write it down: it might be very important to someone else.

Remember

Data protection
 The Data Protection Act 1998 exists to ensure that personal information held on record is not mishandled, mismanaged or used inappropriately.

Dealing with difficult clients

As discussed above, good communication is vital. It will help you deal with many situations. However, not all clients are easy to get along with or to extract information from. Some clients may be angry because they have been made to wait or may be unhappy with the finished style. Some clients may find it difficult to explain what they want or may not understand what you are asking. As a stylist it is your job to remain calm and deal with the situation in a supportive, concerned and caring way.

Angry clients

Stay calm, listen to the client and let them explain why they are angry, use open, friendly body language and maintain eye contact. Keep your speech clear and low when asking questions or giving information to clarify the situation. If you are not in a position to deal with the problem make sure that you get someone who can – this may be a senior stylist or the manager. Never ignore the client; they are angry for a reason and usually the situation can be easily rectified.

Confused clients

Not all clients know what they want when they book for an appointment or what you are suggesting for their hairstyle. Make sure that you give the client time to talk and ask questions. Listen to them again, maintain eye contact, use open body language and gestures such as nodding your head or open palms to confirm your honesty in listening and being ready to support your client. Use simple explanations and questions to extract information. Use visual aids such as style books or colour charts to confirm the requirements.

Dealing with complaints

A client has every right to expect the service that was agreed and paid for and when an unexpected result occurs the client has every right to complain. Dealing with a dissatisfied client is not easy and should therefore be referred to a senior member of staff.

If a client approaches you with a complaint you should:

- move your client away to a quieter area of the salon
- seek assistance from a senior member of staff.

The complaint may then be resolved by the senior who will:

- find out exactly what the problem is
- assess the validity of the complaint
- mutually agree on a suitable course of action
- carry out/organise any corrective work
- record the occurrence and the remedial action that was taken.

Special note If the complaint is serious – such as hair breakage or discolouration – it may be difficult to rectify. The client has a legal right to pursue acts of gross negligence and recently this has proved a popular route to gaining compensation. If a client does follow this course of action the salon's insurers will need to be notified sooner rather than later.

EKU statement

G17.5) how to recognise when a client is angry or confused

Remember

 Don't be in a hurry to solve a problem, you might make it worse. Always remain calm and give careful consideration to the problem, making sure the client understands and agrees to any course of corrective action.

Activity

Preparing for the unexpected is always difficult; but one way of doing this is through a role play. Role play is a way of 'acting out' the different things that could happen during different client situations.

Simple misunderstandings do occur during consultation and this can be due to many different reasons. Unfortunately, the final hair effect that results from poor consultation can be quite different to what the client wanted.

Take it in turns to play client and stylist to see if you can improve your consultation skills before it happens to you!

Activity
Expressions

What do each of these emotions express?

A

B

C

D

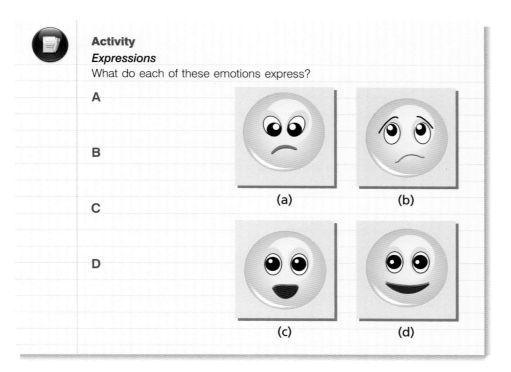

(a)   (b)

(c)   (d)

Activity
Expressions

How is this person feeling?

A angry

B puzzled

C excited

D playful

I-STOCK/©LI KIM GOH

Activity
Getting the right information

> I've got to pick my children up from school at 3.30. I've been sitting here waiting for 25 minutes now. My appointment was for two o'clock! Is there any chance I might be seen within the next five minutes?

First of all, which of the following repeats the main points of the client's complaint?

A The client's appointment is for 3.30 and they're sitting here and waiting for it?

B The client's appointment was at two o'clock and they've been waiting for 25 minutes?

C The client needs to be seen in the next five minutes because they have to pick their children up at 3.30. The appointment was at two o'clock and they've been waiting for 25 minutes?

D The client has to leave now to pick up their children up from school?

What would be the best thing to say to this client?

A You'd better go now to be sure you'll be at the school in time.

B I'm sorry we have kept you waiting so long. Would you like to make another appointment?

C We're really short-staffed at the moment. Everybody is having to wait. Twenty-five minutes is nothing. *She's* been here an hour already.

D I'm sorry you've had such a long wait. Will you accept this sample product with our compliments? Perhaps I can make you another appointment at a time to suit you?

Activity
What is the appropriate thing to say to a client who has been kept waiting for their appointment?

A 'Sorry to keep you waiting. We're always very busy this time of year.'

B ''I'm afraid Sue will be about another fifteen minutes. Can I get you a coffee or some magazines?'

C 'Not long to wait now, Mrs Portman.'

D 'Sue's running late again, Mrs Portman. Here are some magazines while you wait.'

E 'Sorry for the delay, Mrs Portman. Sue will be free in about a quarter of an hour. If you prefer, Mike can cut your hair instead.'

Checkerboard

| | I always explain technical terms eliminating ambiguity and false beliefs | I know and understand the principles of positive communication | I can communicate professionally and know the benefits of good body language |
| I understand the necessity of personal hygiene and presentation | I know when and to whom to refer clients, in situations where external assistance is required | I know the expressions that clients use when they are angry, dissatisfied or confused | I always carry out working practices according to the salon's policy |

Assessment of knowledge and understanding

Project

For this project you will need to gather information from a variety of sources.

For the following legislation find out how:

1   the Disability and Discrimination Act

2   the Consumer Protection Act

affect the way that services can be provided to clients.

In your project pay particular attention to the aspects that would have impact on a business and the implications if this legislation were not considered.

Revision questions

A selection of different types of questions to check your customer communication knowledge.

Q1   Good personal _____ is essential in a personal service industry?   Fill in the blank

Q2   Poor posture leads to clinical fatigue.   True or false

Q3 Which of the following are essential PPE for the clients? Multi selection

Towels	☐ 1
Barrier creams	☐ 2
Aprons	☐ 3
Gowns	☐ 4
Plastic capes	☐ 5
Latex gloves	☐ 6

Q4 Poor quality combs are uncomfortable and can scratch the client's scalp. True or false

Q5 Which of the following is an example of poor customer service? Multi choice

Checking that the towels and gowns are clean	○ a
Cleaning the work surfaces	○ b
Sweeping up loose hair clippings	○ c
Forgetting to offer the client a drink	○ d

Q6 Talking and listening to your client is one of the most important parts of good communication. True or false

Q7 What information should you remember to get when taking messages? Multi selection

Address of contact	☐ 1
Time and place of call	☐ 2
Purpose of call	☐ 3
Details and instructions	☐ 4
Client treatment history	☐ 5
Client service details	☐ 6

Q8 Non-verbal communication is another name for _____ language. Fill in the blank

Q9 Which of the following is poor body language? Multi choice

Maintaining eye contact with the client	○ a
Moving into someone?s personal space	○ b
Smiling when you greet someone	○ c
Maintaining the same eye level as the client	○ d

Q10 Hands at waist height, with palms upward, indicate that the person has nothing to hide. True or false

Preparing for assessment checklist

Remember to:

✔	communicate positively and effectively in the salon at all times
✔	be polite, but confident in carrying out communications with clients
✔	maintain confidentiality and the consequences of failing to keep things private
✔	listen to clients and show them that you care
✔	use positive body language and the reasons why it plays such an important part in good customer service

SANRIZZ ARTISTIC TEAM @ SANRIZZ

Chapter**four**
Reception

More information
Effective communication –
Taking messages – see
Unit G17 page 57

Dealing with confused or
angry clients – see
Unit G17 page 58

Data Protection Act
(1998)
http://www.ico.gov.uk/

G4

G4.1

G4.2

G4.3

G4.4

EKU statement

G4.1) Your salon's
procedures for taking
messages

G4.7) The importance of
taking messages and
passing them on to the
right person at the right
time

G17.5) How to recognise
when a client is angry or
confused

Reception: quick overview

Unit title

G4 Fulfil salon reception duties

This is an **optional** unit and is made up of four main outcomes

Main outcomes

G4.1 Maintain the reception area

G4.2 Attend to clients and enquiries

G4.3 Make appointments

G4.4 Handle payments from clients

What do I need to do for G4.1?

- Always keep the salon reception area clean and tidy
- Maintain levels of reception stationery
- Check and maintain the levels of retail products
- Greet people entering the salon and attend to their enquiries.

What do I need to do for G4.2?

- Attend to salon visitors promptly and politely
- Identify client's needs and respond appropriately
- Record information accurately and communicate effectively
- Multi-task between reception duties effectively

What do I need to do for G4.3?

- Make appointments carefully and without mistakes at mutually convenient times

What do I need to do for G4.4?

- Total the client's bill accurately and inform them of the charge
- Establish payment methods for billing and conduct valid transactions
- Accurately handle payments from clients for salon services

What aspects do I need to cover for G4.1, G4.2, G4.3 and G4.4?

- People who may be confused or angry, or make complaints
- Enquiries and appointments by people arriving at the salon or contacting by phone or electronic means
- Accurate recording of personal identifier information provided by the client
- Different payment methods
- Payment discrepancies in line with salon policy

What do I need to know for G4.1, G4.2, G4.3 and G4.4?

- The salon's policy in relation to greeting clients, making appointments, client confidentiality and payment transactions
- How to communicate effectively with people making contact with the salon in a variety of ways
- How to calculate bills accurately and process payments
- How to recognise valid and invalid payments
- The cost and ranges of the salon's services, treatments and retail products

Introduction

The reception is the most important area of the salon, as it is here that the client makes their first contact with the business. With clients and visitors arriving, incoming telephone calls, stock deliveries, appointments and payments being made, it's a busy place.

Because of all these daily duties that they perform, the receptionist needs a variety of skills: good communication, good organisational abilities, accuracy and above all attention to detail.

Apart from the receptionist's tasks, the reception area is equally important for creating the overall, professional impression. The waiting area, retail displays and reception desk should always be clean, organised and welcoming. It is the job of reception staff to maintain the area throughout the day as things are constantly changing. Stationery items, till rolls, pens and pencils can all run out, retail displays need restocking, magazines and cups and saucers all need attention.

IMAGE COURTESY OF REM

Remember

Meet your client's expectations by offering a prompt, welcoming and efficient service with the minimum of delay.

A professional salon reception

Customer service is at the heart of the hairdressing industry and it is good customer service that brings the clients back again and again. Clients want to feel that their custom is valued and that you and the rest of the staff will respond to their needs and problems with efficiency and empathy.

Making appointments is a complex task requiring literacy and numeracy skills as well as a range of technical knowledge about the salon's services, treatments and retail product ranges.

This chapter covers a range of skills required for reception work. It includes:

- making clients welcome and dealing with enquiries face to face
- using the phone
- handling money, in both cash and non-cash transactions
- balancing the till
- stock control
- working within the law.

Your job in reception is to receive clients and to make them feel welcome, which means greeting them properly, responding to their needs and dealing with them in a professional and friendly way.

You need good communication skills for this type of work, as you will have to deal with a wide range of people who expect the best from you. You also need to know about the services you can offer so that you can explain these to clients and promote your business.

You may also be responsible for making sure that there is enough stock and for accepting payments from clients and giving change. In addition, you may have to check that the money in the till is correct at the end of the day.

All this has to be done within the law, so you need to know which laws apply to you when you are at work.

EKU *statement*

G4.1) Your salon's procedures for client care at reception

Activity

What are your salon's procedures for handling clients at reception?
What things must you do?
Find out the answers to these questions and write them up in your portfolio.

Activity

Think about what happens when you first enter your doctor's or dentist's surgery.
How are you greeted by the receptionist?
For each of the questions below write your answers in the space provided.

Question:	**Your answer:**
Is there anything that annoys you?	
Do you think anything could be done better?	
Does the receptionist use your first or last name?	

G4.1 Maintain the reception area

EKU *statement*

G4.12) The limits of your authority when – attending to people and enquiries – client care at reception

First impressions

Hairdressing is a personal service industry and if we are going to keep our clients happy, we have to provide a complete and professional service. This service is not just focused around the stylist's abilities – cutting, styling, perming or colouring – though, it has to be right from the point of entry and exit from the salon. It's the first and the last impression of the salon.

The reception area is the hub of the salon; clients arrive, calls are received, visitors arrive, bills are paid and appointments are made. As part of your duties as the receptionist you will be

Remember

 Even if we have outstanding communication skills, what clients see around them has a far greater impact on their arrival than anything we have to say.

HOB SALONS

Activity

Match the following operations to the tasks. We have already done the first for you.

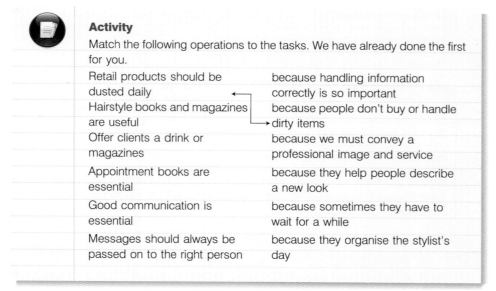

Retail products should be dusted daily	because handling information correctly is so important
Hairstyle books and magazines are useful	because people don't buy or handle dirty items
Offer clients a drink or magazines	because we must convey a professional image and service
Appointment books are essential	because they help people describe a new look
Good communication is essential	because sometimes they have to wait for a while
Messages should always be passed on to the right person	because they organise the stylist's day

EKU *statement*

G4.2) The limits of your authority when maintaining the reception area

Remember

Always make sure that product shelves and retail items are clean and tidy. Nobody will want to handle products that are dusty or on murky shelves!

responsible for making sure that the client waiting area is kept clean and tidy; that magazines are regularly checked for condition and currency and that the style books are replaced after use. A client who has had to wait will feel less angry if they have been attended to, offered something to drink or at least had something at hand to pass the time.

Make sure that the retail displays are regularly cleaned and refilled, that retail products are checked for condition and that price labels are clearly visible. The retail products must look attractive: we want the clients to be encouraged to draw closer, pick them up and handle them.

The reception area is always busy with clients arriving or wanting to pay their bill, the telephone is often ringing with clients wanting to make appointments. Therefore the desk must be well organised. Stationery, such as memo pads, pens and payment-processing items, should be checked each morning before the salon opens, and you should make sure that there is enough to last throughout the day. The receptionist is also responsible for the till; there should also be enough change and card-processing materials to last all day.

Activity

What is your salon's policy in respect to dealing with clients and enquiries? What is the procedure for receiving clients? (Write your answers in the space below.)

Maintaining reception – checklist

Salon tidiness is essential and maintenance in reception is equally important. Make sure that each of these is done every day:

✔	Desk dusted and tidied before clients arrive
✔	Appointment diary close to hand and ready for use

Remember

Clients' expectations of service are high. Always offer a prompt, welcoming, efficient service, be attentive and be helpful.

L'ORÉAL PROFESSIONNEL

✔	Card-payment receipt rolls and till rolls replenished and spares available
✔	Stationery stocks checked and replenished
✔	Shelves and retail products dusted or wiped
✔	Missing items or low stock levels replaced or reordered
✔	Damaged or faulty product packaging removed and reported to the manager
✔	Products rearranged and gaps in product lines removed from displays
✔	Product information and pricing relevant, up to date, close at hand and easy to read
✔	Product promotions clearly displayed, public information available and the correct product items arranged appropriately according to the current offer or promotion

Get organised

Every salon uses the same tabulated system for organising the daily work, although the way that it appears and the way in which it is completed changes from salon to salon. Some salons use the manual appointment book system; others use an electronic, computerised version. Regardless, both types do a similar job by setting out the daily, weekly and monthly work schedule. So, if the reception is the hub of the salon, then the appointment system is the most important business process within the salon. It provides:

- a snapshot of expected levels of business
- a detailed action plan of work for staff
- a minute-by-minute schedule of business activities
- a record of client visits, creating a pattern of repeat business.

From this information you can:

- plan the salon resources, e.g. people, time, stock and equipment
- organise client records, contact details and treatment history
- prepare the till and electronic payment processes.

From this it is easy to see that the appointment system is the centre of an efficiently run business. The information it contains must be clear, accurate and up to date. However, maintaining the appointment system doesn't always guarantee the smooth running of the salon. You will always need to be prepared for the unexpected, such as late or unscheduled arrivals. Regardless of type, all these visitors must be attended to.

Appointment page

G4.2   Attend to clients and enquiries

Good client care at reception

Good customer service and client care are essential to creating a thriving repeat business model. Without returning clients there would be no future for the salon or the people that work within it! So be hospitable, treat the clients well, greet each one with a smile and make sure that your body language (see Unit G17 page 54) is positive.

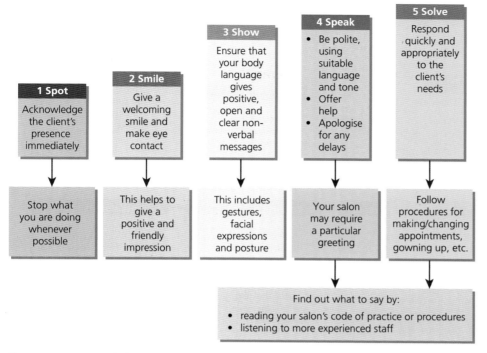

EKU *statement*

G4.8) The importance of
effective communication to
the salon's business

Five steps to good client care at reception

Handling enquiries

EKU *statement*

G4.2) The limits of your
authority when attending to
people and enquiries

G4.13) How to show you
are listening closely to what
people are saying to you

G4.5) The person in your
salon to whom you should
refer reception problems

We want visitors to become clients and there are ways to make this happen. An important part of this process and one that effects the conscious decisions people make about us is communication. We want people to see us as professional communicators. Professional communication occurs when we handle or anticipate the needs of others in a prompt and businesslike manner.

Effective communication takes place in the following ways:

- *speech* – what we say to others and the way in which we say it
- *listening* – hearing the requests of others properly
- *writing* – recording information accurately and clearly
- *body language* – the way we communicate our feelings and attitude to situations by posture, expression and mannerisms.

Enquiries made by a client either in person (i.e. face to face) or on the telephone should be handled in the same way. In both instances, we need to respond promptly and politely. If you don't know the answer to a question, ask someone who does: accurate information is essential. So stop! Listen to what is being said, hear the request and act on the information.

Misinterpreting what has been said will lead to giving or recording the wrong information.

On the telephone

Good telephone skills are important to give a good impression and deal with clients effectively. You will be judged by what you say, so you should be polite, cheerful and helpful from the moment you pick up the telephone receiver to the moment you replace it.

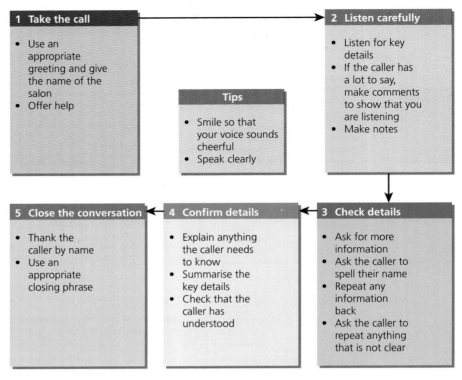

Five steps to handling calls

Memorandum

TO: John

FROM: Linda

DATE: 1/10

SUBJECT: Staff absence

_____

Jayne will not be in for the rest of the week as she has a virus. Please could you reschedule her appointments, and advise all clients accordingly

Thanks.

Smile when you answer the telephone: people will 'hear' the friendliness in your voice. At the same time speak clearly so that the caller can understand everything you say. After listening to the caller's request, confirm the main points back to them. This summarises the information and ensures that all details are correct. Keep in mind the length of the call: calls cost money and waste valuable salon time.

Face to face

When clients arrive in person, they should be attended to promptly, their appointment and time should be checked before they are directed to a seat. Always make a point of making them feel welcome; perhaps offer a magazine or a drink before informing the stylist that their client has arrived. This is important as it will avoid any unnecessary waiting or possible embarrassment when the stylist realises (perhaps much later) that their client has actually arrived.

There will be occasions when you need to seek assistance or advice from others. Being able to recognise situations where you are unable to help is not a failure, it is all part of professional communication. There will be situations that require the attention of someone else, perhaps when the window cleaner arrives and says 'Shall I just get on with it?' or when stock arrives and the signature of a person responsible for taking delivery and accepting condition of goods is required.

The visual impressions made from a person's body language are equally important (see Chapter 3 on Unit G17 Give clients a positive impression of you and your organisation).

Confidentiality

Certain circumstances need special care and attention and probably the most important aspect of professional communication is confidentiality. During our day-to-day work it is possible that we come into contact with information that others consider private. It is important that you recognise these situations and handle them accordingly. This confidential information will be disclosed in numerous ways: during routine conversation between staff or clients and from business contacts and enquirers. Whatever the source, it is vitally important that you do not divulge personal or potentially sensitive information to anyone. Failure to maintain client confidentiality is not only a breach of professionalism and customer loyalty; it could in some cases (under the Data Protection Act (1998); see page 86) be against the law!

Late arrivals

Hardly a day will go by where there isn't someone who is late for their appointment. People are not deliberately late, it's just one of those things put down to modern living, transportation hold-ups, last-minute duties and trying to fit too much into a busy day. All have an impact on time. Unfortunately, it's not your time they are using: in most cases it's the next client's! In a situation where the client has arrived late above all you do need to be sympathetic and understanding. The first thing to do is be sympathetic, find out if there is still enough time to complete the service without over-running throughout the rest of the day. If there isn't enough time left, see if one of the other stylists can help out: often a bit of 'juggling' will put things back on track.

Will the client have to wait? Is there going to be a delay? Tell the client immediately, let them choose between staying and waiting, coming back a little later or, if there is no other option, rebooking for another appointment at some other time.

Unscheduled arrivals and 'walk-ins'

The client who arrives without an appointment should always be accommodated if at all possible. If you think about the situation from their point of view, they have made the decision to come into your salon. Why? Is it because they have been recommended by someone else? Did they like the look of the salon from the outside? Or did they just happen to be in the area at the time? Whatever the reason, it's all good business.

Double bookings

Overbooking, or double booking, does occur, but shouldn't do too often. It is usually the result of either a staff member or the client making a mistake, or through poor communication. Don't try to beat the appointment system; you may upset clients,

EKU statement

G4.1) Your salon's procedures for maintaining confidentiality

G4.3) The consequences of breaking confidentiality

Remember

Always keep a pad for notes handy at reception. It will provide a far more useful aid than writing over the appointment page!

EKU statement

G4.14) How to adapt what you say to suit different situations (i.e. the amount you say, your manner and tone of voice)

Remember

 Never attempt to carry out any hairdressing service without the client's consent.

colleagues or both. Providing a high-quality service includes making sure people know the expected time-scales and duration of services and if there will be any waiting.

Deliberate overbooking is only done by the over-optimistic staff member. (This could be likened to the large airlines: they gamble in the belief that something will crop up and some of the passengers will not turn up.) It doesn't work, it only causes bad feelings and disappointment, and make sure you don't do it!

Activity

What is your salon's procedure for handling telephone enquires? Write in the space provided what you are supposed to say when you answer a call.

Changes to booked services

There will often be occasions where a client has booked for one service, but by the time they reach the salon they have changed their mind and want something else totally different. People change their minds all the time. Don't worry, this could be good business – a client may come in expecting a restyle, cut and finish, and go out with highlights too. In fact many salons set incentives around this very activity; for example, staff performances and commissions may be based on 'upselling' or 'client conversion'.

Staff absences

Staff absences will always stretch the salon's resources to its limits but your salon should have a contingency plan to cover this situation. Generally this will involve:

- checking to see if other salon staff can or have provided services to the client before
- rearranging appointments to accommodate the disruption
- if all else fails – contact the client before they set out to schedule a reappointment.

Remember

 Even if our communication skills are perfect, what clients see around them has a far greater impact on their opinions than anything that we have to say.

Remember

 Never give advice that you are unsure of. Check it out first!

Remember

 Never bill a client for an amount that was not agreed.

Activity

Typical assessment questions and model answers: when clients arrive at the salon...

Q1 What's the first thing you should do when a client arrives?
A1 Check the client's name, appointment time, what they are having done and who it is with.
Q2 What should you do next?
A2 Take their coat and any shopping etc. and put them away carefully and safely.

Q3 The stylist is not quite ready for the client. What should you do next?

A3 Ask the client to take a seat and offer them a drink and something to look at for the time being.

Dealing with people

Every salon needs clients to exist. The clients come because they know what the salon has to offer; this includes the salon ambience, the services and treatments provided and most of all the people with whom they feel comfortable.

Good technical skills are achieved through patience and hard work. Good customer communication is achieved in exactly the same way and the realisation of this simple formula and how you handle it is your key to success. Poor communication, bad manners and disagreements have no place in a successful business and therefore they must be eliminated or resolved.

Activity
Explain why taking messages and passing them on to the correct person is so important.

Remember

First impressions are lasting impressions
The human brain can take in a wide variety of information from different channels at the same time. How is that? We are aware of our surroundings by using any number of the five senses: sight, hearing, smell, touch and taste. These senses analyse and interpret the information we receive, helping us to create an overall impression, whether right or wrong! We all process the information so quickly that we are trying to create a judgement or understanding for what we see. Generally speaking our first and lasting impression is created in fewer than ten seconds! Hence, 'You don't get a second chance to create a good first impression'.

G4.3 Make appointments

Know the salon's services

The appointment system is the very centre, the 'hub' of the whole salon operation. Without an appointment system the business would stop! So it is essential that appointments are made accurately and promptly, every time, whether a client makes an appointment over the telephone or in person.

Before you can schedule appointments you must know the services available. Each salon provides a unique 'menu' of services. Different stylists will have different abilities and skills, and so might be available for certain services at certain levels. You need to know the variety of services available, their timings and relevant costs.

Making appointments needn't be difficult. It's about matching client requests with the time available. We want to help the customer make the booking, while bearing in mind the time that it will take and who will be providing the service. When clients are contacting the salon by telephone you should always speak first saying, 'Good morning/afternoon, this is Head Masters hair salon. This is Clare speaking, how may I help you?' This friendly and positive approach will immediately give a professional image of both the salon and yourself.

EKU *statement*

G4.1) Your salon's procedures for making and recording appointments

G4.2) The limits of your authority when making appointments and dealing with payments and discrepancies

G4.12) How to speak clearly in a way that suits the situation

G4.28) The importance of making appointments correctly

G4.29) The common systems available for making appointments within the hairdressing industry (e.g. manual and electronic)

Making appointments

Each salon has its own system for making appointments but, generally speaking, appointment scheduling maximises the time available with appropriate staff members. Bearing this in mind, we should always remain ready, prompt and polite in attending to the client's requests.

Make sure that when the booking is made that you record the information accurately and clearly and that you have considered all the factors:

- date and time
- service required
- stylist required
- the client's name
- client contact details.

Record the client's name clearly in the appointment system, alongside the service, and check that it is scheduled for the correct day and time with the appropriate stylist. As a matter of customer service it is also useful to give the client an approximate idea of service cost and length of appointment time. At the end, summarise all the information back to the client, thus ensuring that all the details are correct.

Checklist for making appointments

✔	*You need to know the abbreviations the salon uses for different services*
✔	*You need to know the system the salon uses for making appointments*
✔	*You need to ask questions to get extra information*
✔	*You need good listening skills*
✔	*You need to know the prices of the different treatments and services*
✔	*You need to fill in appointment details*
✔	*You need to know the days and hours that each stylist works*
✔	*You need to know which treatments each stylist does*
✔	*You need to spell people's names correctly*
✔	*You need to be able to manage times and dates*
✔	*You need to know how much time the salon allows for each service*

EKU *statement*

G4.15) The services available, their duration and cost

G4.16) The products available for sale and their cost

G4.4) Who to refer to with different types of enquiries

G4.18) How to identify any current discounts and special offers (e.g. two-for-one offers, coupons, etc.)

When in doubt ask!

There may be situations where you are not sure. It is always better to ask someone else than to make mistakes such as:

- making incorrect or inaccurate bookings
- providing inaccurate information e.g. incorrect costings of services or products.

When unsure always ask someone for help. There is nothing worse than a stylist who is running late, particularly if this is the result of someone else's booking error. The situation will be stressful for the stylist but, more importantly, we do not want any clients waiting longer than absolutely necessary, whatever the reason.

Service abbreviations

Cut and blow-dry	CBD
Blow-dry	BD
Shampoo and set	S/S
Ladies' wet cut	WC
Gents' wet cut	G W/C
Gents' cut and blow-dry	G CBD
Highlights T section	H/L T
Highlights full head	H/L fh
Highlights half head	H/L$^{1}/_{2}$
Retouch colour	Col rt
Full head colour	Col fh
Permanent wave	PW
Chemical straightening	Strght

Activity

In this exercise you need to read the following service information and then complete the blank appointment sheet accordingly with the appropriate abbreviations.

A salon employs three experienced hairstylists:

Jane: A stylist who works part-time 1 pm to 5.30 pm

Samantha: A stylist who works full-time 9 am to 5.30 pm and has an hour for lunch

Tina: A colourist who works mornings only 9 am to 12 noon

Service		Duration
Cut and blow-dry	(CBD)	45 mins
Blow-dry	(BD)	30 mins
Wet cut only	(WC)	30 mins
Dry trim	(DT)	15 mins
Highlights T section	(HLT)	30 mins (plus 30 mins' development)
Highlights full head	(HL fh)	45 mins (plus 30 mins' development)
Retouch colour	(Col rt)	30 mins (plus 45 mins' development)

Add the name of each stylist at the top of the appropriate column. Now read the following service information and complete the blank appointment page.

Miss Cooper and her daughter would like full head highlights at the same time as each other with a cut and blow-dry back with Samantha later.

Mrs Ford wants the earliest appointment available with Jane for a cut and blow-dry and would like to bring her two children for dry trims with whoever is available at the same time.

Miss Jones would like a mid-morning cut and blow-dry appointment with Samantha.

A Miss Collins telephones to ask if there is an appointment for retouch colour and then a cut and blow-dry back with Samantha after 10.30 am. Mark out time for Samantha's lunch.

Two college girls, Miss Green and Miss Dorkin, call in and ask if there are any appointments for cut and blow-dry after lectures and as near to 2.00 pm as possible. They don't mind who they have, but they would like their appointments at the same time.

Someone telephones at 1.00 pm and asks for their children, Paula and Cheryl Tombs, to have a wet cut and a dry trim respectively, before 3.00 pm. Where can they be fitted in?

Remember

Always introduce yourself when handling calls. People like to speak to people with whom they can associate, not strangers or machines!

Remember

When making appointments ensure you have a contact number for the client.

ERROL DOUGLAS USING MATRIX

MICHAEL BARNES FOR GOLDWELL

KARINE JACKSON @ KARINE JACKSON HAIR & BEAUTY

Appointment sheet

Date:			
Time			
9.00			
9.15			
9.30			
9.45			
10.00			
10.15			
10.30			
10.45			
11.00			
11.15			
11.30			
11.45			
12.00			
12.15			
12.30			
12.45			
1.00			
1.15			
1.30			
1.45			
2.00			
2.15			
2.30			
2.45			

Appointment sheet

3.00			
3.15			
3.30			
3.45			
4.00			
4.15			
4.30			
4.45			
5.00			

G4.4   Handle payments from clients

Different types of payment

When the hairdressing services have been completed and the client is satisfied with the result, the last thing that takes place before leaving the salon is the payment. The payment is made and kept in either a manual or automatic till.

- The manual till is a lockable drawer, often attached or built in to the reception desk. At the end of the day the money is cashed up and manually recorded onto the salon's accounting system.

- The electronic till has a freestanding cash drawer that is built in to the till's body; this automatically opens when the payment process is complete. The till sits upon the desk or (because these tend to be quite bulky) sits in a specially shaped reveal that makes it less conspicuous. During daily use, the till records the payments and allocates them to individuals automatically. Electronic tills can be programmed for a number of functions. Each person may be given a department key which identifies their takings; this code can be used to calculate commission payments. On an automatic till, a turnkey system can display X and Z totals. These readings when printed out are used to check the amounts registered against the actual amount in the till.

X readings may be used to provide subtotals throughout the day: this is particularly useful in larger companies where it may be helpful to check takings when the cashier or receptionist leaves the till, removes cash etc. from the till, or leaves the reception for break or for lunch. The Z reading is a figure taken at the close of business at the end of day. This provides a breakdown of the payment types, the times that payments were made and the allocations of sales against individuals.

The computerised till like the electronic till has a built-in cash drawer and sits upon the reception desk. The advantage of this type of till over the others is its ability to provide a better analysis of salon sales as well as keeping a central point of access to all the clients' records and treatment history. During daily use they will monitor the individual sales, client repeat patterns and stocks sold or used; they will also provide a range of management reports.

I-STOCK/@GILLES DUMOULIN

Sales-related equipment

- *Calculator* – Always a useful and necessary item to be kept somewhere handy on the desk for totalling large bills or during end-of-day summaries.
- *Till rolls and spare rolls for card-processing machines* – These provide records of sales and provide the client with a receipt for payment. Always keep spares handy just in case they run out in daily use. As the rolls get close to running out you will notice a red continuous marking, indicating that the roll must be changed at the earliest possible moment.
- *Credit card equipment* – If the business accepts payment by cards you will have an electronic terminal which processes payments automatically, through a telephone connection (e.g. 'chip and pin'). The machine is loaded with a two-ply receipt roll and the details of the sale are automatically printed onto the receipt. However, in the event of breakdown, i.e. power outage or telephone communication breakdown, a manual imprinter is used as a back-up system. The manual imprinter is a system whereby the client's embossed credit card details are transferred to a self-carbonating sales voucher. The details of the sale are written on to the voucher and the client checks all the details and provides a signature to confirm.
- *Cash float* – At the start of the day a small sum of money in low-denomination notes and smaller coins is put in the till in order to provide change to clients paying in cash. This float is removed at the end of the day before any of the rest of the money is tallied. (A typical float, say £50.00, would be made up of the following: 1 × ten-pound note,

2 × five-pound notes, 5 × two-pound coins, 10 × one-pound coins, 10 × fifty-pence coins, 10 × twenty-pence coins, 20 × ten-pence coins, 20 × five-pence coins.)

- *Cash book* – Used as a way of accounting for sales by manually writing up the day's totals.

Methods of payment

Cash

When taking cash from clients make sure that you follow these simple steps:

1 Carefully 'ring up' all the services and products provided to the client into the till and press 'subtotal'.

2 Inform the client of the amount to be paid.

3 Look carefully but not suspiciously to make sure that the money offered is legal tender (you should check that the notes are still valid, not out of date and not counterfeit i.e. fake!).

4 Place the money tendered to you on the ledge at the top of the till drawer, so that it can be seen by the client too.

5 Press the numeric keys of the till to equal the amount tendered by the client.

6 Press the total button. The till will automatically show the amount of change to be given and the till drawer will open.

7 Take out and count back this amount into the client's hand.

8 Tear off the till receipt and don't forget to thank them as well as asking, 'Would you like to make your next appointment now?'

9 If the amount given back to the client is disputed, ask how much is missing. It is quite simple to make a genuine mistake, but if you are in any doubt call for a senior member of staff to assist. (If there is any dispute the till will need to be cashed up there and then to check for discrepancies.)

Remember

Fraud is happening all the time! Find out what your salon's policy is in relation to fraudulent or attempted fraudulent transactions.

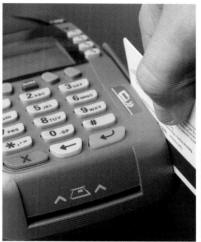

I-STOCK/©JEFFREY SMITH

EKU statement

G4.10) How to balance giving the correct amount of attention to individual clients whilst maintaining a responsibility towards other clients in busy trading periods

G4.20) Common methods of calculating payments including point-of-sale technology and physical calculations

G4.21) How to keep cash and other payments safe and secure

G4.22) The types of payment that you are authorised to accept

G4.23) How to gain electronic authorisation for payment cards

G4.24) How to identify suspected counterfeit payments

G4.25) How to identify suspected stolen cheques, credit cards and payment cards

Remember

Checking the validity of notes
Hold the note in front of you with the Queen's head uppermost and on the right. You are looking for:

- a clear, detailed watermark of the Queen (facing to the right) in the lower centre of any denomination note

- a continuous metal strip through the note on the left which, if looked at from the back, appears to be a woven and an intermittently shiny foil

- a hologram decal in the mid-left section of the note. When this is turned in the light it will disclose the denomination, matching the face value above it.

The note should feel crisp and fine without any distortion even if it has been accidentally washed.

The note should be intact without tears or sign of tampering. (A torn note can be accepted providing that the note remains in one piece – a damaged note is discretional and can be refused. However, damaged notes can easily be exchanged at a bank or post office.)

EKU *statement*

G4.26) How to deal with customers offering suspect tender or suspect non-cash payments

G4.27) Consequences of failure to handle payments correctly

EKU *statement*

G4.1) Your salon's procedures for dealing with suspected fraud, dealing with customers whose cards are over limit, client care at reception and personal safety

ISTOCKPHOTO.COM/PAUL HEDDITCH

Cheques

Some clients still prefer to pay their bill by cheque. Cheques must be accompanied by a cheque guarantee card. These are normally a debit card and denote a spending limit which is etched into a hologram on the back of the card. Normally this limit is set at £100, although limits up to £250 are available on credit cards which can also be used for cheque guarantees in certain situations. It is not advisable to accept cheques drawn for amounts above the guarantee limit, even if the client is a regular.

When receiving payment by cheque follow these steps:

1 The cheque must have the correct date in the top right-hand corner.
2 The cheque must be payable to the firm or company (you may have a pre-printed stamp for this).
3 The amount in figures must match the amount written in words.
4 Any mistakes or errors made must be initialled by the client.
5 The cheque must be signed and must match the signature on the back of the cheque guarantee card.
6 The sort code and account number on the cheque must match those on the guarantee card.
7 The payment date must be within the valid from and to dates on the cheque guarantee card.
8 The cheque cannot exceed the guarantee limit.

Remember

A post-dated cheque, i.e. a cheque made out for a date later than the current day's date, is an invalid form of payment.

EKU *statement*

G4.1) Your salon's procedures for authorising non-cash payments

Payments by card

Payment by card is the most popular form of payment and there are a number of reasons why clients prefer to use this type of payment.

- *Cash availability* – Most people are paid directly into their bank accounts, therefore it is easier to draw down on these funds by debit card than to queue at an ATM (automated teller machine) to get cash out.

- *Cost of drawing out cash* – Many competing banking organisations will charge for withdrawing cash. If you can't find a branch of the bank with which you have an account, you could be charged for withdrawing from another bank's ATM.
- *Easier to account for expenditure* – It is simpler to keep a tally on the bank account as each amount drawn will be itemised on a monthly statement.
- *Different types of card* – There are many different types of card, so people can make choices on how they pay. Therefore people can manage their money easier by opting to pay by debit card, credit card or charge card.

Remember

 Card-issuing companies believe that customer spend is greater on credit cards and that is why they charge a percentage of the total bill as opposed to a fixed charge per transaction.

Card types

There are three basic types of card:

- debit card
- credit card
- charge card.
- *Debit cards* – Switch/Maestro and SOLO cards all act as an automated cheque: the transaction process is the same as for a cheque or credit card, but once processed the salon's account is electronically credited and the client's bank account is debited. The card-processing company applies a nominal fixed fee to the salon for each card transaction made.
- *Credit cards* – These are accepted as a method of payment at the discretion of the salon. When a card has been accepted as the method of payment, a fixed percentage of the total bill is charged by the card-processing company for the use of this facility. A list of cards that are accepted by the salon for payment should be clearly displayed on the door or front window as well as the reception desk. Clients tend to assume that payment by card will be acceptable so failing to inform them otherwise could cause an embarrassing situation to arise. Card payments are given a 'floor limit' by the card company: payment will be honoured up to a specific amount; for large amounts prior authorisation by telephone is required. Thorough training needs to be given if staff are to understand these procedures.
- *Charge cards* – These provide another payment alternative. Many businesses now accept charge-card payments too – American Express is the main operator in this field. Charge-card payments are made in a similar way to credit or debit cards and therefore can be treated the same way. The difference is more for the card holder. The cards are often used as business cards, for travel, accommodation and business expenses. Each month the card holder receives a statement for the purchases made on the card over the period. This statement is a request for settlement and the bill must be paid.

I-STOCK/©JEFF GYNANE

Processing payments

Before you accept a card payment you should make sure that the card is genuine and valid. Within the salon information pack you will find a card recognition guide for each card that is permitted. The guide provides the following information:

1 *Card symbol* – This is a logo (Visa, MasterCard) which will appear at the front lower right corner of the card. On charge cards, i.e. American Express, the Centurion head is printed across the centre of the card.
2 *Card hologram* – The card hologram service mark is in the centre right-hand edge of the card. This service mark is etched on to a foil decal which is

superimposed on the card's printed background. The service mark on the holographic service mark (e.g. Visa, which appears as a dove ascending) is visible when angled in the light. The hologram changes according to the angle from which it is viewed.

3 *Card member number* – The card member's number will be embossed on to the surface and across the width of the card. When you use an electronic terminal, always ensure that the card member number matches that which is printed on your terminal receipt.

4 *Card validity dates* – The card will show a 'valid from' date as well as an 'expires end' date. If the card is not in date it can not be accepted.

5 *Card member's name* – Check that the name on the card and the title of the card member, if it is embossed, match the person presenting it.

EKU *statement*

G4.1) Your salon's procedures for dealing with suspected fraud and authorising non-cash payments

Chip and pin payments

1 Check that the terminal is in sale ready mode.

2 Insert the card into the chip reader.

3 Enter the amount by using the key pad (if you make a mistake you can clear the figures using the 'clear' button).

4 Press 'enter', which will connect the terminal to the card-processing company.

5 The customer details are automatically accessed and after a few moments, a message will prompt for 'Enter customer pin'. The customer can enter their four-digit pin on the customer keypad and press enter. The payment is authorised or declined automatically.

6 Separate the receipts. Pass the bottom copy back to the client and retain the top copy for the till.

Calls for authorisation

As a safeguard against fraudulent payment you may find that during a transaction that you are required to call for authorisation (or if you are in any way suspicious of the card, its presenter or the circumstances of the sale, you must seek authorisation).

Having ensured that no goods are within the customer's reach, take the card and the completed sales voucher, with a ballpoint pen, to the telephone. Dial the authorisation number and you will be connected to the authorisation operator. Be ready to provide the following information:

Remember

All information regarding clients should be handled in strict confidence. This safeguards all concerned and helps to reduce the possibility of embarrassment and loss of clients.

- the salon's merchant number (a unique registration number allocated by the card processing company)
- the number embossed on the client's card
- the amount of the transaction.

Occasionally you may be asked to obtain some form of positive identification from the customer presenting the card.

When the sale is authorised you will be given a numeric code. You enter this code in to the terminal and the payment is then completed and the authorisation code is printed on the receipt.

However, if the card is declined, no reason will be given. You should return the card to the customer and ask for some other form of payment.

Code 10 authorisation calls

There are times when it is necessary to seek authorisation for a transaction where it is not possible to speak freely over the telephone – particularly if you are suspicious of the circumstances surrounding the transaction. To avoid any difficulties, when it is not possible to speak freely you simply state that it is a Code 10 call. The operator will understand your predicament and will deal with your call sympathetically. If you are able to speak freely and are suspicious of the circumstances surrounding the transaction, let the operator know immediately.

Hot card warnings

From time to time notification will be sent to the salon about cards that cannot be accepted. If a customer attempts to purchase goods on a hot card you should retain the card and telephone authorisation. The full instructions on how to handle hot cards will be sent with each hot card warning to the salon.

Retaining a suspicious card

There are occasions when the authorisation operator will require you to retain a card. When this is so politely inform the customer without causing embarrassment or putting yourself at risk. Preserve the evidence for further action and take the following steps:

- cut off the bottom left-hand corner from the front of the card
- preserve intact the signature panel and magnetic strip
- handle the card by its edges to preserve fingerprints and other forensic evidence
- return both pieces back to the card company along with any receipts or sales vouchers
- claim your reward! All card companies want to stamp out card fraud and pay generous rewards for the recovery of wanted cards.

RUSH LONDON

Other payment types

- *Accounts* – Your salon may provide an account facility for regular clients, and a formal arrangement whereby all bills for an individual or a family are paid at agreed intervals. It is advisable to ask the client to sign the bill at the time of service. It should be clear to the stylist when the commission will be paid – either at the time of service or at the time of the account payment.

- *Traveller's cheques* – These are often accepted as payment by companies who operate in tourist locations. However, to avoid losing out in currency conversions, traveller's cheque for the moment should only be accepted in pounds sterling. As these are not normally used by regular clients they should be checked against the bearer's passport for proof of identity.

- *Gift vouchers* – These may be sold by the salon for payment against hairdressing and beauty services or retail sales. When the salon is operating as a concession, gift vouchers may be available for purchase from the host company. You in turn will require reimbursement from the source of the voucher. Company policy should outline procedures for issuing and receiving gift vouchers.

Activity

Make a list of all the different card types that may be used for payment in your salon, and the differences between them.

Discrepancies

Inconsistencies, disagreements or differences – invalid currencies being tendered, out-of-date cheque cards or unsigned cheques – should be dealt with as soon as possible. Where a payment card is being fraudulently used or there is a payment dispute, such as a bill totalling more than was previously agreed, then a senior member of staff should be referred to. Should an illegal transaction or even one suspected of being illegal be attempted, it may be decided to refer the matter to the police. This decision should always be made by the manager alone; however, in these circumstances you must act discreetly as serious allegations must be backed up with a formal statement and or evidence.

Discrepancies within the till where the sales don't balance with the money in the till could be a genuine mistake or, alternatively, indicate dishonesty. The till should be neither up nor down at the end of the day and your salon will have a procedure for looking into 'unders' or 'overs' more closely.

Theft

Theft is a crime. If someone is caught in the act of theft or if it is proven that a previous theft has taken place, then it should be reported to the police.

Police strongly urge businesses to prosecute staff who have stolen from the business. Theft is an act of gross misconduct and any person found guilty of it will be dismissed immediately without any justifiable recourse.

Computers

ISTOCK/©IZVORINKA JANKOVIC

As more people come into contact with computers and the Internet as part of their daily life, computer-based salon solutions are now a fixture in all forward-thinking modern salons. And there are a number of purpose-built applications for running and operating a salon system to choose from.

Most of these database applications provide a very comprehensive package and have features that address the following business aspects:

- *appointment booking system*
- *client records*: patterns of repeat business and history, as well as contact information product usage, stock control and retail sales
- *staff details*: sales, commissions, hours of work, sickness, holidays etc.
- *sales functions*: sales audits, tracking and VAT, as well as normal till operation
- *management information*: reports, accounting, financial breakdowns, trading patterns.

The individual features of particular products are usually very similar; however, the main difference between systems is more to do with look and functionality. Some systems tend to go for a more graphical front end (pictorial information depicted upon the screen) whilst others go for a more business-type look that is more like a typical (Microsoft Office™) application.

As more clients do their business, accounts and shopping online, a growing number of salons communicate to their customer base either through their website or by e-mail.

It's just as easy to make an appointment online as it is on the telephone, so there will be a big take-up over the next few years in hairdressing and beauty therapy online booking systems.

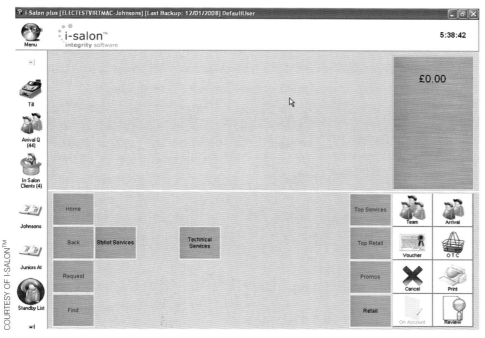

Online booking systems

Activity
Collect information about the different types of computer-based systems available. When you have information on say two or three make a comparison between them. See what features and benefits each one has to offer.

Reception Security

The reception is the first part of the salon that people walk into off the street, so this area must maintain a high level of security. All monies must be kept safely locked away and products should be monitored so that they are not maliciously removed. Records relating to the business, client details, accounts books etc. should never be left unattended. If a client were to see these things left around that would be bad enough, but if an unknown viewed them, then the salon's security measures would have been breached and personal information disclosed. In order to avoid these situations:

- the salon reception should be manned at all times;
- money is not kept on the premises when the salon is shut and keep cash in the till during working hours to an absolute minimum;
- never leave the till drawer open when it is not in use;

EKU *statement*

G4.1) Your salon's procedures for personal safety

- check all notes that have been handed over in payment to avoid counterfeits;
- always leave the cash drawer, or at least the chassis that it fits into, open overnight: this discourages forced entries;
- money should be regularly transferred to the company safe or banked;
- never make regular visits to the bank at the same times;
- receipts should be given for all payments;
- never use the cash in the till for petty cash purchases;
- any other money removed for whatever reason must always be recorded;
- follow the salon's safety and security procedures at all times.

Activity

What is your salon's policy in respect to your personal safety in aspects of salon security?

Find out and put this information in your portfolio.

EKU *statement*

G4.6) Relevant rights, duties and responsibilities relating to the Sale of Goods and Services Act and the Data Protection Act

Legal requirements in the salon

Data Protection Act (1998)

Any organisation that records information about staff or clients, whether on a card index system or a computer, must register with the Data Protection Registrar. This information must be kept accurate and up-to-date and be available to the person whose information it is to see on their request. In salons, this means that information about clients must be kept confidential, as must any information held about the staff. All staff have a responsibility to maintain this confidentiality at all times.

Data Protection Act 1998

The Data Protection Act (DPA) applies to any business that uses computers or paper-based systems for storing personal information about its clients and staff.

It places obligations on the person holding the information (data controller) to deal with it properly.

It gives the person that the information concerns (data subject) rights regarding the data held about them.

The duties of the data controller:

There are eight principles put in place by the DPA to make sure that data is handled correctly. By law, the data controller must keep to these principles. The principles say that the data must be:

1 fairly and lawfully processed

2 processed for limited purposes

3 adequate, relevant and not excessive

4 accurate

5 not kept for longer than is necessary

6 processed in line with your rights

7 secure

8 not transferred to other countries without adequate protection.

For more information see http://www.ico.gov.uk/

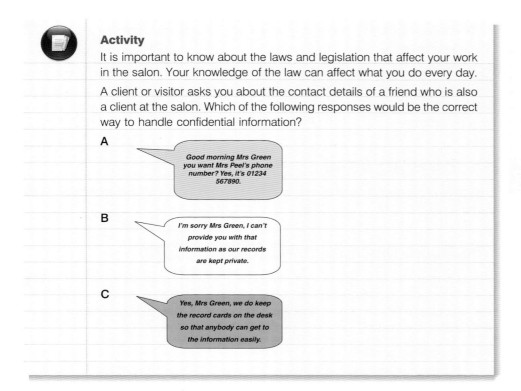

Activity

It is important to know about the laws and legislation that affect your work in the salon. Your knowledge of the law can affect what you do every day.

A client or visitor asks you about the contact details of a friend who is also a client at the salon. Which of the following responses would be the correct way to handle confidential information?

A

Good morning Mrs Green you want Mrs Peel's phone number? Yes, it's 01234 567890.

B

I'm sorry Mrs Green, I can't provide you with that information as our records are kept private.

C

Yes, Mrs Green, we do keep the record cards on the desk so that anybody can get to the information easily.

The Sale of Goods Act (1979) and Sale and Supply of Goods Act (1994)

The Sale of Goods Act 1979 and the later Sale and Supply of Goods Act 1994 are the main legal instruments helping buyers to obtain redress when their purchases go wrong. It is in the interest of anyone who sells goods or services to understand the implications of these Acts and the responsibilities they have under them. Essentially, these Acts state that what you sell must fit its description, be fit for its purpose and be of satisfactory quality. If not, you – as the supplier – are obliged to sort out the problem.

Briefly these Acts requires the vendor:

- To make sure that goods *conform to contract*. This means that they must be as you describe them, e.g. highlight shampoo stops your highlights from fading.
- The goods must also be of *satisfactory quality*, meaning they should be safe, work properly and have no defects.
- You must also ensure the goods are *fit for purpose*. This means they should be capable of doing what they're meant for. For example, a brush shouldn't fall apart when it is first used.

The Consumer Protection Act (1987)

This Act follows European laws to protect the buyer in the following areas:

- *product liability* – a customer may claim compensation for a product that doesn't reach general standards of safety
- *general safety requirements* – it is a criminal offence to sell goods that are unsafe; traders that breach this conduct may face fines or even imprisonment
- *misleading prices* – misleading consumers with wrongly displayed prices is also an offence.

The Act is designed to help safeguard the consumer from products that do not reach reasonable levels of safety. Your salon will take adequate precautions in procuring, using and supplying reputable products and maintaining them so that they remain in good condition.

M. BALFE

The Prices Act (1974)

The price of products has to be displayed in order to prevent a false impression to the buyer.

The Trades Descriptions Act (1968 and 1972)

Products must not be falsely or misleadingly described in relation to their quality, fitness, price or purpose, by advertisements, orally, displays or descriptions. And since 1972 it has also been a requirement to label a product clearly, so that the buyer can see where the product was made.

Briefly, a retailer cannot:

- mislead consumers by making false statements about products
- offer sale products at half price unless they have been offered at the actual price for a reasonable period.

The Resale Prices Act (1964 and 1976)

The manufacturers can supply a recommended price (MRRP or manufacturers' recommended retail price), but the seller is not obliged to sell at the recommended price.

Activity

It is important to know about the laws and legislation that affect your work in the salon. Your knowledge of the law can affect what you do every day.

1 How many days must a product have been on sale before you can advertise it as a sale item at a reduced price?

    A 14 days ?

    B 28 days?

    C 90 days?

2   Who is responsible for the state of the products sold in a salon?

    A the person who made it?

    B the person who sold it?

    C the person who bought it?

3   A client buys a hairbrush from the salon and returns the next day saying.

    'This hairbrush you sold me is plastic. It says on the box it has natural bristles.'

    Which of these is the correct response that you should give?

    A 'I'm sorry. The boxes must have got muddled up. I'll find you a real bristle brush.'

    B 'Plastic bristles would be best for your hair.'

    C 'I'm sorry. There's a muddle in the stock room. Somebody needs to sort it out.'

IMAGE COURTESY OF REM

Checkerboard

I understand my job position and the impact of not keeping information confidential	I know how to record accurate information for messages and appointments	I always follow the salon's policy in respect to client care and customer service
I know how to maintain the reception area and retail displays	I know how to do the reception duties	I know how to attend to clients when they arrive at reception	I always carry out working practices according to the salon's policy
I know how to communicate effectively with staff and customers	I understand the implications of poor client communications	I know how to work the till, handle payments and process payment by card	I know the salon's appointment system and how to make appointments for clients
I know the salon's services; how long they take and how much they cost	I know what to look for in relation to stationery shortages and product imperfections	I understand the extent to which the Legislation affects what I do at work	I understand the necessity of personal presentation when dealing with clients

Assessment of knowledge and understanding

Project

With two of your colleagues you can practise and document the different scenarios that occur in a hairdressing salon.

Let one person take the place of the client and another, the receptionist. The third acts as an observer and takes notes for the others. Take it in turns to cover the following salon situations:

1 An angry client who is not happy with their hair.

2 A client who needs assistance with buying retail products.

3 A client who wants to make several bookings for her daughter's wedding.

In your notes you need to cover how the client was handled, how, if at all, the service could be improved and what information needs to be recorded in each of the different scenarios.

Case study

A client has asked for an appointment with a stylist who no longer works at the salon. Describe your salon procedures for:

- what you say to the client
- the questions you would ask
- the alternatives that you would offer the client
- what you would do if you could not deal with the situation.

Revision questions

A selection of different types of questions to check your reception knowledge.

Q1   Visa and MasterCard are both forms of _____ card.   Fill in the blank

Q2   A charge card is the same as a debit card.   True or false

Q3   Which of the following card types are debit cards?   Multi selection

Loyalty card	☐ 1
Switch card	☐ 2
American Express card	☐ 3
MasterCard	☐ 4
Maestro card	☐ 5
Store card	☐ 6

Q4   A float in the till contains 1 x £10.00 note 2 x £5.00 notes, £20.00 in £1 coins and £5.00 in 50p coins. How much is in the float?   Multi choice

£40.00	○ a
£45.00	○ b
£45.50	○ c
£46.00	○ d

Q5   You should always take a contact number when making appointments.   True or false

Q6   Which of the following are examples of ineffective use of resources?   Multi selection

Explaining services and costs to clients on the telephone	☐ 1
Discarding excess product after application	☐ 2
Overrunning on appointments	☐ 3
Turning the lights off in corridors and staff areas	☐ 4
Washing up in the dispensary	☐ 5
Ordering stock over the telephone	☐ 6

Q7   _____ retail products are for maintaining hair between visits.   Fill in the blank

Q8   Which of the following procedures monitors the usage of products within salons?   Multi choice

Stock control   ○ a

Monitoring wastage   ○ b

Retail product and display cleaning   ○ c

Stock rotation   ○ d

Q9   A job description is a document containing the employee's terms and conditions of employment.   True or false

Preparing for assessment checklist

Remember to:

✔	promote the range of services available in the salon and know what they cost
✔	promote the range of products available in the salon and know what they cost
✔	keep the reception area clean and tidy at all times
✔	keep stationery stocks handy at reception and know where to find replacements
✔	cover all the salon's payment types and methods
✔	always make appointments correctly, according to the salon's policy
✔	take messages and pass them on to the right person promptly
✔	give the right change when payment is made by cash
✔	recognise the current and valid forms of payment that the salon accepts
✔	keep the reception area and the till secure at all times.

Part**two**
Customer-centred services

1 Hair: Richard Ward, Photography: Daniele Cipriani 2 Hair: Damien Carney for Joico, Photography: Hama Sanders 3 Hair: NHF Inspire, Photography: Simon Powell 4 Hair: Lewis Moore@Francesco Group, Streetly, Photography: John Rawson@trp 5 Hair: The Artistic Team@TPL Hairdressing, Photography: John Rawson@trp 6 Hair: Christopher Appleton@George's Hair Salon, Leicester, Photography: John Rawson@trp Left Hair: Reds Hair and Beauty, Sunderland, Photography: John Rawson@trp

FELLOWSHIP FOR BRITISH HAIRDRESSING F.A.M.E. TEAM 2006

Chapter**five**
Consultation and advice

G7

G7.1

G7.2

G7.3

More information See appendices for relevant legislation:

- Data Protection Act (1998) EKU G7.1
- Equal opportunities
- Consumer rights EKU G7.2

Consultation: quick overview

Unit title

G7 Advise and consult with clients

This is a **mandatory** unit in hair dressing *and* barbering and it is made up of three main outcomes

Main outcomes

G7.1 Identify what clients want

G7.2 Analyse the hair, skin and scalp

G7.3 Advise clients and agree services and products

What do I need to do for G7.1?

- Allow clients to express their wishes and ideas
- Find out what clients want with simple questioning
- Use a variety of visual aids to get different ideas
- Ask about uncertainties and confirm your plan of action with the client
- Confirm client's wishes for services and products

What do I need to do for G7.2?

- Look for signs that will influence, limit or change your plan of action
- Carry out any necessary tests beforehand
- Check previous records for any indications that might affect your plan
- Seek help from others when you are unsure

What do I need to do for G7.3?

- Make suitable recommendations for your client
- Agree services, products and processes with your client

- Tell the client how much and how long the processes will be

- Maintain a professional level of contact with the client

- Make sure that all records are kept up to date

What aspects do I need to cover for G7.1, G7.2 and G7.3?

- New and existing salon customers

- The different ways in which you find out about the client's hair

- Any adverse or limiting conditions that affect the client's expectations

- Report any infections or infestations that you find

What do I need to know for G7.1, G7.2 and G7.3?

- The legal and salon requirements affecting your consultation and advice

- The ranges of products and services available in your salon

- How to calculate the costs of services and products

- How hair grows and the effects of different types and textures

- A range of adverse hair and skin conditions, their possible causes and the ways in which they affect styling options

- Why you should look for adverse hair and skin conditions

- Why it is important to carry out tests and how this is done

- The importance of a confidential and professional communication with clients

Introduction

Consultation is arguably the most important service provided in a hairdressing salon; although the professional advice it produces for its clients often seems undervalued in relation to other professional sectors. But make no mistake; the service of consultation is fundamental to all other services and treatments that take place within the salon and, without it, salon-based hairdressing would not survive.

But in many salons consultation is a service that is often 'squeezed into or bolted on to' other booked services. When this is rushed, you run the risk of unexpected outcomes or potential disasters. Conversely, when too much time is taken, it often erodes into the service time, causing a 'knock-on' effect that will either make the stylist and client run late or not allow enough time to do the job properly.

Keywords

Trichology
The scientific study of the hair and scalp

Referral
The situations where you need to redirect clients to other sources of treatment or service, i.e. when there are adverse hair and skin conditions, or because of other services that your salon doesn't provide

Incompatibility
Refers to incompatible chemistry. When incompatibles are present within the hair – e.g. colour restorers, 'Just for Men' or compound henna – no organic chemicals can be used

Adverse hair and scalp condition
Something that will affect the way in which a service is or can be carried out; for example, a double crown – this will influence the way in which the hair can be cut in order to camouflage the growth pattern

Information covered in this chapter

- Hair tests
- Hair and scalp disorders
- Using visual aids
- Limiting and influencing factors affecting styling choices

So, taking all these aspects on board, it is essential that you get the balance right. Enough time must be given to:

- gain the client's trust and professional respect
- use visual aids either brought by the client or available from the salon
- conduct an analysis of the starting situation
- discuss the client's expectations in line with your analysis
- negotiate and then agree the best course of action
- provide home care maintenance and management advice.

G7.1 Identify what clients want

Hairdressing is about relationships – the relationships that are created through good communication.

So your communication skills need to be clear in finding out what the client wants in a clear and mutually understood way. Its not that clients want to mislead us; its more to do with the fact that many people find discussing personal, or things to do with their appearance a difficult thing to talk about.

Most people have no self-visualisation; that means that they haven't an ability to imagine what a style would look like on them and this can be a huge problem for those trying to give advice. Seeing what the clients are seeing is everything, so you have to find ways of establishing what it is that they really want.

Good, effective communication

A good communicator will use a mixture of techniques; this is a sort of 'toolbox,' a mixture of effective communication skills that covers the following.

1 *Listening and hearing*. This is the ability to hear and understand what the client is saying. This is essential when you need to review what has been said later; when you finally agree on the service and course of action to take.

Activity
Communication

1 Can you think of the gestures, posture or expression that would portray at least three types of negative body language?

2 List at least six different ways of communicating.

3 Explain briefly what communication means to you.

Remember

 'Advising clients' means listening to what they have to say about their hair, asking appropriate questions and coming up with suitable suggestions for styles and treatments.

2 *Speaking clearly.* It is important that you are clear with what you say and that you are not misunderstood by the client. During consultation you will be taking the lead; you will be asking questions and trying to find enough information in the time available to make the right decisions for your client. You will be weighing up what the client wants against the limitations that arise during the analysis. You will be getting the client to agree on the various possible options and planning the necessary course of action.

3 *Understanding body language.* The most difficult aspect of consultation is *reading between the lines*. Your ability to understand situations based upon what has been said or not said, is exceptionally useful. There are times when your client will look in a certain way, or say something that makes you stop and think. In these situations, your ability to read the situation, i.e. your perceptiveness in picking this up and responding appropriately, will have a huge impact on what happens next.

4 *Finding help.* There will be times during consultation that you will find that you aren't sure of what the client means, or possibly, not sure of what you see. If you make an inaccurate assessment of these factors it could lead to a disaster. It is vitally important that you clarify the situation at every point along the way and if that means asking for assistance from someone else, then you must go and find a second opinion.

Further information can be found in other parts of this book: G17.3 Communicate information to clients pages 51–60 and G18.3 Gain client commitment to using additional services or products pages 140–141.

EKU *statement*

G7.20) How to use varied vocabulary and expressions to suit your purpose (e.g., to present an argument, express ideas or opinions, exchange information)

G7.21) How to adapt your contributions to suit different situations (e.g., the amount you say, your manner and tone of voice, dealing with those with sight or hearing difficulties)

Asking questions to find out what the client wants

1 You need to ask the right sorts of questions to get the information that you need.

2 You need to ask those questions in a way that your client understands.

The main types of question styles are covered below.

Open questions These are good to use if you want to gain more in-depth information from the client. They start with 'who', 'what', 'when', 'why', 'where' and 'how'. Examples:

- What products do you use on your hair?
- When did you last wash your hair?
- How often do you use the straightening irons on your hair?

Closed questions   These are useful for a quick 'yes' or 'no' elimination response. Examples:

- Have you had permanent colour on your hair before?
- Would you like me to do it in your lunch hour today for you?
- Are you against moving the parting from the centre?

Feeling questions   These types of questions focus upon the client and are good to use when you are trying to gauge a personal opinion or feeling. Examples:

- How do you feel about taking the length back up to the shoulders?
- Do you want me to talk you through the home care for this style now?
- What do you think about a complete colour change today?

'Choices' questions   They could be considered to be leading as they request the client to make a response based on a set number of options. Examples:

- Would you prefer the smaller intense leave-in treatment, or the normal after-shampoo conditioner?
- Shall we see if there is time today to do it all, or would you rather make a separate appointment for the highlights after the cut?
- Where would you like to wear the parting, in the centre where it is now or to move it across so that you can have a sweeping fringe?

Whatever style of question you choose to use, you must make sure that:

- you identify any limitations or influencing factors that affect your styling options
- the client understands what you are saying/doing
- you allow the client time to consider the options that you provide
- you urge the client to give you as much information as possible
- you listen, *hear* and understand the client's responses
- you confirm what you hear before moving on to the next aspect of the consultation.

Remember

 If you find that your line of questions isn't getting the information that you need, try asking again but in a different way. E.g. 'Well, how do you feel about changing the colour?' or, 'What other things do you find that also work well on your hair?'

EKU *statement*

G7.23) How to identify the speaker's intentions (e.g., by manner, tone of voice, vocabulary)

EKU *statement*

G7.22) How to show you are listening closely (e.g., by body language) and responding appropriately (ask questions to show interest)

Open/closed questions

Open questions will result in explanations or descriptions. **Closed** questions will result in short answers such as 'yes' or 'no'.

Feeling questions

Feeling questions ask "how do you **feel** about a fringe?" "What do you **think** if I restyle it today?" "Do you **want** more volume?"

 Questioning styles

Choices questions

"Would you like to keep the parting in the centre, **or** would you like to try it on the side for a change?"

Questioning styles

No misunderstandings

You need to adapt your consultation style to suit the level of understanding of the client. Seek clarification or confirm points as they are discussed; show that you understand by nodding in agreement. When you get to a point in the consultation where you are not sure about something, re-ask your questions in a different way to probe further.

Identify the limitations or influencing factors Some of these will crop up in conversation, but the main influencing factors are going to arise during your visual inspection of the hair and scalp. So whether you do your inspection first or later will depend on the service that you are going to do, or how comfortable the client is with the consultation process.

Allow time for the client to express their wishes And consider your advice. Give the client time to prepare what they want to say. Many people will bring pictures from magazines or off the Internet which will give an impression of what they have in mind. But often those people feel embarrassed to take it out of their handbag when they get to the salon, so why not ask. 'Is there is anything that you have seen or brought with you?'

Don't rush them into making swift decisions; you need to *take them with you every step along the journey*. If they do feel rushed or that you are 'pushy' you will be alienating them from the outset. That's a difficult position to be in as you will be creating a tension during the service that would be uncomfortable for anyone to be in.

Remember

It's easy to confuse clients if you start using technical terms. Keep it simple.

Using visual aids in consultation

Pictures

'A picture paints a thousand words' – the term is an old overworked cliché but very true. Pictures convey aspects of hair styles or effects that are very difficult to put into words. They cut straight through technical jargon and establish a basis for things that you and the client can see and confirm.

Pictures are an immensely important visual aid and another form of language that hairdressers understand very well. One reason for this is hairdressers' understanding of shape, proportion and balance. As a stylist, you are trained in looking into pictures to

Activity

Consultation

We can define consultation as a way of providing advice during a meeting.

In order to carry out a thorough consultation there are a number of steps that should take place. Write down in order the sequence of events that should take place during client consultation.

A.

B.

C. etc.

see more than just an overall image. You see things like how volume is distributed, where hair needs to be shaped in a certain way and how colour can impact an overall effect. However, you can't expect the client to see these technical aspects too, so beware when pictures are used to express a feeling or a mood. You need to make sure that you are seeing the same things.

Colour charts

Colour charts are extremely useful for hairdressers. We rely on them every day. However, they are not always a very helpful medium for the client. We tend to treat others as we would want to be treated ourselves. This is a good philosophy, but there are times when our expectation of others is a little over-optimistic. Generally speaking, clients have very little ability for self-visualisation, but that's why they are asking you for your opinions and advice.

Remember colour charts tend to have very small samples of coloured wefts. Unless you can help the client visualise the

- amount and placement
- colour intensity, and
- density and saturation of colour

then the value of using a chart is greatly reduced.

IMAGE COURTESY OF GOLDWELL UK

Activity

Online consultation

There are several websites that show hairstyles, makeovers and provide good technical advice for men and women.

You should keep abreast of this information and make a note of the more useful sites so that you can recommend these sites for clients to look at home.

To start you off take a look at the resources at www.best4hair.co.uk.

Confirm and agree Whatever methods you have used during your consultation, make sure that you confirm and summarise, at all the points along the way. Only after you have both agreed a course of action can you take things to the next stage.

Activity
For discussion
Empathy and sympathy – is there any difference?
Discuss with your colleagues the differences between these emotions and why they are useful.

Activity
For discussion
Discuss with your fellow staff members how different client personalities will affect the style and method of consultation. Discuss also how you can vary the consultation delivery to ensure that a mutually beneficial outcome is derived.

Lead the consultation process

Take control of the situation; it is essential that you guide the client throughout the service. Your professionalism will be measured at the moment when the client realises that it is you who is going to conduct the consultation. Everything is summed up (rightly or wrongly) by the client and you in a few moments and, contrary to customer service beliefs, you will not be able to satisfy the client fully unless you are in charge of this situation. You have to guide and steer the whole process in order to satisfy the client and those of your salon.

Activity
Body talk
What would be the visible signs of someone who:

1 Is being defensive?

2 Shows no interest?

3 Seems confused?

4 Wants to know more about your in-salon promotion?

Write down your answers in your portfolio.

Remember
Visual aids are an extremely useful way of conveying information.
What types of visual aid do you use during client consultation?

Remember
During consultation with your client, take enough time to find out what they want.

Remember
Trust is hard earned. Gaining a customer's trust and loyalty takes time. Once you have earned this, the bond remains fragile, so handle with care.

Remember
You have to have the confidence to lead during consultation. It is your positive approach and outlook that will draw your client in to the conversation and draw the vital information out.

The analysis of the client's hair takes the form of a visual inspection. You need to brush and separate the hair in several directions in different areas over the head so that you can look for any signs that will either limit or modify the options available for your client.

You are looking for anything that could affect your decisions and this could relate to:

- **hair texture** – the thickness of individual hairs; is it coarse, medium or fine?
- hair length – is it layered, graduated or all one length?
- hair growth patterns – what directions does the hair grow in at the front, or the nape or over the crown?
- **hair tendency** – is the hair straight, wavy or curly?
- hair amount – how much hair do they have, how is it distributed over the scalp?
- hair condition – is the hair **chemically treated**, natural, dry or damaged?
- **hair colour** – is the colour natural or has it been highlighted or coloured?
- hair problems – damaged **cuticle**, split ends etc.
- face shape – is the shape **oval, round, oblong** or **square**?
- infections and infestations – is there any adverse signs or indications?
- tests – elasticity, skin, colour etc.
- lifestyle – manageability and the time available to maintain the look.

EKU *statement*

G7.13) The basic structure of hair and skin

G7.14) The growth cycle of hair

G7.15) The characteristics of different hair types and textures

G7.10) The indications of suspected infections and infestations and disorders visible to the naked eye

The aspects to consider:

Structure of hair and skin page 105	**Cortex**, cuticle, medulla, physical properties of hair and skin, hair **follicle**
Growth cycle of hair pages 109–112	Anagen, catagen, telogen
Hair texture page 110	Coarse, medium, fine
Hair tests pages 111–114	Sensitivity test, strand test, colour test, test cutting, test curl, curl check, peroxide test, incompatibility test, elasticity test, porosity test
Infectious skin and scalp pages 116–117	Impetigo, scalp ringworm (tinea capitis), head lice (pediculosis capitis)
Non-infectious skin and scalp pages 117–119	Folliculitis, dandruff (pityriasis capitis), alopecia, seborrhoea, psoriasis, eczema
Hair defects page 119	Split ends (fragilitis crinium), damaged cuticle, trichorrexis nodosa, monilethrix
Head and face shapes page 121	Oval, round, rectangular, square, heart-shaped
Other important physical features pages 122–123	Hair growth patterns, ears, nose, eyes, etc.

Structure of hair and skin

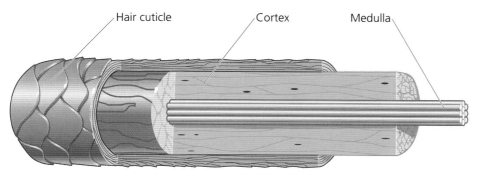

Hair cuticle   Cortex   Medulla

The hair shaft

EKU *statement*

G7.16) The general factors that contribute to healthy hair (e.g. health, environment, chemicals)

Hair

The cross-section taken through the hair lengthways shown in the diagram provides us with a microscopic view of the three specific layers.

The cuticle is the outer layer of colourless cells which forms a protective surface to the hair. It regulates the chemicals entering and damaging the hair and protects the hair from excessive heat and drying. The cells overlap like tiles on a roof with the free edges pointing towards the tips of the hair. The amount of layers is proportional to hair texture. Hair with fewer layers of cuticle is finer than coarser hair types which have several layers. Hair in good condition has a cuticle that is tightly closed, limiting the entry of moisture and chemicals. Conversely, hair that is in a dry or porous condition has damaged or partially missing cuticle layers. One simple indicator of cuticle condition relates to the time taken to blow-dry hair. Hair in good condition will dry quickly in proportion to the amount of hair on the head (*density*). The closely packed cuticle allows the dryer to chase the water from the hairshaft. Porous hair absorbs moisture and therefore takes far longer to dry and is unfortunately subjected to more heat, which exacerbates the problem.

Remember

 A closed smooth cuticle is the most important sign of healthy hair: hair imparts shine, dryes more quickly, is resistant to chemical treatments and holds styles and colours better than hair with a raised/damaged cuticle.

The cortex is the middle and largest layer. It is made up of a long fibrous material which has the appearance of rope. If looked at more closely, each of the fibres is made up of even smaller chains of fibres. The *quality* and condition of these bundles of fibres will determine the hair's strength. The way in which they are *bonded* together has a direct effect upon curl and ability to stretch (*hair elasticity*). It is within this part of the hair that the natural hair colour and permanent synthetic colour is distributed and perms make the permanent chemical changes.

EKU *statement*

G7.16) The general factors that contribute to healthy hair (e.g. health, environment, chemicals)

The *medulla* is the central, most inner part of the hair. It only exists in medium to coarser hair types and is often intermittent throughout the length. The medulla does not play any useful part in hairdressing processes and treatments.

Physical properties of hair

Hair *naturally* contains a certain amount of moisture that allows it to stretch and return, giving it elasticity. Hair that is dry and in poor condition is less elastic. Hair is hygroscopic: it absorbs water from the surrounding air. How much water is taken up depends on the dryness of the hair and the moistness of the atmosphere. Hair is also porous. There are tiny tube-like spaces within the hair structure and the water flows into these by *capillary action*, rather like blotting paper absorbing ink. Drying hair in the ordinary way evaporates only the surface moisture, but drying over long periods or at too high a temperature removes water from within the hair, leaving it brittle and in poor

Remember

 Hair in good condition has moisture that helps to give it elasticity and shine.

condition. Damaged hair is more porous than healthy hair and easily loses any water, which makes it hard to stretch and mould.

Curled hair returns to its former shape as it takes up water, so the dryer the atmosphere, the longer the curl or set lasts. Similarly, curling dry hair is most effective just after the hair has been washed because, although the surface is dry, the hair will have absorbed water internally. Blow-styling and curling with hot irons, heated rollers, hot combs and hot brushes all have similar temporary effects.

Hair health and condition

Moisture levels within the hair are essential for maintaining good condition. We can see the evidence of this moisture from the shine that we associate with great-looking hair. 'Bad hair' denotes poor condition and the lack of shine is due to the unevenness of the hair's surface, i.e. the cuticle. A roughened cuticle surface is an indicator of either physical or chemical damage. Each of these states is difficult to correct. In mild cases of dryness, treatments can be applied to improve the hair's manageability and handling. In more serious situations of porous hair, the hair's ability to resist the ingress of chemicals and moisture is severely impaired. There are no long-lasting remedies for this so regular reconditioning treatments must be used.

So the health and the condition of the hair is your starting point. Whatever happens next should be a process of improving what went on before. A client will expect the service or treatment that you advise to be a step in the right direction. You will need to look for each of the following properties and aspects:

Features of hair in good condition

- Shine and lustre.
- Smooth outer cuticle surface.
- Strength and resistance.
- Good elasticity.
- Good natural moisture levels.

Features of hair in poor condition

- Raised or open cuticle.
- Damaged torn hair shaft.
- Split ends.
- Low strength and resistance.
- Over-elastic/stretchy.
- Dry, porous lengths or ends.

Physical hair damage is caused by

- harsh or incorrect usage of brushes and/or combs
- excessive heat from styling equipment.

Chemical hair damage is caused by

- incorrect over-timing of all colouring and perming treatments
- effects of hydrogen peroxide
- over-bleaching and highlighting services
- excessive overuse of colouring/tinting products
- perm products that are too strong or over-processing
- chlorine from swimming pools.

DR. JOHN GRAY

Good condition

DR. JOHN GRAY

Poor condition

Weathering

- Hair is also damaged by excesses of ultra violet radiation found in sunlight.

And generally speaking

- The normal and abnormal working of the body has a direct effect on the hair and scalp. Good health is reflected in good hair and skin. A balanced diet with plenty of fresh foods contributes to good health.
- Disease and drugs used in the treatment of disease take their toll on the hair and skin.
- Genetic factors affecting hair growth determine hair strength and texture.
- The hair of women is usually at its best during pregnancy.
- Deterioration of the hair and skin after giving birth is usually due to stress and tiredness.

Remember

 It is far easier to keep good-conditioned hair in good condition than it is to try to correct hair in bad condition.

The skin

The skin is the largest organ of the body and if laid flat would cover an area of about 21 square feet. It forms the barrier to a multitude of external forces and is made up of many layers.

The epidermis

The epidermis is the front line of defence. This outer protective layer of the skin is called the *stratum corneum* and is a hard, cornified layer, consisting of 15 to 40 layers of flattened skin cells or corneocytes, which constantly migrate up from deeper regions and fully replace themselves about once a month. The corneocytes are filled with keratin and a fatty *lipid* that make a barrier to prevent loss of water through the skin.

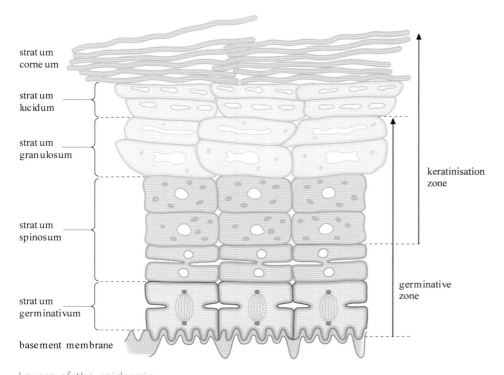

Layers of the epidermis

The dermis

The dermis is the thickest layer of the skin. It is here that the hair follicle is formed. The dermis is made up of elastic and connective tissue and is well supplied with blood and lymph vessels. The skin receives its nutrient supply from this area. The upper part of the dermis, the *papillary layer*, contains the organs of touch, heat and cold, and pain. The lower part of the dermis, the *reticular layer*, forms a looser network of cells.

The subcutaneous fat

The subcutaneous fat lies below the dermis. It is also known as the *subcutis*, or occasionally as the *hypodermis*. It is composed of loose cell tissue and contains stores of fat. The base of the hair follicle is situated just above this area, or sometimes in it. Subcutaneous tissue gives roundness to the body and fills the space between the dermis and muscle tissue that may lie below.

The hair follicle

Hair grows from a thin, tube-like space in the skin called a hair follicle.

- At the bottom of the follicles are areas well supplied with nerves and blood vessels, which nourish the cellular activity. These are called *hair papillae*.
- Immediately surrounding each papilla is the *germinal matrix* which consists of actively forming hair cells.
- As the new hair cells develop, the lowest part of the hair is shaped into the *hair bulb*.
- The cells continue to take shape and form as they push along the follicle until they appear at the skin surface as *hair fibres*.
- The cells gradually harden and die. The hair is formed of dead tissue. It retains its elasticity due to its chemical structure and keratin content.

Sebaceous glands

The oil gland, or *sebaceous gland*, is situated in the skin and opens out into the upper third of the follicle. Oil or *sebum* is secreted into the follicle and onto the hair and skin surface.

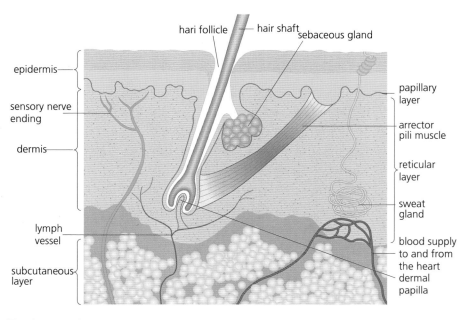

The hair in skin

Sebum helps to prevent the skin and hair from drying. By retaining moisture it helps the hair and skin to stay pliable. Sebum is slightly acid – about pH 5.6 – and forms a protective antibacterial covering for the skin.

Sweat glands

The sweat gland secretes sweat which passes out through the sweat ducts. The ends of these ducts can be seen at the surface of the skin as sweat *pores*. There are two types of sweat gland: the larger, associated closely with the hair follicles, are the *apocrine glands*; the smaller, found over most of the skin's surface, are the *eccrine glands*.

Sweat is mainly water with salt and other minerals. In abnormal conditions sweat contains larger amounts of waste material. Evaporation of sweat cools the skin. The function of sweat, and thus the sweat glands, is to protect the body by helping to maintain the normal temperature.

HAIR: NHF INSPIRE

The hair muscle

The hair muscle, or *arrector pili*, is attached at one end to the hair follicle and at the other to the underlying tissue of the epidermis. When it contracts it pulls the hair and follicle upright. Upright hairs trap a warm layer of air around the skin. The hairs also act as a sensor of touch: for example, you soon notice if an insect crawls over your skin.

Hair growth

Hair is constantly growing. Over a period of between one and six years an individual hair actively grows, then stops, rests, degenerates and finally falls out. Before the hair leaves the follicle, the new hair is normally ready to replace it. (If a hair is not replaced then a tiny, bald area occurs.) The lives of individual hairs vary and are subject to variations in the body. Some are actively growing while others are resting. Hairs on the head are at different stages of growth.

Stages of growth

The life cycle of hair is as follows:

- *Anagen* is the active growing stage of the hair, a period of activity of the papilla and germinal matrix. This stage may last from a few months to several years. It is at this stage of formation at the base of the follicle that the hair's thickness is determined. Hair colour too is formed in the early part of anagen.
- *Catagen* is a period when the hair stops growing and cellular activity decreases at the papilla whilst the follicle shrinks.
- *Telogen* is the final stage, when there is no further growth or activity at the papilla. The follicle begins to shrink and completely separates from the papilla area. This resting stage does not last long. Towards the end of the telogen stage, cells begin to activate in preparation for the new anagen stage of regrowth.

The new anagen period involves the hair follicle beginning to grow down again. Vigorous papilla activity generates a new hair at the germinal matrix. At the same time the old hair is slowly making its way up and out of the follicle. Often the old and new hair can be seen at the same time in the follicle.

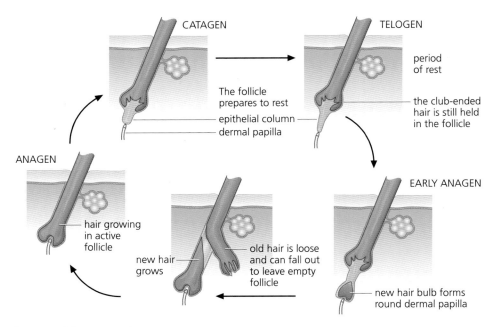

Stages of hair growth

In some animals most of the hairs follow their life cycle in step, passing through anagen, catagen and telogen together. This results in moulting. Human hair, however, develops at an uneven rate and few follicles shed their hair at the same time. (If all hairs fell at the same time we would have bald periods.)

Hair texture

Individual hair thickness is referred to as **hair texture** and the main types are:

- very fine hair
- fine hair
- medium hair
- coarse hair.

The main differences between the hair textures relate to the number of layers of cuticle.

Remember

Hair texture
The more layers of cuticle that the hair has, the greater its resistance to absorbing moisture and chemicals. Therefore coarse hair in good condition can often take longer to perm than finer hair types.

Curly	Wavy	Straight
Flat ribbon-like	Less oval	Round

Hair types

Hair and skin tests

There are a number of tests that you can carry out to help diagnose the condition and likely reaction of your client's skin and hair. These tests will help you to decide what action to take before, during and after the application of hairdressing processes.

You will need to carry out and record all these results in line with your own salon's policy for conducting tests.

Development/strand test

A strand test or hair strand colour test is used to assess the resultant colour on a strand or section of hair after colour has been processed and developed. It is carried out as follows:

1 Most colouring products just require the time recommended by the manufacturer – check their instructions.

2 Rub a strand of hair lightly with the back of a comb to remove the surplus colour.

3 Check whether the colour remaining is evenly distributed throughout the hair's length. If it is even, remove the rest of the colour. If it is uneven, allow processing to continue, if necessary applying more colour. If any of the hair on the head is not being treated, you can compare the evenness of colour in the coloured hair with that in the uncoloured hair.

Colour test

This test is used to assess the suitability of a chosen colour, the amount of processing time required and the final colour result. Apply the colour or bleaching products you propose to use to a cutting of the client's hair and process as recommended.

Sensitivity Test

(Also known as patch test or skin test)

The sensitivity test is used to assess the reaction of the skin to chemicals or chemical products. In the salon it is mainly used before colouring. Some people are allergic to external contact of chemicals such as PPD (found in permanent colour). This can cause dermatitis or, in more severe cases, permanent scarring of skin tissue and hair loss. Some are allergic to irritants reacting internally, causing asthma and hay fever. Others may be allergic to both internal and external irritants. To find out whether a client's skin reacts to chemicals in permanent colours, the following test should be carried out at least 24 hours prior to the chemical process.

Note: Skin testing is not just for new clients, it has now been found that clients can develop sensitivity to chemicals through prolonged use of the same or similar products. Therefore periodic testing for adverse reactions is essential and should be carried out routinely from time to time as recommended by the manufacturer.

1 Mix a little of the colour to be used with the correct amount of hydrogen peroxide – as recommended by the manufacturer.

2 Clean an area of skin about 8mm square behind the ear or in the fold of the arm. Use a little spirit on cotton wool to remove the grease from the skin.

3 Apply a little of the colour mixture to skin.

4 Cover the colour patch with a simple dressing to protect it. The client should remain in the salon for the duration of the processing time. Ask your client to report any discomfort or irritation that occurs over the next 24 hours. Arrange

EKU *statement*

G7.3) Salon procedures and manufacturers' instructions in relation to conducting tests

G7.11) How and when tests are carried out on hair

G7.12) The importance of carrying out tests and the potential consequences of failing to do so

Remember

Tests are a vital part of general hairdressing services. If they are missed or ignored you and the salon run the risk of a potential disaster.

Skin test

L'ORÉAL PROFESSIONEL

EKU *statement*

G7.4) Salon rules for maintaining confidentiality

EKU *statement*

G7.8) Why it is important to identify factors that may limit or affect services and products which can be used

to see your client at the end of this time so that you can check for signs of reaction.

5 If there is a *positive response*, i.e. a skin reaction such as inflammation, soreness, swelling, irritation or discomfort, do not carry out the intended service. Never ignore the result of a skin test. If a skin test showed a reaction and you carried on anyway, there might be a more serious reaction which could affect the whole body.

6 If there is a *negative response*, i.e. no reaction to the chemicals, then carry out the treatment as proposed.

Warning: In recent years there have been a growing number of successful personal injury claims made against salons where the necessary precautions have not been taken.

Remember

Contra-indications

A contra-indication is something that signifies that a service CANNOT be carried out.

Activity

Carry out a skin test

To do this you will need:

1 A. Materials for 'skin test': i.e. dark permanent hair colour, 6 per cent hydrogen peroxide, alcohol wipes, cotton buds and a sterile plaster.

2 B. Record card.

When you have completed the test you have to wait 24–48 hours for the result. Record your findings of the skin test on the record sheet by ticking the relevant box, and complete a salon record card.

1 If you have a positive result what advice would you give to the client?

2 If you have a negative result what would you be able to do?

3 What other names is a skin test also known as?

Remember

Incompatible chemistry

Henna is still widely used throughout the world as a hair- and skin-dyeing compound. In the UK people using natural henna will often add other ingredients such as coffee, wine, lemon juice, etc. to intensify the final colour. However, other countries also add compounds to henna; e.g. India and Turkey sometimes add iron ore deposits which are crushed into the powder to increase the 'reddening' effect. If this mixture were to come into contact with hydrogen peroxide (either through colouring or perming), a chemical reaction would take place and in that exchange permanent damage and breakage would occur.

Test cutting

In this test a piece of hair is cut from a place from the head where it won't be noticed. The hair can then be processed to check its suitability, the amount of processing required and

Activity

Incompatibility test

To do this you will need the following materials

1   perm lotion

2   hydrogen peroxide

3   glass bowl

4   a small piece of hair treated with a product containing metallic salts

5   a small piece of untreated hair (cut from a friend or colleague).

Record your findings – what happened when the different hair samples were immersed in the solutions? what did you see?
For:

1   treated hair

2   untreated hair

the timing, before the process is carried out. The test is used for colouring, straightening, relaxing, reducing synthetic colouring, i.e. decolouring, bleaching and incompatibility.

Test curl

This test is made on the hair to determine the lotion suitability, the strength, the curler size, the timing of processing and the development. It is used before perming.

Curl check or test

This test is used to assess the development of curl in the perming process. The test is used periodically throughout a perm and for final assessment of the result.

Peroxide test

This test is made on hair that has been decoloured or stripped of its synthetic colour. The test is used to assess the effectiveness of the process and to check that no synthetic pigment remains. Any synthetic colour remaining will oxidise later and darken again within two or three days. If the hair darkens after testing, remove all the chemicals from the test section, then reapply the decolourant. It may take several applications to strip all of the unwanted colour.

Incompatibility test

Perm lotions and other chemicals applied to the hair may react with chemicals that have already been used such as home-use products. The incompatibility test is therefore used to detect chemicals/elements which could react with hairdressing processes such as colouring and perming. The test is carried out as follows:

1   Protect your hands by wearing gloves.

2   Place a small cutting of hair in a small dish.

3 Pour into the dish a mixture of 20 parts of 6 per cent hydrogen peroxide and one part ammonium thioglycolate (general purpose perm solution). Make sure that you are not bending over the dish to avoid splashing the chemicals on to your face or inhaling any resultant released fumes.

4 Watch for signs of bubbling, heating or discolouration. These indicate that the hair already contains incompatible chemicals. The hair should not be permed, coloured or bleached if there are any signs of reaction. Perming treatment might discolour or break the hair and could burn the skin.

Pull test

A pull test helps to evaluate excessive and/or abnormal scalp hair loss. It is particularly relevant to the attachment of hair pieces and hair extension services.

To conduct a pull test:

1 Gently pull small sections of hair whilst sliding the fingers from root to point on at least three areas of the scalp.

2 If more than 12 hairs per hand are shed, it could be indicating an abnormal hair loss.

3 This is a contra-indication and the attachment service should not be provided.

Tensile strength test

A test to determine the breaking point of hair. This test is carried out in a similar way to an elasticity test, although the strength of the internal structure of the hair is tested to breaking point.

Elasticity test

This test is carried out on a dry single hair and used to determine how much the hair will stretch and then return to its original position. It is an indicator of the internal condition of the hair's bonded structure and ability to retain moisture. By taking a hair between the fingers and stretching it you can assess the amount of spring it has. If the hair breaks easily, care needs to be taken before applying any hairdressing process and further tests are indicated – a test curl or a test cutting, for example. Natural healthy hair in good condition will be elastic and more likely to retain the effects of physical curling, setting or blow-shaping longer. It will also take chemical processes more readily. Hair with little elasticity will not hold physical shaping or chemical processes satisfactorily.

Porosity test

The porosity test is used to assess the ability of the hair to absorb moisture or liquids – another indicator of condition. If the cuticle is torn or broken, it will soon lose its moisture and become dry. It may be able to absorb liquids quicker, but its ability to retain them is reduced. If the cuticle is smooth, unbroken and tightly packed, it may resist the passage of moisture or liquids. By running the fingertips through the hair, from points to roots, you can assess the degree of roughness. The rougher the hair, the more porous it will be and the faster it will absorb chemicals.

Remember

Natural moisture levels

The natural moisture levels in hair play a significant part in the way that hair responds to treatments and styling. If the natural levels can be retained following perming, colouring and bleaching the client's hair will remain manageable, easier to detangle and able to hold thermal styling effects for far longer.

Deplete those natural levels and the hair becomes porous and will tangle easily, is less manageable and not able to hold a set for long. Pre-chemical treatments help to reduce the hair's moisture reduction.

L'ORÉAL PROFESSIONNEL

Porosity test

L'ORÉAL PROFESSIONNEL

Porosity test

Hair and scalp diseases, conditions and defects

Diseases of the hair and scalp may be caused by a variety of infectious organisms and particular tell-tale signs or symptoms enable us to identify them. An initial examination should be carried out before any hairdressing process occurs, so that any adverse conditions can be identified. If this is not done a variety of serious outcomes can occur. However, not all hair and scalp conditions are dangerous; some non-infectious conditions can easily be addressed within the salon.

You have to differentiate between them.

EKU *statement*

G7.8) Why it is important to identify factors that may limit or affect services and products which can be used

G7.17) The likely causes of adverse hair and scalp conditions visible to the naked eye

Activity
Parts of the skin

The skin is the outer covering of the body. It is a complex organ, made up of different layers and contains many parts: oil (sebaceous) and sweat glands, hair muscles, blood and nerves.

Complete the table below by explaining what these parts of the skin are and what they do.

Parts of the skin	Explain what this is and what it does
Epidermis	
Dermis	
Hair follicle	
Sebaceous gland	

Infectious diseases

Bacterial diseases

Condition	Symptoms	Cause	Treatment	Infectious
Folliculitis Inflammation of the hair follicles	Inflamed follicles, a common symptom of certain skin diseases	A contact bacterial infection, or due to chemical or physical action	Medical referral to GP	Yes
Impetigo A bacterial infection of the upper skin layers	At first a burning sensation, followed by spots becoming dry; honey-coloured, crusts form and spread	A staphylococcal or streptococcal infection	Medical referral to GP	Yes
Sycosis A bacterial infection of the hairy parts of the face	Small, yellow spots around the follicle mouth, burning, irritation and general inflammation	Bacteria attack the upper part of the hair follicle, spreading to the lower follicle	Medical referral to GP	Yes
Furunculosis Boils or abscesses	Raised, inflamed, pus-filled spots, irritation, swelling and pain	An infection of the hair follicles by staphylococcal bacteria	Medical referral to GP	Yes

COURTESY OF MEDISCAN
DR M H BECK
DR ANDREW WRIGHT
DR ANDREW WRIGHT

Viral diseases

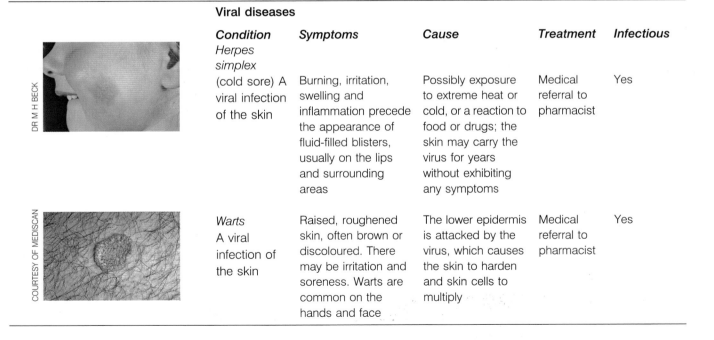

Condition	Symptoms	Cause	Treatment	Infectious
Herpes simplex (cold sore) A viral infection of the skin	Burning, irritation, swelling and inflammation precede the appearance of fluid-filled blisters, usually on the lips and surrounding areas	Possibly exposure to extreme heat or cold, or a reaction to food or drugs; the skin may carry the virus for years without exhibiting any symptoms	Medical referral to pharmacist	Yes
Warts A viral infection of the skin	Raised, roughened skin, often brown or discoloured. There may be irritation and soreness. Warts are common on the hands and face	The lower epidermis is attacked by the virus, which causes the skin to harden and skin cells to multiply	Medical referral to pharmacist	Yes

DR M H BECK
COURTESY OF MEDISCAN

Animal (parasite) infestations

	Condition	Symptoms	Cause	Treatment	Infectious
COURTESY OF MEDISCAN	*Head lice* (pediculosis capitis) Infestation of the hair and scalp by head lice	An itchy reaction to the biting head louse, 'peppering' on pillow-cases and minute egg cases (nits) attached to the upper onto the hair shaft for hair shaft close to the scalp	The head louse bites the scalp feeding on the victim's blood. Breeding produces eggs, which are laid and cemented in incubation until the immature louse emerges	Referral to a pharmacist	Yes
COURTESY OF MEDISCAN	*Scabies* An allergic reaction to the itch mite	A rash in the skin folds around the midriff and on the inside of the thighs, extremely itchy at night	The itch mite burrows under the skin where it lays eggs	Medical referral to GP	Yes

Fungal diseases

	Condition	Symptoms	Cause	Treatment	Infectious
DR JOHN GRAY	*Tinea capitis* Ringworm of the head	Circular bald patch of grey or whitish skin surrounded by red, active rings; hairs broken close to the skin, which looks dull and rough. The fungus lives off the keratin in the skin and hair. This disease is common in children	Fungal infection of the skin or hair	Medical referral	Yes

Non-infectious diseases

Conditions of the hair and skin

	Condition	Symptoms	Cause	Treatment	Infectious
COURTESY OF MEDISCAN	*Acne* Disorder affecting the hair follicles and sebaceous glands	Raised spots and bumps within the skin, commonly upon the face in adolescents	Increased sebum and other secretions block the follicle and a skin reaction occurs	Medical referral to GP	No
HMSO	*Eczema* and *dermatitis* In its simplest form a reddening of the skin	Ranging from slightly inflamed areas of the skin to severe splitting and weeping areas with irritation and soreness	Many possible causes, eczema often associated with internal factors, i.e. allergies or stress Dermatitis a reaction or allergy to external factors.	Medical referral to GP	No
I-STOCK	*Psoriasis* An inflamed, abnormal thickening of the skin	Areas of thickened skin, often raised and patchy. Often on the scalp and also at the joints (arms and legs)	Unknown	Medical referral to GP	No

	Condition	Symptoms	Cause	Treatment	Infectious
COURTESY OF MEDISCAN	Dandruff (Pityriasis capitis)	Dry, small, irritating flakes	Fungal (yeast-like) infection, or physical or chemical irritants	Anti-dandruff treatments	No
COURTESY OF MEDISCAN	Seborrhea	Very greasy, lank hair and greasy skin, making styling difficult	Over-production of sebum	Astringent shampoos	No

Alopecia (hair loss)

	Condition	Symptoms / Description			Infectious
DR ANDREW WRIGHT	Alopecia areata	The name given to balding patches over the scalp. Often starts around or above the ears, circular in pattern ranging from 1–2.5 cm in diameter			Trichological referral
COURTESY OF MEDISCAN	Traction alopecia	Hair loss as a result of excessive pulling at the roots from brushing, curling and straightening. Very often seen with younger girls tying, plaiting or braiding long hair			None
COURTESY OF MEDISCAN	Alopecia totalis	Complete hair loss sometimes as a result of alopecia areata spreading and joining up across the scalp			Trichological referral
COURTESY OF MEDISCAN	Cicatrical alopecia	Baldness due to scarring of the skin arising from chemical or physical injury. The hair follicle is damaged and permanent baldness results			

Condition	Symptoms	Cause	Treatment	Infectious
Male pattern alopecia	Premature male pattern baldness occurs in teens or early 20s Senile pattern baldness occurs in late 30s–50s. Hair recedes at the hairline or loss at the crown area. Condition is hereditary (passed on in families)			Remedies currently being developed

COURTESY OF MEDISCAN

Defects of the hair

DR JOHN GRAY

Condition	Symptom	Cause	Treatment
Split ends (Fragilitis crinium) Fragile, poorly conditioned hair	Dry, splitting hair ends	Harsh physical or chemical treatments	Cutting off or special treatment conditioners

REDKEN

| Monilethrix Beaded hair | Beadlike swellings along the hair shaft, hair often breaks at weaker points | Irregular development of the hair forming during cellular production | None |

DR JOHN GRAY

| Trichorrexis nodosa Nodules forming on the hair shaft | Areas of swelling at locations along the hair shaft, splitting and rupturing the cuticle layer | Harsh physical or chemical processing | None, although cutting and conditioning may help |

COURTESY OF MEDISCAN

| Sebaceous cyst Swelling of the oil gland | Bumps, lumps and swellings on the scalp containing fluid, soft to the touch | Sebaceous gland becomes blocked allowing a build-up of fluid to take place | Medical referral |

WELLCOME IMAGES

| Damaged cuticle Broken, split, torn hair | Rough, raised, missing areas of cuticle; hair loses its moisture and becomes dry and porous | Harsh physical or chemical processes | None, although cutting and conditioning may help |

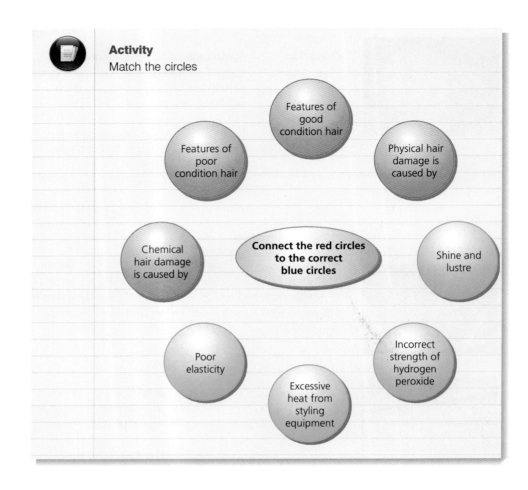

Activity
Match the circles

Features of good condition hair

Features of poor condition hair

Physical hair damage is caused by

Chemical hair damage is caused by

Connect the red circles to the correct blue circles

Shine and lustre

Poor elasticity

Excessive heat from styling equipment

Incorrect strength of hydrogen peroxide

Influencing factors and features

EKU *statement*

G7.8) Why it is important to identify factors that may limit or affect services and products which can be used

G7.9) How lifestyle, adverse hair, skin and scalp conditions, and incompatibility of previous services and products used limit or affect the services and products that can be offered to clients

The purpose of consultation is to arrive at a suitable hairdressing outcome through the process of analysis and evaluation. It should be done in a way that gives the client confidence in both the salon and in you.

During consultation you will be considering all the aspects of the client's physical features. Is there anything that doesn't work? Is the client happy with the existing style? They may point to areas which you feel are wrong or unnecessary, so you need to be able to express your technical appraisal in a clear, simple way without confusion. Avoid using any technical jargon or trade terms.

Consultation is *customised* for the client. It is personal and individual on each and every occasion. We therefore have to consider technical and personal image aspects:

- cutting and final shape of the hair
- volume or colour which will enhance the style
- finishing options of blow-drying or dressing the hair
- hair type, hair growth, natural colour and face shape
- their personal image, lifestyle and personality
- amount of time they can give to their hair.

Look for responses to your suggestions

The client's facial expression reflects their mood and how they are feeling. You need to pick up on these expressions and react to them appropriately. This will help to understand the client's wants and needs more easily. Expression is an important part of communication; remember, even if your client looks disgruntled or is scowling, you will need to use a friendly, pleasant expression to encourage them to relax.

Hair growth patterns

The hair's movement refers to the amount of curl or wave within the hair lengths. However, its growth pattern denotes the direction from which it protrudes from the scalp. Natural hair fall can be seen on wet and dry hair and strong directional growth will have a major impact on the lie of the hair when it is styled. So it is essential that it is taken into account during consultation.

- *Double crown* The client with a double crown will benefit from leaving sufficient length in the hair to over-fall the whole area. If it is cut too short, the hair will stick up and will not lie flat.

- *Nape whorl* A nape whorl can occur at either or both sides of the nape. It can make the hair difficult to cut into a straight neckline or tight 'head-hugging' graduations. Often the hair naturally forms a V-shape. Tapered neckline shapes may be more suitable, but sometimes the hair is best left long so that the weight of the hair over-falls the nape whorl directions.

- *Cowlick* A cowlick appears at the hairline at the front of the head. It makes cutting a straight fringe difficult, particularly on fine hair, because the hair often forms a natural parting. The strong movement can often be improved by moving the parting over so that the weight over-falls the growth pattern. Sometimes a fringe can be achieved by leaving the layers longer so that they weigh down the hair.

- *Widow's peak* The widow's peak growth pattern appears at the centre of the front hairline. The hair grows upward and forward, forming a strong peak. It is often better to cut the hair into styles that are dressed back from the face, as any 'light fringes' will be likely to separate and stick up.

Face and head shape

The basic, natural shape of the head, face and features are what form the underlying structure in styling. The proportions of the hair mass and distribution in relation to the face and head are vital in choosing a style. The outer hair shape should fit the face shape to achieve a suitable hair arrangement.

The contours of the head are its focal points. Those on the side of the head are formed by the parietal and temporal bones. Those on the back of the head and nape are formed by the occipital bones, which can be concave or convex: curving inwards or outwards. The frontal bone forms the forehead shape. It is the beginning of the profile, which follows along the nose to the lips and chin. This can vary in shape and may be concave or convex.

The face shape is made up of straight or curved lines, and sometimes a mixture of the two. Straight, fine shapes appear angular and chiseled or firm and solid. They can be triangular, rectangular, square or diamond shaped. Curved line shapes appear soft and may be round, oval, pear shaped or oblong. Shapes which have some straight and some curved lines are defined as heart shaped or soft square shaped.

Remember

Always make and maintain eye contact with your client.

Be aware of your client's expressions and react appropriately.

Remember

Give your clients time to consider your suggestions and advice.

Remember

Look at the amount and quality of your client's hair. Remember that clients with fine hair want volume. Look at the proportion, partings and distribution of the hair.

How much natural movement has the hair got? Will it affect the styling plan?

Are there any strong growth patterns to contend with?

Remember

Hair growth, i.e. the directions in which the hair grows, will have an impact on the choice of styling and general style maintenance.

To create a pleasant balance, the hairstyle and face shape need to be compatible. Generally speaking, an angular hair cut will not suit a soft, rounded face. A soft hair shape will not complement a chiseled face. Hair shape outlines can be made to look quite different from the front by simply changing a parting from side to centre. Side partings tend to make the face appear wider, whilst centre partings close down the width of a wide forehead.

An oval face shape suits any hair style. Round faces need height to reduce the width of the face. A centre parting can also help to reduce width. Long facial proportions are improved with short, wider hairstyles. Square-shaped faces need round shapes with texture on to the face to soften them. Longer lengths beyond the jaw line improve the balance and proportion.

Ears, nose and mouth

Often ears are out of balance, which can affect the cut if you use them as a guide. Generally, large ears or even large lobes are accentuated by hair cut short or dressed away from the face. It is often better to leave hair longer over the ears unless it is an essential part of the style's impact.

Your client may wear a hearing aid and this may be a sensitive issue. Some clients wish to have all signs of an aid hidden, but others do not mind and even display it. You should discuss this with your client carefully and with sensitivity; they may feel too embarrassed to bring up the subject herself. The size of the aid will need careful consideration when completing the total image.

The position, shape, size and colour of the nose and mouth are very important in the facial expression. The angles that are created can be softening or harsh and must not be ignored when the image is being planned. Hair shape and make-up can contribute to create the required effect.

Activity

Hair growth patterns

Hair growth patterns do have an impact on the way that hair can be styled. For each of the listed growth patterns below, write down in what ways this will influence your styling options.

Widow's peak

Nape whorl

Double crown

Cowlick

Remember

Checklist

- What are the shape, position and size of the client's ears?
- What is the shape and size of the client's nose and mouth?
- Are these features a major concern to your client?
- What shape is your client's facial and head shape?
- Are there any significant features that need to be accounted for?
- Small faces need 'opening up' while larger faces need narrower framing effects.

Remember

The eyes are the focal point of the face. Good images in magazines use this aspect to sell everything from clothes to hairdressing. Your client will be drawn to strong images, but are they wearable in everyday life? The majority of 'hair shots' use hair in ways across the eye line to create artistic impact. These may be stimulating but not feasible. You must make a point of this during your consultation.

Neck and shoulders

The length, fullness and width of the neck will affect the fall of the back and nape hair. Longer necks allow better positioning of long hair. They are complemented by high, neat lines; for example, mandarin collars or polo-neck tops. Short necks need to be uncluttered, with short hair and low collars. Long and thin necks are more noticeable with short styles and will therefore be better suited to longer hair around them. Shorter necks can be counterbalanced with height or upswept hair styles.

Body shape

The body shape also needs to be considered. You need to carefully balance the amount, density and overall shape of the hair to your client's physical body shape. This is particularly important if your client considers their shape or size a particularly important factor. For example, a small, clinging hairstyle would look wrong on a large body shape.

Lifestyle, personality and age

Remember that people are constrained by what they do for a living or what they like to do in their spare time. Usually, people who work in environments where they have face-to-face contact with clients have to be more particular about the image they portray. This is a very important factor in style selection.

From a leisure point of view, you should find out whether the client does a lot of sport or exercise. If so, the hairstyle will have to be versatile and able to withstand a lot of washing and possibly heat styling. Also, think about how the style could be handled to create a number of different effects when the client is going out. If you are styling for a special occasion, it is worth asking what dress will be worn. A beautiful gown needs to be accompanied by an elegant hairstyle. However, this style will need to be altered for normal wear.

- Many clients want practical and manageable styles for work.
- Nurses, doctors and caterers, among others, may require styles which keep the hair off the face, or they may have to wear face and head coverings at work.
- Dancers and sporty people need hairstyles which will not get in their eyes and obscure their vision.
- Fashion models may require elaborate styles for special photographic or modelling sessions or displays.

Character and personality can often override physical features when you are choosing a style for your client. A self-confident client will be able to wear looks that a self-conscious client cannot. Make sure you take this into account so that mistakes are not made. Is your client confident and outgoing or shy, timid and retiring, not wishing to stand out in a crowd? Are they professional and businesslike?

Remember

How long or short is your client's neck?

How wide or narrow is your client's neck?

Have you taken these features into consideration?

Remember

What is the purpose of the style – fashion, special occasion?

Work, social and leisure pursuits are all factors to be considered.

Different styles suit certain age groups.

Will the final effect suit the lifestyle requirements?

EKU *statement*

G7.9) How lifestyle, adverse hair, skin and scalp conditions and incompatibility of previous services and products used limit or affect the services and products that can be offered to clients

ISTOCKPHOTO.COM/JACOB WACKERHAUSEN

And what age group does your client fall in to? There are basic rules that apply to people at certain ages:

- *Children* – simple, practical shapes (although parents often try to suggest fashions).
- *Teenager* – fashionable, trendy and willing to try new things.
- *Young married* – something suitable for work, attractive easier to maintain styles.
- *Parents* – practical and attractive styles, often shorter styles.
- *Middle-aged* – softening shapes to disguise wrinkles.
- *Older women* – softening shapes.
- *Business people* – fashionable cuts.
- *Older men* – simple, practical styles.

These are only general guides – there will always be exceptions to the rules.

G7.3 Advise clients and agree services and products

Being able to recommend services and products to clients relies upon having a good working knowledge of what your salon provides. This range of services and products changes from time to time and you will need to keep abreast of those changes.

You will need to know:

- the ranges of services and products that are suitable for your clients' needs
- the prices and timings of those services and prices of the products available
- how to keep abreast of current fashions.

Making suitable suggestions and recommendations

Suitability relies upon matching the client's needs with the correct selection of services and products that your salon offers. We are all familiar with the salons that make a name for themselves by turning people out looking all the same. Similarly, there are other salons that have a seasonal collection of work and really push their clients into wearing the current look, just because they think its good PR for the salon.

Both of these types of environments may be easy or fun to do from the stylist's point of view, but the client hasn't been considered at any point in the process. So sadly, in these sorts of salons, there is no consultation taking place. They just process people like a *mechanical production line*.

So, from your point of view as a junior stylist it would be unprofessional to recommend a shoulder-length bob to a client who had long hair down their back, just because you were really good at good at doing classic bobs!

The same goes for recommending products too; you may have a core of favourites that the salon uses and those are really good on your hair. Great, you have a product regimen that works for you. But that's as far as it goes. Your client has individual and particular needs and it is your job to match their needs with the features and benefits of products that your salon provides.

You may also think that the packaging of the new range really looks good and it smells great too. But do these features actually benefit your client?

Most people need products to do a job for them like sorting out dry and damaged lengths or provide volume and lift. Remember it's not what it looks like that makes it work; it's what's inside the bottle that really counts.

Always look at people as individuals; match their needs to those products that offer benefits that suit them.

When you do recommend a specific remedy as a course of treatments, don't forget to explain the benefits of prolonged, continual applications as opposed to a 'one-off' treatment. Although people generally want their problems sorted out immediately, this is seldom the case. You need to subtly express the values of continual usage even if the visible signs seem slow to work. A good way of doing this is to make a note on their client records that prompts you to review the results next time. This makes sure that you do a good job in remembering your client's specific needs and also helps to get them to return in the normal reappointed time-frame.

Remember

Keep a breast of all your salon's services and products. If new products are introduced, then it's your job to find out; what they do, how they work and how long they take and how much they cost.

Discussing costs and durations for services

You need to be aware of:

- the time it will take to provide the discussed service(s)
- the cost for the service(s) to the client
- any additional costs that could be involved to complete the service
- the costs of any products or treatments that could be purchased for home use
- any special offers in force at the time.

HAIR: MARK WOOLLEY

Most salons have a standard tariff that shows the costs of their services and in most cases the price shown is the price it will be, but that isn't the same in every case. It would be impractical for a salon to try and produce a tariff that covered service costs for every hair type, hair length and hair density! Just think, the price list would be several pages long and it would be so confusing for you to read, let alone the clients.

So the standard price list covers the main services for the average range of people. This might extend to pensioners as well as children, but it will definitely cover the average range of men or women in between.

You need to be aware of the time it takes to complete a task for any service across the range and a good idea of what that will cost. Your clients have a right to know what they are spending before they commit to having the service or product.

Are there any hidden costs?

Clients don't like unpleasant surprises. If your salon does have additional costs that aren't clearly displayed you would be better off stating them from the outset. For example, if you offer a client a coffee they might think that it is complementary. Similarly, if you say that you are going to put on a new treatment on their hair while they are at the basin, will there be an additional cost for that?

EKU *statement*

G7.24) How to move the discussion forward (e.g., summarise, develop points, focus on purpose)

Retail products

Most salons offer a comprehensive range of retail services that supplement the services that they offer. Keep up to date on the ranges that the salon offers. If your client shows an interest in the products on display or asks how they can benefit her, you need to be ready to provide those answers without: 'Err, umm, I don't know what that does.'

It will undermine your professionalism and it won't improve the likelihood of making a sale. If you aren't sure about the costs or benefits of a product, say to the client; 'I'll find out for you, let me see if Sally is free.'

Agreeing the course of action

When you have covered everything in your consultation, you need to summarise the points back to the client.

You could say:

> So, Mrs Jack, we've talked about the time and cost of your cut and blow-dry. Let me just run through what we are going to do. We will take X off the length of the hair and introduce some layers to give it more texture and movement, then I'll finish it off with a smooth blow-dry look and apply some of that serum I was telling you about. Is that correct?

Whatever your summary is, you <u>must</u> ask a question at the end of it. Unless you have the client's expressed wishes before you start then you haven't given them the opportunity to accept or decline your plans. In other words they haven't agreed the services or products and they have every right to dispute this at the end!

Activity
Home-care advice
Good home-and aftercare advice is about giving the client the correct advice on looking after their hair.
This will include advice on:

- products

- tools and equipment

- future salon services.

1 What advice should you give regarding products?

2 What advice do you need to provide regarding tools and equipment?

3 What advice could you provide regarding future salon services/ treatments?

Some services also need additional preparation or special conditions
Before they can be carried out. For example; your salon may do hair-pieces for hair-up work; some salons may do added clip-on hair extensions; others may offer the complete bonded extensions systems. In any of these cases it would be unlikely that all the necessary materials to do all of these services will be in stock. So you need to be able to

tell your client exactly when those items will be available, the differences, benefits and pitfalls, how long it will take, how they will look after them and how much it will cost.

You will also need to check to see if a deposit is needed. Often in situations where there is a large investment of salon time or stylist's time, then other preparations need to be arranged in advance and it would be normal practice to take a deposit.

There are other special situations too. You may wish to offer a colouring service to a new client, but you know that you will have to conduct your skin test first. So you will need to tell the client what they can expect and also what you need to know should there be any adverse, contra-indications. All this needs to be pointed out well in advance.

Keeping abreast of current fashions

Your knowledge should be up-to-date and there are numerous ways in which you can do this:

- trade shows and exhibitions
- courses and seminars
- trade magazines
- fashion magazines
- TV and the Internet.

HAIR: NHF INSPIRE

You should keep in touch with what's happening in the celebrity world. These well-known icons create fashion; they are prepared and groomed by personal stylists who are employed by production and promotional companies so that they are always in the eye of the public. People are stimulated by the entertainment industries and the media are always following the lives of celebrities from film, TV and music. The success of magazines such as *OK* and *Hello* is due to the attention they pay to these peoples' lives and what they are up to.

Your customers will expect you to be aware of what is happening in these sectors and you will need to be ready to advise whether these new looks are going to suit them. In many cases, they will not and you have to be ready to provide alternatives. You may have to consider many other alternatives, but try to incorporate something from the theme. If the main impact of the style that your client wants requires a fringe, but you feel that by taking the bob-line short to the chin is going to make their face appear too 'podgy' , what about incorporating the fringe into a longer version of the look?

NHF INSPIRE

As you can see, there is always another way of tackling the problems. When you can't provide what the client wants, always offer suitable alternatives.

Referrals (see adverse hair and scalp conditions)

There will be situations where the clients anticipated service can not be provided.

This could be due to:

- adverse hair and skin problems
- your salon doesn't do that particular service or treatment.

Specialist remedial referral

Some hair and scalp conditions can be treated in the salon, but many more will require specialist remedial attention. You need to know which ones are handled by the various specialists.

For example, a mother who brings a child in for a haircut who obviously has nits cannot be dealt with in the salon. You need to be sympathetic and not over-reactive. If you suspect an infestation has occurred, *go and find* a senior member of staff. They will help you to explain the benefits to the mother of looking out for infestations on a regular basis and the signs that she would probably see, i.e. small whiteish/grey nodules attached to the hair close to the scalp, generally around the back and nape, or evidence of the louse itself as a peppering of brown speckles over the child's pillow at night and itching.

But that is as far as your comments should go. Your supervisor or senior stylist will need to refer them to a pharmacist so that the mother can purchase a remedy and apply herself at home.

A client with eczema may be aware of their condition, but you may be concerned that a planned service may aggravate the condition further. A referral to their doctor first is preferable, if only to eliminate the concern that your planned service won't make the condition worse.

If you find a condition that you are not sure about, get your senior stylist or supervisor to intervene. They will probably say to the client, 'I'm not sure what the problem is but I do think you should get it checked out before we continue our planned services.'

Remember

If you are not sure what the problem is and it looks medical, the client will need a referral to a pharmacist or their GP. (For more information on adverse hair and skin conditions see pages 115–119.)

Remember

If you need to refer clients to a trichologist, you can find a listing through the trichological institute on the Internet www.trichologists.org.uk.

EKU *statement*

G7.7) How to calculate the likely charge for services

Activity
Contra-indications
What would you do and say if:

1 a client was found to be infected with head lice?

2 a client had cuts or abrasions on their scalp?

3 a client wanted a service that you felt because of their condition, was in too poor a condition for this to be carried out?

4 during the consultation you suspected that metallic salts were present within the hair and the client wanted to have a chemical process?

Salon referrals You need to keep abreast of the salons in your area that offer special services that your salon doesn't, services such as trichological analysis, hair extensions, hair transplants, wigs and hairpieces. But remember with referrals – you must follow your salon's policy for external redirection. You may not be permitted to do this yourself; speak to a senior or supervisor before you say anything to the client.

Activity

With a work colleague pretend that you have a selection of clients waiting to pay their bill at reception. Taking turns now calculate a variety of bill totals for a range of your salon's services, treatments and products.

Keep notes on the services etc. that each of you have stated to one another, so that you can check each other's ability to add up the imaginary clients' bills.

EKU *statement*

G7.1) Salon rules of confidentiality

G7.19) The importance of confidentiality and what might happen if this is not observed

Client records

Keeping proper client records is essential for good salon management and to ensure clients receive a service appropriate for their individual needs. The records also give vital information should there be any subsequent client complaint or worse, if there was any pursuance in a legal case against the salon.

Different salons use different systems for recording information. Some salons use handwritten cards whereas others use computerised systems. The information required will change from salon to salon.

Remember this is personal and private information, it must be handled confidentially and you have a duty to uphold the rights of your clients if you keep their personal information on file. (For more information see *Data Protection Act (1998)* in Appendix 1.)

(For more information about client confidentiality see Chapter 4, unit G4 Reception Page 71.)

Client record cards

L'OREAL PROFESSIONAL

Remember

Consultation checklist

✔ Listen carefully to what is requested
✔ Use visual aids to assist the consultation process
✔ Communicate the possible effects
✔ Explain why certain effects are not possible
✔ Give good reasons for suggested actions
✔ Ensure that the client understands what is being said
✔ Agree on a final and suitable course of action
✔ Assure and reassure throughout
✔ Make it clear if follow-up appointments are necessary
✔ Carry out the agreed service or treatment
✔ Encourage the client to rebook the next visit before she leaves
✔ Maintain the client's goodwill and safety throughout the appointment
✔ Record the details for future reference.

Remember

Make sure that records are found prior to consultation and used to check on previous client history. Update the records in line with your actions taken after consultation.

Remember

If you don't tell the client how to maintain their hair after the salon visit, how do you expect them to achieve a similar result at home?

Checkerboard

I know and understand the principles of positive communication	I can communicate positively and professionally with the clients	I always recognise the adverse hair and scalp conditions when I analyse the client's hair
I can identify the range of hair and scalp problems	I know how to negotiate, reaching a mutually beneficial conclusion	I always carry out working practices according to the salon's policy	I've covered most of it!
I always explain technical terms, eliminating ambiguity and false beliefs	I know when and who to refer clients to in situations where external assistance is required	I understand the necessity of personal hygiene and presentation	I know how to advise, promote and sell other services and products to clients
I know and respect the client's rights, equal opportunities, data protection, anti-discrimination and consumer legislation	I always provide the client with advice on how to maintain their hair themselves at home	Done it all	

Assessment of knowledge and understanding

Project

For this project you will need to gather information from a variety of sources. List the services, treatments and products that are available in your salon. Then for each one listed explain:

1   what the features and benefits are to the client
2   how you would go about explaining these to clients
3   the costs of each of these.

Revision questions

A selection of different types of questions to check your consultation and advice knowledge.

Q1	The three stages of hair growth are anagen, _____ and telogen.	Fill in the blank
Q2	The cortex is the outermost layer of the hair.	True or false
Q3	Which of the following are infectious diseases (select all that apply)?	Multi selection

Impetigo	☐ 1
Scalp ringworm	☐ 2
Alopecia	☐ 3
Head lice	☐ 4
Psoriasis	☐ 5
Eczema	☐ 6

Q4	The natural colour of hair depends on the amount of melanin within it.	True or false
Q5	Which of the following is commonly known as split ends?	Multi choice

Trichorrhexis nodosa	○ a
Monilethrix	○ b
Tinea capitis	○ c
Fragilitas crinium	○ d

Q6	Dandruff is a condition of the scalp usually caused by fungal infection.	True or false
Q7	Which of the following tests are carried out *during* technical services?	Multi selection

Skin test	☐ 1
Strand test	☐ 2
Development test curl	☐ 3
Incompatibility test	☐ 4
Porosity test	☐ 5
Test cutting	☐ 6

Q8	The layer of the skin below the epidermis is called the _____.	Fill in the blank
Q9	Which face shape suits most hairstyles and lengths?	Multi choice

Square	○ a
Oblong	○ b
Oval	○ c
Triangular	○ d

Q10	During consultation and hair analysis, a contra-indication will not allow the planned service to be carried out.	True or false

Preparing for assessment checklist

Remember to:

✔	communicate effectively in the salon
✔	listen to clients and show them that you care
✔	listen to the client's requirements and discuss suitable courses of action
✔	adhere to the safety factors when working on clients' hair
✔	use positive body language and the reasons why it plays such an important part in good customer service
✔	acknowledge the legal rights of clients and what might happen if they were breached
✔	identify the factors that affect the variety of choices available to the client
✔	promote the range of services, products and treatments with the salon
✔	recognise the adverse conditions that prevent salon services
✔	conduct the tests that are needed and avoid the risks of not taking appropriate action
✔	record the outcomes of the tests for future purposes.

Chapter**six**
Promote services and products

G18

G18.1

G18.2

Promoting services/products: quick overview

Unit title

G18 Promote additional services or products to clients

This is an **optional** unit at Level 2 and is made up of three main outcomes

Main outcomes

G18.1 Identify additional services or products that are available

G18.2 Inform clients about services or products

G18.3 Gain client commitment to using additional services or products

What do I need to do for G18.1?

● Keep abreast of the salon's services and products

● Check with others when unsure of new services or products

● Spot the products or services that would be useful to certain clients

● Spot the chances to introduce those products or services

What do I need to do for G18.2?

● Choose the right times to introduce services or products with clients

● Choose the right ways to introduce services or products with clients

● Give sufficient, accurate information that would help the client to buy the introduced services and products

● Give the client the time to respond to introduced services and products

What do I need to do for G18.3?

● Know when to close discussions when clients show no interest

● Continue with promotional information when the client is interested

More information
Legal requirements (see appendices)

● Consumer and retail legislation

- Establish agreement when the client commits to a purchase
- Pass the client on to the relevant service or product provider

What aspects do I need to cover for G18.1, G18.2 and G18.3?

- The ranges of services and products that your salon offers

What do I need to know for G18.1, G18.2 and G18.3?

- The salon's procedures for promoting additional business
- How the services and products will benefit the client
- How the sales of services and products will benefit the salon
- How the features and benefits of services and products are communicated
- How to overcome reservations about services and products
- How to give balanced information to clients

Keywords

Features
The aspects of a product or service that state its functions; i.e. what it does

Benefits
The ways in which the functions provide advantages

Information covered in this chapter

- How to promote products and services
- How to make the clients aware of the promotions
- How to gain client commitment as a result of salon promotion

Introduction

The services and treatments that salons provide to their clients are constantly being updated so that they meet an ever-increasing customer expectation.

So, by offering new or improved services and products, your salon is able to:

- increase client satisfaction
- retain client loyalty for the future.

For salons these two factors are directly linked and are therefore essential for a business to succeed. It is possible to make a really good job of satisfying our clients, but unless they continue to return (and within a reasonable time scale) the financial and ongoing success of the salon is drastically affected. So we need to stimulate the client's loyalty by encouraging them to:

- buy our other services, products and treatments
- return on a regular basis
- share their experiences with other people.

G18.1 Identify additional services or products that are available

Good customer service is being customer focused. It is centred upon the needs of the client and is reflected within all of the aspects that are involved within routine salon operations: the telephone response times, salon refreshments and magazines, visually pleasing interiors and the polite and friendly staff. It is your duty to be upbeat, outgoing and positive when you communicate with the clients.

Remember

 Try to put yourself in the client's position. How would you like and expect new services or products to be introduced to you?

EKU *statement*

G18.1) Your salon's procedures and systems for encouraging the use of additional services or products

G18.2) How the use of additional services or products will benefit your clients

G18.3) How your clients' use of additional services or products will benefit your salon

Salon services and products

Most salons have tariffs and point-of-sale material that provide information about the services and products they provide. This is a good way of providing information to clients as they can easily be seen and provide a talking point in the salon. But printed material is not always at hand or available, particularly when services and product ranges are being continually updated.

You need to be aware of changes and additions, so that you can provide advice on available services or products that would benefit your clients. You also need to keep up to date on all the features and benefits of newly introduced services and products. If you find that there are recent additions in the salon that you haven't seen before, you will need to ask your manager or supervisor for more information.

The products available in your salon can come from a lot of different sources and suppliers and this can often make it harder to keep abreast of developments. But this is often the way that salons have to operate in order to cover a constantly changing, comprehensive range of options at a competitive price.

IMAGE COURTESY OF REM

Products are not wallpaper!

Products should never be treated as wallpaper. They are not decorative items used to cheer up a 'dingy' corner; they have far more important purposes. Retail displays are an expensive investment for the salon and stock resting on shelves is an expensive cost. Products provide a useful, additional input to the salon's income and many salons look for a significant proportion of their turnover to be derived from these sales.

EKU *statement*

G18.4) The main factors that influence clients to use your services or products

There are hidden benefits to the purposes of retailing which you may not have thought about. The promotional displays are an integral part in supporting the salon's image. If you think about it another way, the salon *only* purchases products for use and resale that are befitting the quality of services that your salon wants to be *identified* with. It therefore enables the clients to gain an extension of the salon experience, in the products that they take home.

Features and benefits

In order for you to promote and ultimately sell your salon's services, treatments and products, you need to recognise how they are viewed by clients. To do this you need to consider each service or product in terms of its features and its benefits and how these aspects would meet the needs your clients:

● 'Features' are the functions; i.e. what the service, treatment or product does.

● 'Benefits' are the results of the functions; i.e. advantages, what the service or products achieves.

For example, suppose you recommend a client to spend £11.50 on a conditioning treatment. Why should they do this? What are the benefits of the service?

● The feature is: it re-conditions dry, damaged hair.

● The benefits for them are: it improves the dryness and helps to smooth damaged lengths; therefore it will improve handling, make the hair easy to manage and comb and enhance the hair further with shine and lustre. So these benefits justify the investment on their hair.

Knowledge of service and product features enables you to sell your clients the benefits. You thereby create a need, and once the client has accepted the need, you are in a good position to make the sale.

The first step is therefore for you to gain a thorough knowledge of each service and product available in the salon, and to *translate* this knowledge into an understanding of the features and benefits for each one.

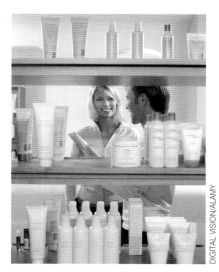

DIGITAL VISION/ALAMY

EKU *statement*

G18.5) How to introduce additional services or products to clients outlining their benefits, overcoming reservations and agreeing to provide the additional services or products

G18.2 Inform clients about services or products

New clients that come in to our salons are part of a very special group. They have probably found us through the network of already satisfied customers. Those satisfied customers feel confident enough in our expertise to promote our skills and services by recommending us to their friends and colleagues.

If recommendation is such a powerful channel of communication, why don't we use it more?

Well we can. The perfect time to talk about the variety of services and treatments available to clients is when they are in the chair in front of us. Recommendation is the simplest way of extending the range of services to our clients and enhancing the professional relationship.

The most effective way of introducing clients to products that will benefit them is to use them on their hair in the salon. This style of introduction creates a close relationship between:

● something that the client needs (with the added benefit of)

● seeing how it is applied (through to)

● the results that it achieves.

This style of promotion is improved further by not only showing the product to the client but by passing it to them so that they can experience the product by:

● holding it and

● smelling the fragrance.

Activity
Promoting business

The services and products that the salon provides to its clients generate the income that the business exists on. If the clients do not return on a regular basis, the business will fail. Therefore, client loyalty is vital to the success of the business and this can only happen if the client is satisfied with the services they receive.

Give three ways in which you think client loyalty may be maintained.

Now give suggestions for how to promote the business to its clients.

How do we inform clients?

In-salon promotions are the most popular way of conveying *messages* to the clients which, in turn, become a topic of conversation whilst they are having their hair done. However, any form of salon activity costs money and that outlay has to be budgeted for.

So the first part of the process is to find out what is the promotion about? If it is linked to a new product introduction, then there will be some form of supporting resources to help inform the clients. Whenever a new product or range of products is introduced, the manufacturer will produce a variety of point-of-sale material that provides people with professionally produced information, posters etc. to help with its launch. The amount of supporting material tends to be distributed in line with the levels of purchases made by the salon.

So, a small independent salon that has bought an entry-level intro deal from the supplier may only have a small amount of supporting material or resources to use within the salon, whereas another, larger, chain-type salon will be bulk-buying a larger amount and will get more resources to help promote the product.

EKU *statement*

G18.1) Your salon's procedures and systems for encouraging the use of additional services or products

G18.2) How the use of additional services or products will benefit your clients

Implementation stages of product or service promotion

The following information provides you with a checklist for implementing an in-salon promotion.

✔	Find out the budget
✔	Make individuals aware of the product's features and benefits
✔	Let staff know what their roles and targets are
✔	Implement the promotion
✔	Evaluate the effectiveness of the promotion

The budget is set by management and may include the initial outlay figure for purchasing the products as well as the additional cost of setting up the promotional activities. Everyone involved should be informed well in advance of the promotion about the nature and purpose of the event. This provides staff with a clear idea of what the newly introduced products do, their application and how they benefit the clients and the product selling costs.

Usually on a product launch there would be an introductory period that may entice customers with special offers or deals.

The most popular promotions are usually in the form of;

- introductory discounts – where products are available for a set period at a lower price
- multi-buys – typically two-for-ones or get three for the price of two
- special offers – buy all three and get a free beach towel or scarf.

Staff should be made aware of the promotional plan, any incentives linked with the promotion and their personal targets for the introductory period. Each member of staff might have an individual role to play in the overall team plan. For example, the junior may ask the client if they want to try the new conditioner on their hair at the basin. From this a client gets the chance to gain their first experiences of the product.

HAIR BY TERRY CALVERT & THE CLIPSO ARTISTIC TEAM

The promotion continues at the styling position where display materials – e.g. show cards or leaflets – inform the client of the benefits from using the product. This is further backed up by the stylist's recommendation and advice. The client would be asked if they noticed and liked the *smell* of the conditioner when it was applied, or if they can *see* and *feel* the difference that it has made to their hair.

Then finally, before the client leaves, they *connect* again with the promotion when they see a well-put-together display in reception. The receptionist could now ask if the client would like to add the product to their bill so they can use it at home.

You can see from this example that it can be a whole-team approach. This is particularly important for larger salons where clients are handled by a number of different individual members of staff: this increases the likelihood of continuity being lost. In these situations, passed-on communications are paramount as useful sales can be lost.

Common senses

When a promotion is implemented, a plan of action is put into effect and all successful promotions have to be a *sensory event*. Effective selling is experiential; it provides the purchaser with a variety of experiences that they can:

- see
- touch
- smell
- hear or
- taste.

HAIR BY TERRY CALVERT & THE CLIPSO ARTISTIC TEAM

Our five senses provide the only ways in which people can be influenced in making a purchasing decision. The more sensory *channels* that are involved in the promotional environment, the more chances are that the customer will buy.

At the end of the promotional period the success and impact of the event can be evaluated by team discussion, reviewing sales reports and listening to feedback from the clients on how the promotion was received.

Activity
Using the senses

You can see how the senses are used when you go shopping. For example, what do you notice when you go into a shopping mall? The shops that sell toiletries open their doors so that the fragrance of the goods can fill the air.

Again, why do you think that supermarkets put their fresh produce or coffee shop next to the front door? It's so they can stimulate the client's senses with the things that they can touch and smell.

How do you think the senses are used in your salon to help in the promotion of products? Write down the types of experience that the client would get from the introduction of a new styling product.

Promotional materials

A typical product promotion will consist of:

- point-of-sale merchandising – central 'island', open cabinet, shelf displays
- shelftalkers – printed promotional slips/cards fixed to/dangling from shelves; 'mobile' ones that bob or bounce deliver best results

L'OREAL PROFESSIONEL

- eye-catching displays – these are instantly informative – locate them where they'll be seen at reception or centrally in treatment areas
- arrangement of popular lines at eye level with price details – use 'price watch' stickers
- linking displays with money off and other special offers – first visit, loyalty, recommend-a-friend discounts and promotional tie-ins with major local stores.

Window displays

Window displays are an essential way of advertising services, their costs and displaying products. They are relatively inexpensive to dress, if they are maintained by salon staff. But care needs to be given to the quality of dressing, as public expectations of retail window space are generally high. Part of the secret to creating eye-catching displays is constant change. Therefore the display windows need to be changed frequently, if they are to have any impact on the passing trade.

New salon customers find us through a variety of different ways and the image of the salon created by the front window is part of that formula; although we shouldn't forget that reputation, location, advertising campaigns and, the most important, personal recommendation, all have a major impact too.

Website

In the past the only way for people to locate and find out about businesses was through directory listings. This form of advertising, e.g. *Yellow Pages and BT Phonebook*, was poor in quality, often badly printed and, if a large display advert, very expensive. This type of business finder is quickly becoming obsolete as most businesses are turning to more engaging forms of media.

Now the most popular and interesting way to find out about what a business has to offer from a remote location is through its website. Most salons now have an Internet presence and as managing the information upon a website gets easier; many salons can upload their own photographs, edit textual content and can provide engaging, interactive and fun ways to sell their services and products.

The website can be a very powerful marketing tool for any business and providing people can find the www address, then this will continue to be the fastest and most effective way of reaching customers when they are not in the salon.

Remember

Physical contact
Most people are embarrassed by physical contact from someone they do not know well.

EKU statement

G18.6) How to give appropriate balanced information to clients about services or products

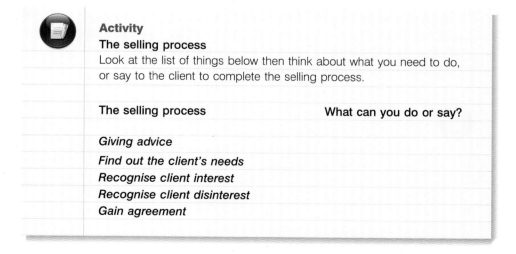

Activity
The selling process
Look at the list of things below then think about what you need to do, or say to the client to complete the selling process.

The selling process	What can you do or say?
Giving advice	
Find out the client's needs	
Recognise client interest	
Recognise client disinterest	
Gain agreement	

G18.3 Gain client commitment to using additional services or products

Remember

 A client not only shows her interest through body language, she will show her lack of interest too!

Remember

 Genuine interest is expressed by the client wanting to know more and/or showing it by what they do.

 Diversion: See Unit G17.3

Recognising interest – buying signals

You need to be able to differentiate between genuine interest and a polite and friendly, but negative response. Just because someone responds in a polite or friendly way is not an indication of 'I want to buy that'.

Genuine interest is expressed in at least two ways:

1 The client will *ask* how that will benefit them, e.g. 'Would that be suitable for my type of hair?' or, 'How does that work?'

2 The client will *show* their interest by taking the product and holding it for closer examination, or through their positive body language.

Therefore when you introduce or recommend the client to a new service or product, you will need to look for the signs of interest above.

Anything other than these signs could indicate a lack of interest and you should be careful how you proceed. There is little point pursuing the issue if you are receiving little or no response; even if you think it's the best product or service that she could have. The last thing that you want to be seen as is 'pushy' or a 'commission seeker'. It won't help your professional standing and it may tarnish your professional relationship too!

Communication

So from the information already covered in this section you can see that there are many ways in which we communicate with our clients. Establishing an effective communication between you and the client is the most important aspect that determines your success in your role. The relationship between stylist and client is built on quality of service, professional advice, trust, support and a listening ear. Good communication ensures productive and effective action. On the other hand poor communication can lead to misunderstandings, misinterpretation and mistakes.

Verbal and non-verbal communication

For more information on question styles, open questions, closed questions, and body language, see Chapter 3, which covers Unit G17 Give Clients a Positive Impression of Yourself and Your Organisation (pages 44–61), particularly the section on G17.3 Communicate information to clients (pages 51–57).

Remember

 Body zones
Do not crowd or appear over familiar with your client. Imagine how you would feel if someone came up to you and got a little too close. What do you do? Immediately back off and go onto the defensive.

Activity
Features and benefits
Put yourself in the clients' position; think about how they view and experience the salon's services, treatments and products.

1 What is meant by the term 'features'?

2 Now explain what is meant by the term 'benefits'.

Now in terms of features and benefits, give the features and benefits to the client for the following services:

1 A new haircut.

2 A semi-permanent colour.

3 A conditioning treatment.

4 Temporary 'clip-on' hair extensions.

Remember

 Excellent communicators are good listeners, they understand how to ask the clients the right questions and listen effectively to responses, building on the information given to them and then finally, helping the client to buy.

Good and bad selling techniques

Key factors indicating GOOD selling techniques

- Listening, asking questions, showing interest
- Using the client's name
- Empathy (putting yourself in the client's place), establishing a bond
- Recognising non-verbal cues (dilated pupils = 'I approve'; ear-rubbing = 'I've heard enough')
- Identifying needs; helping clients reach buying decisions
- Knowing your products/services
- Highlighting the results or user benefits; demonstrating these where possible
- Thinking positively, talking persuasively, projecting confidence and enthusiasm

Key factors indicating BAD selling techniques

- Doing all the talking
- Not listening, not 'hearing' unspoken thoughts, arguing
- Interrupting – but never letting the clients interrupt you – thus losing an open opportunity for giving extra information
- Hard selling, 'spieling' (working to a script)
- Threatening – 'You won't get it cheaper anywhere else', knocking the opposition
- Manipulating – 'Oh dear, I'll miss my sales target'
- Knowing nothing about the product
- Treating 'no thanks' as personal rejection
- Blinding clients with science
- Staying mainly silent waiting for an order
- Insisting the client should buy the product

Consumer legislation

The rights of your customers should not be compromised; they are protected from fraudulent and sharp practice by a variety of consumer legislation. For more information see Appendix 3 on pages 460–461.

EKU *statement*

G7.2) Your legal responsibilities for describing the features and benefits of products and services

Checkerboard

	I always explain technical terms eliminating ambiguity and false beliefs ☐	I know and understand the principles of positive communication ☐	I can communicate professionally and know the benefits of good body language ☐
I know how the ranges of our salon's services and products can benefit clients ☐	I know our salon's policy in respect to promoting services and products to clients ☐	I know the expressions that clients use when they are angry, dissatisfied or confused ☐	I know the main factors that influence peoples' purchasing decisions ☐
I know how to counter reservations and give balanced information ☐			

Assessment of knowledge and understanding

Project

For this project you will need to gather information from a variety of sources.

For the following legislation find out how:

- the Health and Safety at Work Act
- the Data Protection Act

affect the way that services can be provided to clients.

In your project pay particular attention to the aspects that would have impact on a business and the implications if this legislation were not considered.

Revision questions:

A selection of different types of questions to check your sales and promotion knowledge

Q1 Selecting opportunities occur when the features and _____ of products are explained.   Fill in the blank

Q2   Business develops without promotion or advertising.   True or false

Q3   Which of the following are types of in-salon promotion?   Multi selection

Radio advertising ☐ 1
Hairdressing competitions ☐ 2
Hairdressing demonstrations ☐ 3
Point of sale material ☐ 4
Reception displays ☐ 5
Merchandising ☐ 6

Q4   PR is a term which refers to professional media handling.   True or false

Q5   What is the most cost-effective way of selling services to clients?   Multi choice

External demonstrations ○ a
Internal promotions ○ b
Client consultation and advice ○ c
Point of sale material ○ d

Q6   Merchandising is a retailing strategy.   True or false

Q7   Which of the following are laws protecting consumer purchases?   Multi selection

The Consumer Protection Act ☐ 1
COSHH ☐ 2
Trades Descriptions Act ☐ 3
RIDDOR ☐ 4
The Prices Act ☐ 5
The Data Protection Act ☐ 6

Q8   The vendor must ensure that goods they sell are of _____ quality.   Fill in the blank

Q9   When handling complaints avoid which of the following?   Multi choice

Maintaining eye contact with the client ○ a
A discussion in a quieter area of the salon ○ b
Telling the manager about the event ○ c
Folding your arms and being defensive ○ d

Q10   A prospective client bases their first impressions of salon staff in less than ten seconds.   True or false

Preparing for assessment checklist

Remember to:

✔	communicate effectively in the salon
✔	maintain confidentiality and be mindful of the consequences of failing to keep things private
✔	listen to clients and show them that you care
✔	use positive body language and the reasons why it plays such an important part in good customer service
✔	acknowledge the legal rights of clients and what might happen if they were breached
✔	promote the range of services, products and treatments with the salon
✔	use your time efficiently and effectively
✔	work towards personal targets and know why they should be achieved.

Part**three**
Hairdressing technical services

1 Hair: Lewis Moore@Francesco Group, Streetly, Photography: John Rawson@trp 2 Hair: Richard Ward, Photography: Daniele Cipriani 3 Hair: Christopher Appleton@George's Hair Salon, Leicester, Photography: John Rawson@trp 4 Hair: The Artistic Team@TPL Hairdressing, Photography: John Rawson@trp 5 Hair: Tim Lawton@TPL Hairdressing, Nantwich, Photography: John Rawson@trp 6 Hair: NHF Inspire, Photography: Simon Powell Left Hair: Reds Hair and Beauty, Sunderland, Photography: John Rawson@trp

VICKY TURNER @ GOLDSWORTHY'S

Chapter**seven**
Shampooing and conditioning hair

GH8

GH8.1

GH8.2

GH8.3

GH8.4

**More
Information** Personal
hygiene and general salon
hygiene see G20 Health and
Safety Chapter EKU GH8.18
EKU GH8.21 EKU GH8.36
How to communicate with
clients G18 EKU GH8.52
Promote additional services
or products to clients
See also Appendices for
following relevant
legislation:

- COSHH EKU GH8.6
- Electricity at Work
  Regulations EKU
  GH8.7, EKU GH8.19
- Data Protection Act
  EKU GH8.8

Shampoo and conditioning: quick overview

Unit title

GH8 Shampoo, condition and treat the hair and scalp

This is a **mandatory** unit for hairdressing *and* barbering and it is made up of four main
outcomes

Main outcomes

GH8.1 Maintain effective and safe methods of working when shampooing, conditioning
and treating the hair and scalp

GH8.2 Shampoo the hair and scalp

GH8.3 Condition and treat the hair and scalp

GH8.4 Provide aftercare advice

What do I need to do for GH8.1?

- Take adequate precautions in preparing yourself and the client before any shampoo
  or conditioning procedure.

- Prepare and maintain the basin area.

- Work tidily, safely and effectively at all times.

- Identify the client's hair and scalp requirements

- Seek assistance when not sure of client's requirements

What do I need to do for GH8.2?

- Use the appropriate methods and products to shampoo and condition the client's
  hair and scalp

- Shampoo and condition different hair lengths, types and densities correctly

- Maintain a comfortable water temperature and pressure for the client throughout the
  process

- Detangle and prepare the client's hair for the next service

What do I need to do for GH8.3?

- Apply suitable conditioning products to the client's hair and scalp using the appropriate method

- Rinse to remove the products from the hair after the specified timing

- Detangle and prepare the client's hair for the next service

What do I need to do for GH8.4?

- Give advice to the client on how they can maintain the condition of their hair

What aspects do I need to cover for GH8.1, GH8.2, GH8.3 and GH8.4?

- Hair that is damaged by chemicals, heat, sun or styling products

- Scalp conditions that are oily, dry or affected by dandruff or styling products

- Different hair lengths using surface or penetrating treatments

- A variety of hair and scalp massage treatments

- Recommendation or advice for maintaining healthy hair and scalp at home

What do I need to know for GH8.1, GH8.2, GH8.3 and GH8.4?

- Health and safety requirements that affect you and the client

- How to recognize types of hair conditions and select appropriate products to use

- A range of wash-point products, their purposes and applications

- The different massage techniques used in shampooing and conditioning operations.

- Basic hair science about how shampoos work and how pH values affect hair

- How different products work or affect the hair

- How different massage techniques are used

- How to work efficiently and effectively during shampoo and conditioning procedures

- The sorts of advice that you should give to clients about their hair needs

Keywords

Effleurage
Gentle stroking movement used in shampooing

Rotary
Quicker and firmer circular movement used in shampooing

Petrissage
Slower circulatory kneading movement used during scalp massage when applying conditioner

Chemically damaged hair
Hair condition worsened by the effects of chemical processing

Surface conditioner
A light conditioner that works on the outside of the hair to smooth and fill areas of damaged, missing or worn cuticle until next shampoo

Penetrating conditioner
Deep-acting conditioner working on the inside of the hair

Information covered in this chapter

- The types of products used and how they work

- The range of hair types that you will need to cover

- How shampoos and conditioning treatments work

Information covered in this chapter (cont.)

- How to work safely, effectively and efficiently
- How shampoos work and how pH values affect hair
- How shampooing, conditioning and treatments are carried out
- The massage techniques involved in shampooing and conditioning

Introduction

Shampooing and conditioning are an integral part of 90 per cent of hairdressing processes. If done properly these services are personal, invigorating and stimulating therapeutic experiences. When they are not, the client is left feeling that they are part of an inferior production line, in a salon where staff take no interest in their jobs.

The action of shampooing cleans the hair by removing dirt, grease, skin scale, sweat and product build-up; leaving the hair ready for blow-drying, setting or perming. Conditioning treatments are applied to smooth the cuticle layer, provide protection for the hair, improve handling and combing, make the hair look healthier and help the hair to resist external elements.

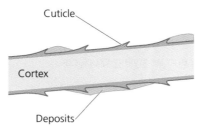

Dirt on hair cuticle

| GH8.1 | Maintain effective and safe methods of working when shampooing, conditioning and treating the hair and scalp |

This part of the chapter looks at the preparations needed for these services and the other aspects that you must be aware of in order to fulfil the requirements in your particular salon. It covers the following parts of the service:

- cleaning and maintaining the shampoo/conditioning area
- preparation and protection of both you and the client
- working efficiently, safely and effectively
- recognising different hair and scalp requirements
- maintaining records.

EKU statement

GH8.1) Your salon's requirements for client preparation

EKU statement

GH8.3) The person to whom you should report low levels of resources

Cleaning and maintaining the shampoo and conditioning area

Your health and safety and that of the client are vitally important. Because of this you should make sure that you always follow the manufacturer's instructions when handling any chemicals or equipment. Shampoos and conditioners are chemicals and therefore you must wear adequate protection to reduce risks from skin conditions such as dermatitis. Always wear the personal protective equipment (PPE) provided by the salon such as, non-latex disposable gloves and a plastic apron.

Because of the risks to health and safety, the wash-point area must be kept clean and tidy at all times and all items of waste should be removed and disposed of in a covered bin. Always use the cleaning materials provided by the salon to clean the wash-point areas, this will ensure that only hygienic sprays etc. are used in areas where there is a risk to public health and prevents infection from spreading.

The basins are in continual use and the clients may be coming and going back to these during different services. For example, a client who is having a cut and blow-dry will have their hair washed at the beginning of the services, whereas a client having a colour will arrive at the basin much later in the process. So, with all these different types of services going on, lots of different situations occur. A client who has had a perm may have all their cotton neck wool removed at the basin; this may be saturated with alkaline chemicals and must be removed and disposed of.

Always keep a check on the levels of wash-point products and materials, during use; towels, shampoos and conditioners will eventually run out and these will need replenishing at different times throughout the day.

Preparation and protection of both you and the client

The client's clothes must be protected from spills and splashes at all times whilst they are in the salon with a clean freshly laundered gown. Similarly, a fresh clean towel is placed around the shoulders and can be fixed with a sectioning clip so that it doesn't slip or fall away during the shampoo/conditioning process. You should also keep a look out through shampooing and conditioning processes for the position of the towel in relation to the basin and the client's neck. If there isn't enough towel between the basin and neck then water can seep down the client's neck and wet their clothes. Conversely, too much fabric may initially feel comforting to the client, but will soon get saturated and again the client will feel uncomfortable and their clothes will get wet. Sometimes you will need to apply a plastic cape on top of the towel as this provides extra protection, particularly for chemical services or special conditioning treatments.

It is very important that after sitting the client at the basin, you make sure that they are comfortable and that their back and neck are fully supported by the position that they are in at the basin. When the client is correctly seated, the basin forms a supportive barrier at the nape of the neck, that neither pinches causing discomfort, nor does it allow water to leak over the rim.

Your standing position is equally important from your safety's point of view too. You should be standing close enough to the basin to be upright when either in a *side or front wash position* (your arms and shoulders are positioned above the torso and hips without having to twist or lean forwards) or from in a *back wash position* (your arms and shoulders are directly above your hips and feet and slightly behind the position of the client's head when they are laying back). You need to maintain this posture throughout the shampoo or conditioning process otherwise you will be exposing yourself to the risk of injury and longer term back condition or fatigue.

EKU *statement*

GH8.6) Your own responsibilities under the current Control of Substances Hazardous to Health Regulations in relation to the use of shampoos and conditioning products

GH8.11) The type of personal protective equipment available

GH8.15) Why it is important to keep your work area clean and tidy

GH8.16) Methods of working safely and hygienically and which minimise the risk of cross-infection and cross-infestation

GH8.37) The manufacturers' instructions relating to the use of shampooing and conditioning products in your salon

Remember

Shampooing and conditioning should be a relaxing, enjoyable experience when it is done well; conversely, if it is done badly, it will imply something negative about the other salon services that follow.

IMAGE COURTESY OF CLYNOL

IMAGE COURTESY OF CLYNOL

EKU statement

GH8.10) The range of protective clothing that should be available for clients

GH8.12) Why it is important to use personal protective equipment

EKU statement

GH8.13) How the position of your client and yourself can affect the desired outcome and reduce fatigue and the risk of injury

GH8.14) The safety considerations which must be taken into account when shampooing, conditioning and treating hair and scalp

GH8.18) The importance of personal hygiene

Working efficiently, safely and effectively

During the shampoo process you will be controlling the water pressure to make sure that it is fast enough to rinse the hair properly, but slow enough so that it doesn't spray the client's face at the same time. You will also be keeping a regular check on the water temperature too. Many water systems are affected by other staff drawing water at the same time, as well as other appliances elsewhere in the building, such as washing machines, toilets and sink, all drawing from the same water supply. This can make the water temperature fluctuate at the wash-point very quickly and you need to be sensitive to those changes in temperature so that the client doesn't get burned!

Keep an eye on the clock; you must remember that all wash-point activities are part of a wider hairdressing service, the stylist will need the client back in the styling chair as soon as possible so that they don't overrun and that they don't make the client late.

Water is essential to all the salon's services and shampooing alone can take five to ten litres for each wash. So it is vitally important that this valuable and expensive resource is not unnecessarily wasted. Always use water sparingly and never leave the taps running between shampoos, even if it is just the cold water!

Many hairdressing procedures create potential blockages and for this reason salons are very careful about the materials put down the drain. Beneath each basin is a waste trap. This fitting serves two purposes:

1 it forms a seal that stops vapours and smells coming back from the sewerage system

2 it provides a safeguard for stopping hair and debris from entering into the sewerage system.

In addition, if a client loses an earring during shampooing it can be retrieved by undoing the waste trap. But since this procedure could be difficult and is certainly disruptive during opening hours, some salons now also use plastic hair traps which are inserted from above. These are ideal for stopping any small items from penetrating further below. Make sure that they are regularly cleaned and free of tangled hair. This will keep the drainage clear and stop water backing up in the basin!

Recognising different hair and scalp requirements

Choosing a shampoo

Shampoos come in a variety of forms, including creams, semi-liquids and gels, and a range of different sizes too.

There are many different types of shampoo bases (the substances that form the bulk of the shampoo) and some are kinder and gentler on the skin than others. The balance of these various shampoo ingredients is important; for example, the detergent content in shampoos for oily scalp is higher than those for normal and dry hair. So too is their ability to deal with different hair types and conditions.

Shampoos are named after the ingredients or essences within them: henna, camomile, rosemary, jojoba, aloe vera and mint are just a few typical varieties available in the supermarkets today. Choosing the right shampoo for the hair condition or following service is important. If the wrong choice is made the hair may become difficult to manage afterwards: it may become brittle, flyaway, static, oily or even dry.

> ### Activity
> See if you can match the shampoos on the right with their appropriate applications on the left.
>
> | | |
> |---|---|
> | Moisturising shampoo | Dandruff |
> | Medicated shampoo | Fine, lank hair |
> | Volumising shampoo | Dry or porous hair |
> | Colour-protecting shampoo | Coloured or highlighted hair |

If the shampoo doesn't remove all of the styling products that have been previously applied, they could block products used as part of the next service that you want to carry out. For example, hair wax that is applied on a daily basis adheres to the hair and creates a product build-up. This must be removed in order to achieve a final satisfactory result.

Shampoo types

Type	Effects on the hair
Aloe vera	A popular, mild natural base ideal for healthy hair and scalps that can be used on a frequent basis
Camomile	Better on oily scalps; has a natural lightening effect
Clarifying	Strong, deep-acting, often used prior to chemical services to remove build-up of styling products and dirt
Coconut	Contains an emollient which helps dry hair to regain its smoothness and elasticity
Jojoba	A natural base better on normal to drier hair types
Lemon	Contains citric acid; ideal for oily scalp types or for removing product build-up
Medicated	Helps to maintain the normal state of the hair and scalp; contains antiseptics such as juniper or tea tree oil
Mint	A natural base suited to normal to slightly oily scalps, often used as a frequent use shampoo
Oil	Can contain a range of natural bases such as pine, palm and almond; these are used to smooth and soften drier hair and scalps
Soya	Helps to lock in moisture for the hair and scalp
Tea tree oil	A natural essential oil, which is like an antiseptic which will fight infections on the scalp

EKU statement

GH8.5) Your salon's expected service time for shampooing, conditioning and treating hair and scalp

GH8.30) The effects of water temperature on the scalp and structure of the hair

GH8.48) The importance of using shampoos and conditioning products cost effectively

> ### Remember
> Always wear gloves when handling chemicals. This will reduce the risk of contact dermatitis.

EKU statement

GH8.31) How the 'build-up' of products can affect the hair, scalp and the effectiveness of other services

GH8.32) How the formulations of shampoos and conditioning products vary to suit different hair conditions

GH8.38) When and how to use shampoos and conditioning products to treat the hair and scalp conditions in the range

IMAGE COURTESY OF GOLDWELL UK

EKU *statement*

GH8.36) Range of available shampooing and conditioning products and equipment

EKU *statement*

GH8.40) What may happen if the incorrect shampooing and conditioning products are used

Remember

 Make sure that you match the correct products to the identified hair and scalp conditions. If you use the wrong products you will probably making the condition worse than it is. If in doubt ask a senior or your supervisor.

EKU *statement*

GH8.39) When the shampooing process should be repeated

Preparing to shampoo – checklist

✔	Prepare the client with a clean fresh gown and towel.
✔	Look at the client's hair and scalp to see what condition they are in.
✔	Ask questions such as: 'What products do you use at home?' 'How often do you shampoo your hair?' 'How often do you style your hair?'
✔	Look for any signs of infection, infestation or injury that would stop you from carrying out any other hairdressing processes.
✔	If you recommend any treatments, confirm them with the client before you apply them and advise the client of any additional time and costs involved.

Making the right choices about shampooing

The right choice of shampoo depends on the following factors:

- *Type, texture and condition of hair*:
  - *fine hair* (without product build-up) requires a single wash shampoo that will not make it too dry or fluffy. Choose a shampoo that will add body and volume;
  - *coarse hair* usually requires two washes with a shampoo that will tend to soften it and make it more pliable;
  - *thicker hair* usually requires two washes with shampoo that will penetrate and make good contact with all the hair and scalp;
  - *frequency of shampooing* – If hair is washed once or more daily, choose a shampoo specially designed for frequent use;
  - *water quality* – If the water in the salon is in a hard water area, more shampoo is needed to form a good lather. In soft water areas shampoos foam more easily, so less shampoo is required to do the job.
  - *shampoo purpose* – Is the shampoo intended just for cleaning or is it to treat the scalp, or condition the hair, or colour the hair?

Activity
Shampooing is a process that can differ between salons: what is the preferred process for shampooing in your salon and how long should it take? Write down your response in the space provided.

1

2

3

4

- *planned services* – What are you going to do with the hair later? Some shampoo ingredients (Pro V or dimethicone) produce a flexible coating on the hair shaft. This could be beneficial in adding protection and locking in moisture or, conversely, in the case of conditioning-type shampoos and most conditioners, it could prevent or prolong the processing of some treatments such as perms.

Choosing a suitable treatment

There will always be times when you don't recognise a certain hair or scalp condition. In these situations always seek help from a senior stylist or your supervisor. If you suspect a condition that could put the salon at risk from cross-infection or infestation, you must report it immediately and without over-reacting in front of the client. The following information covers the signs of the most common hair and scalp conditions. (For more information of specific hair and scalp problems see Chapter 5 on consultation, pages 116–119.)

How do conditioners work?

Conditioners use a combination of chemical and electrical (ionic) properties to achieve their effects. They can balance and counteract the effects that the chemical services and physical processes have upon the hair. There are two ways in which they bond with the hair:

- *Absorption* – This relies upon the natural state of the hair. Dry and porous hair has many tiny spaces within the hair's internal structure. These areas suck in the conditioning agents by capillary action, just as water is drawn into a sponge.
- *Attraction* – This occurs after the hair has been shampooed. The action of the detergent on the hair during shampooing ensures that all product, dirt and dust are removed. When these particles are removed it leaves the surface of the hair in a 'charged' state. This prepares the hair for the conditioner which is now attracted to the sites upon the hair that have been electrically charged. (This ionic attraction principle can be explained another way. Do you remember how you stick balloons to the wall or ceiling at a birthday party? After blowing the balloons up, you rub them vigorously on the sleeve of your jumper. This removes electrical particles and now makes the balloon stick to anything it comes into contact with, just like a magnet!)

IMAGE COURTESY OF GOLDWELL UK

Remember

 If oily deposits remain on hair they may cause a barrier to other chemical processes. If you believe that the client's hair has build-up, you can use a clarifying shampoo as a deep cleanser first.

EKU *statement*

GH8.4) The person to whom you should report unrecognised hair and scalp conditions

GH8.17) The importance of promptly reporting unrecognised hair and scalp conditions

EKU *statement*

GH8.32) How the formulations of shampoos and conditioning products vary to suit different hair conditions

EKU *statement*

GH8.26) How to identify hair and scalp conditions and their causes (i.e. chemically damaged hair, heat damaged hair, environmentally damaged hair, dandruff affected scalp, oily scalp, dry scalp, product build-up on hair and scalp)

GH8.34) How shampoos and conditioning products affect the hair and scalp

Remember

A protective conditioner is used before chemical processes to prepare the hair and even out the porosity of the hair before the process is carried out.

Remember

A corrective porosity balancing conditioner is used after chemical processes to replenish moisture and shine or to return the hair back to its natural pH-balanced state.

Different types of conditioner

There are three different types of hair conditioners:

- surface conditioners
- penetrating conditioners
- scalp treatments.

Surface conditioners

These conditioners do not enter the hair but remain on the cuticle surface. Their main purpose is to coat the hair and improve the look and feel by adding shine and moisture. Some of these conditioning rinses are used after perms and chemical straighteners to return the hair back to its natural pH balance. This group of conditioners would normally contain:

- vegetable and mineral oils
- lanolin
- fats and waxes
- mild acidic compounds which close the cuticle, could be citric or acetic-based.

Penetrating conditioners

Penetrating conditioners have deeper-acting benefits. They enter the hair shaft through the cuticle layer and are deposited into the cortex by capillary action. This suction of the product is like a natural magnetism, drawing the product in to the cellular spaces within the hair. These penetrating conditioners, often called *restructurants*, are designed to temporarily repair the physical structure of the fibres within the cortex and damaged areas within the cuticle layers. Apart from smoothing the hair and adding shine, they tend to make the whole hair structure much stronger. (Examples are hair strengtheners such as L'Oréal's Kerastase Ciment Anti-Usure or Wella's Liquid Hair.)

Their composition is more chemically complex. They are based on:

- *quaternary ammonium compounds*
- *proteins* – amino acids
- *humectants,* which lock in moisture to the hair
- *emollients,* which soften, smooth and moisturise the hair.

Before and after chemical services

Where the cuticle has been damaged, the hair cortex becomes more porous, like a sponge soaking up any chemicals applied to the hair. Older hair is more likely to be damaged than newer growth. The porosity must be reduced before hair can be successfully permed or coloured. Pre-straighteners or pre-perm treatments will balance the porosity evenly through the hair. This enables the chemical service to be carried out in the confidence that no parts of the hair will be unduly damaged through the action of additional chemical application.

The pre-colouring treatments have a similar effect. These products will 'fill' the damaged sites along the hair shaft, repairing the cuticle layer and maintaining an even absorption, i.e. 'take-up', of colouring products into the cortex.

After chemical services the hair may need rebalancing. The normal state of hair is slightly acidic (pH 5.5) and many of the processes use caustic – ammonium-based compounds – or corrosive – acid-based compounds. In these situations it is always advisable to use an *acid-balancing conditioner*. Acid-balancing conditioners will act either as an anti-oxidant (to remove unwanted 'free oxygen', which may be left in the hair after using hydrogen peroxide in operations such as neutralising, colouring and lightening) or to reduce the alkaline state of hair with mild acidic compounds following perming and straightening.

Scalp treatments

Other than improving the look, feel and condition of hair, the final group of conditioners are designed to remedy a variety of skin problems. These scalp-active treatments are chemical preparations that are developed to target specific disorders. Therefore, your correct analysis of the client's scalp condition is essential. You will need to be able to identify and distinguish between:

IMAGE COURTESY OF GOLDWELL UK

- dry scalp conditions
- dandruff problems
- excessively oily scalp conditions.

Dry scalps

Dry scalps can often be mistaken for dandruff. A dry scalp has some of the symptoms of dandruff, such as flaking on the surface of the epidermis, but if this is wrongly diagnosed, the corrective treatment may make the problem worse. A dry scalp can occur for a number of reasons. It may be from:

- a natural moisture imbalance, within the client's skin
- shampoos or styling products
- other chemical services

An dry skin condition is often a chronic or long-term problem; you should recommend a scalp-active treatment that will nourish and moisturise the scalp, whilst getting an agreement with the client that this is followed up at home as well. The type of treatment will depend upon the condition of the hair too. If the client has a dry scalp it doesn't necessarily follow that the hair will be dry too. This will have a bearing on how the treatment is to be applied. If the hair is normal and healthy you would not want to overload it with heavy moisturisers and emollients, so a more 'topical', carefully applied solution is required. Your client will also need to learn that not all products are the same. An application that is generally applied and combed through will have little effect! The product must target the problem and therefore the hair will need to be divided and the application should be made directly to the scalp.

Dry scalps can occur from intolerance to hairdressing products. A client can get a reaction when they use something different on their hair. Ask them whether they have tried something new. A typical cause would be newly introduced styling and finishing products such as 'root lift' mousse or heavy definition waxes. However, even a simple change of shampoo can cause dryness.

A dry scalp can also occur after chemical treatments. Many of the solutions we use in hairdressing have a quenching effect upon the skin. Alkaline solutions create this continual drying 'thirst' upon the scalp, so this is particularly relevant to perming and chemical straighteners. However, a reaction can be caused by any exposure

Remember

Always use balancing conditioners after any chemical processes.

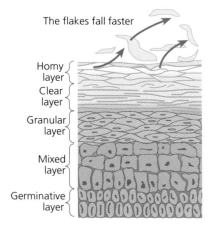

The flakes fall faster

Horny layer
Clear layer
Granular layer
Mixed layer
Germinative layer

Flaking scalp

to chemicals and you can prevent this by taking particular care when you apply any chemical service to the client.

Dandruff

Dandruff can sometimes in its simplest form be mistaken for a dry scalp. Unfortunately, if you wrongly diagnose this condition, you will either make the problem worse or have no effect at all.

Normally, the skin cells produced in the lower dermis take up to 30–45 days to work up through to the surface of the epidermis. Once there, the cells are shed daily in the form of a fine visible dust. In the case of dandruff, though, this process becomes erratic.

In the diagram you can see that, as the layers of dermal cells work up towards the surface of the epidermis, they eventually 'lift' and come away as 'shedding'. This is commonly noticeable as 'scurf', white skin cells, when you brush or comb the client's hair. More often, it is deposited onto their clothes.

Dandruff or *Pityriasis capitis* is caused by the overproduction of skin cells. It initially appears as small white flakes that loosen and continually shed from the scalp, rather as is the case with dry skin. A secondary condition occurs if the problem isn't rectified: the scalp becomes infected by bacteria and larger yellowier, waxy flakes now appear that usually stick to the scalp. When dandruff has progressed this far you often smell it too! This condition is often more prevalent in people with oilier scalps.

In tackling this problem in its earliest stages, you should ask the client if they have or have had a dry skin condition. If they say no, then the scurf is probably due to this skin production imbalance. This can be rectified over a period of time by regular home use of the correct shampoos and conditioners.

If the dandruff has progressed to the second stage, it must be treated initially in the salon, and then with a follow-up at home over a longer period in time. The first objective would be to combat the bacterial infection, then to clear the scalp of the scaly build-up. This degree of infection cannot be rectified by one scalp-active application. It will usually involve a course of treatments often in liquid forms applied onto pre-sectioned hair, directly onto the infected areas.

Oily scalps

An oily scalp, or 'seborrhoea', is caused by overproduction of natural oil (*sebum*) from the skin. The sebaceous gland in a normal state produces moderate amounts of oil, which is generally sufficient to lubricate the hair shaft and create natural moisture for the skin. This moisture, in turn, keeps the skin supple and helps to 'lock in' flexibility and elasticity. When the glands work overtime, then the imbalance of moisture becomes a nuisance. This is seen as excessively greasy hair and scalps that require frequent washing to give lank hair volume and body.

The normal approach to combating oily scalps is to shampoo it every day. When a client is asked how often they wash their hair and they give the answer 'at least once a day', there is a strong likelihood that there's a reason behind it. Sometimes people wash their hair every day because they fall into the routine of doing it when they take a shower. This is particularly obvious if they have easy-to-manage hairstyles, their lifestyle dictates it or they just have short hair.

However, when you do notice that the frequency of washing is more than just a habit and a problem exists, then there are a number of medicated preparations that are designed to sort it out.

These astringent-type lotions will cause the skin to contract slightly; this will temporarily constrict the glands and reduce the production of oil. A treatment like this could initially be undertaken in the salon but, to have any long-lasting effect, it will have to be followed up at home.

Oily skin surface

Sebum collects in follicle

Excess sebum

Extended sebaceous gland produces too much sebum

Oily scalp

Activity
Answer the following questions in the space provided:

Q1 What types of products are available in your salon?

Q2 What shampoo would you use for dry or porous hair in the salon?

Q3 What shampoo would you use for fine or lank hair in the salon?

Q4 What shampoo would you use for an oily scalp in the salon?

EKU *statement*

GH8.2) When and how to complete client records

Maintaining records

At the end of the process you need to update all treatment records including what shampoos and conditioners were used for future purposes. It is hard to remember what has been used on a client from one salon visit to another and someone else may be conducting the wash-point operations next time. Apart from this, even if you do attend to the client next time, it is unlikely that you will remember everything that you used previously and this may be particularly embarrassing if the client specifically asks for the same regimen again.

Remember

When treating conditions of very oily scalps or dandruff, it is best to try one product at a time, giving it the full opportunity to do its job. It is all too easy to give up on a new introduction before it has had time to make a significant difference.

GH8.2 Shampoo the hair and scalp

As we have already discussed; the shampoo process is used in most hairdressing services as a prelude to some other service happening after. It is your duty to make this a pleasurable yet invigorating experience. As shampooing is so often undertaken as part of a service it is considered best practice to wear gloves. The risk of dermatitis is increased during wet work, particularly when undertaking such tasks for more than 2 hours per working day. Take protective measures to reduce the risks such as wearing non-latex disposable gloves and regularly moisturising.

Special note: shampoo equipment Most references in this book refer to the backwards-style, wash-point; these make up 90 percent of all typical salon shampooing equipment. In salons where there is insufficient space or room to move clients around, or for the type of service being offered, such as shaving in barber shops, the front or

Remember

Some specific injuries or neck complaints prevent the client from lying back at the basin. In some cases this has led to clients passing out when pressure is applied to the back of the neck. Ask your client if they know of any reason why they cannot use a backwards-style wash-point.

EKU *statement*

GH8.20) The importance of thoroughly rinsing hair to remove shampoos and conditioning products, when necessary, at the end of the service

GH8.42) When and how rotary and effleurage massage techniques should be used when shampooing different lengths and densities of hair

GH8.46) The importance of removing excess water from the hair at the end of the service

forwards wash is still used. Although this may not be the most pleasurable way to provide services to the client it still addresses specific needs; particularly if the client has a neck complaint and cannot lie backwards.

Step-by-step: Shampooing technique

1 Sit the client at the basin, put on a clean fresh gown and visually check the hair and scalp.

2 Place a freshly laundered towel around the client's neck and across their shoulders.

3 Adjust the basin so that when the client's head is tilted back their position is comfortable with the minimum of towel supporting their neck.

4 When working on longer hair carefully disentangle the hair by initially working the fingers through the lengths and then by brushing or with a wide-toothed comb.

5 Turn on the water and adjust the mixture of hot and cold. Test the temperature on the back of your hand to ensure the temperature is neither too hot nor too cold.

6 Carefully place your hand across the client's hairline, 'damming' the water from splashing forward onto the face. Start rinsing the hair from the forehead, down either side, cupping the ears and through to the lengths.

7 Check the flow of water pressure and temperature and ask the client throughout.

8 After the hair is thoroughly wet, apply a small amount of the correct shampoo to the palms of the hand; lightly rub them together, then apply evenly to the client's hair.

9 With your fingers clawed, massage the scalp with the correct massage technique. Cover the whole scalp ensuring that no part is missed.

10 Rinse the hair thoroughly, checking water temperature and pressure.

11 Finally, rinse all traces of shampoo lather away from the hair and lightly squeeze out the excess water so that the hair is free of lather and ready for the next process. Repeat steps 5–11 if a second shampoo is needed.

It is best practice to wear gloves when washing clients' hair to avoid dermatitis.

Step 5 Checking the water temperature.

Step 6 Carefully dampening the hair.

Step 8 Using the dispenser to meter the correct amount of shampoo.

Step 9 An even and balanced shampoo massage technique.

Step 11 Rinsing away the lather.

Massage techniques used in shampooing

There are three types of shampooing massage techniques:

1 Begin shampooing with effleurage, gentle stroking movements with the flat of the hand that help to spread the products evenly.

2 Continue with firm but gentle rotary massage (circular movements). Let the fingertips glide over the scalp, whilst moving your hands towards each other in the centre (up from the sides, over the top and down into the nape). Move your hands in decreasing circles around the head to make sure you cover the scalp fully.

3 Occasionally change the rotary massage to friction, a quicker rubbing movement with the fingertips used to deep clean any difficult areas.

4 Finally, use soothing effleurage movements again to complete the shampoo process.

Shampooing: Finger positions

What is dermatitis?

Dermatitis is a painful, itchy skin condition that affects the skin. Generally speaking, when hairdressers have this condition, it appears as a sore, sometimes moist reddening of the skin between and along the fingers and hands. The skin takes on this condition due to frequent contact with chemicals: shampoos, hair colourants, perm solutions and neutraliser. You must take adequate precautions to prevent this from happening. Always wear non-latex disposable gloves for technical processes at the wash-point. (See Unit G20, 'Bad hand day' page 14 for more information.)

Shampooing: Finger movements

Remember

 While shampooing:

- make sure the client is comfortable at all times

- be careful, especially with your hand positioning and massage technique, water flow and temperature, and client's head and neck positioning throughout the process

- work in a clean, methodical and hygienic way.

After shampooing:

- make sure the water is turned off and replace the shower head in its place

- apply suitable conditioning treatment (see conditioning process later in this chapter)

- lift the hair away from the face and basin and carefully wrap in a towel. Place either side of the towel up and around the hairline, overlapping, and the remainder at the back, up and balanced evenly on the top

- lead the client from the basin area back to the work point

- remove the towel and comb the client's hair through.

Remember

 Hard, linear and circulatory massage movements are uncomfortable for the client. Practice the right pressure with your colleagues at the salon.

Remember

 Always record the products that you have used on the client's record card so that they can be charged for and used again in the future.

Remember

Wet hair can tangle very easily which makes it very painful to comb through. So when you comb through your client's wet hair, you should always disentangle the ends first, then work back up through the lengths getting closer to the scalp. This makes the process simpler, it takes less time and it doesn't hurt either!

Remember

If your client is in the habit of washing her hair every day advise her to use a mild frequent use shampoo. Anything else may be too strong or may create a build-up in regular use.

Remember

Regular brushing helps to remove products, dirt and dust from the hair.

EKU *statement*

GH8.9) What is contact dermatitis and how to avoid developing it whilst carrying out shampooing and conditioning services

Remember

Shampooing dos and don'ts

- Always use clean, fresh towels and gowns.
- Make sure that your hands and nails are hygienic and clean.
- Wear non-latex disposable gloves
- Avoid splashing water or shampoo lather onto the client's face or near their eyes as the chemicals will cause discomfort if not injury.
- Always keep your hand in contact with the water whilst rinsing so that you can detect any sudden change in its temperature.
- Always direct the water spray away from the hairlines and into the basin.
- Carefully comb the hair after shampooing to remove any tangles.
- After using the basin, always clear and clean the area before it is used again.
- Turn off the water in between shampoos and conditioning to avoid wastage.
- Rinse and dry your hands afterwards to remove any shampoo or conditioning chemicals and reapply a barrier cream.

Science

If you look at the ingredients on the packaging of shampoos you will find somewhere the term *SLS* or *TLS*. These are the common chemical terms for the detergents *Sodium Lauryl Sulphate* or *Triethanolamine Lauryl Sulphate*. Detergent in shampoo will, with prolonged use, cause contact dermatitis. You must take adequate precautions to avoid this happening. Barrier creams are an effective way to do this. They should always be applied to clean dry hands before any backwash activity takes place. They will need regular reapplication throughout the day to get maximum protection.

Remember

Health and safety

- Raising the client too quickly from the basin can be dangerous; for some, it may make them feel dizzy when they try to stand up and, for others, if they have had any neck problems, it could cause injury.
- Make sure that you do not apply too much pressure on the back of the neck or 'joggle' the client's head around by wrongly applying uneven pressure on either side.
- Always test the water temperature on the back of your hands before transferring the flow to the client's head. Look out for changes and fluctuations in water temperatures and pressures.

The detergent in shampoo – how does it clean the hair?

Water by itself will not spread easily over the hair and scalp. This is because water molecules are attracted together by small electrical forces. These have their greatest effect at the water's surface, creating the effect called 'surface tension'. On hair, water by itself would form droplets. The detergent in shampoo reduces surface tension, allowing the water to spread easily over the hair and scalp, wetting them. *Detergents* are therefore '*wetting agents*' and shampoos contain detergents.

Each detergent molecule has two ends similar to a magnet. The 'hydrophilic' end is attracted to water molecules; the other 'hydrophobic' end repels water and is attracted to dirt and grease instead.

Detergent molecules lift the grease off the hair and suspend it in the water. This suspension is called an 'emulsion'. The grease holds the dirt so, as the grease is removed, the dirt loosens too. The emulsion containing the dirt is be rinsed away with water leaving the hair clean.

Remember

Good shampooing is physically soothing, psychologically calming and, overall, an enjoyable experience. A poor shampoo has the opposite effects!

EKU *statement*

GH8.28) How shampoo and water act together to cleanse the hair

Activity

You can always find out if your own shampooing practices are acceptable if you shampoo your colleagues' hair at work. Ask each other in what ways you need to modify or change your techniques.

Attracted to grease, repelled by water

Detergent molecule

Attracted to water, repelled by grease

A detergent molecule

Water | Grease

Detergent molecules surrounding grease

Science

Acidity and alkalinity

Like many other chemicals, shampooing can affect the surface of the skin. This changes its natural pH balance and removes essential moisture. The pH scale measures acidity or alkalinity. It ranges from pH1 to pH14. Acid compounds have pH values 1 to 6 and alkalis have pH values of 8 to 14. A compound with a value of 7 is neither acidic nor alkaline and is therefore neutral.

EKU *statement*

GH8.29) How the pH value of the products used affects the current state of the hair

EKU *statement*

GH8.34) How shampoos and conditioning products affect the hair and scalp

Science

Approximate values of substances

Substance	pH value
Acid	0.1–6.9
Alkali	7.1–14.0
Neutral solutions	7.0
Normal hair and scalp	5.5
Pre-perm shampoo	7.0
pH balanced shampoo/conditioner	5.5

The normal pH of the hair and the skin's surface is 5.5. This is referred to as the skin's 'acid mantle'. The acidity is due in part to the sebum, the natural oil produced by the skin. Sebum production is an important skin function. Skin protects the underlying tissue, acting as a barrier; it prevents liquid loss from inside and keeps excess liquid outside the body. It also protects the body from infection. An acid skin surface inhibits, i.e. slows down, the growth of bacteria and makes them less likely to enter the skin. If the acidity of the skin is reduced and rises above pH 5.5 infection is more likely to occur.

Hairdressing procedures can affect this natural equilibrium, so pH-balancing products are used after perming and straightening, to return the skin to the natural acid mantle.

The pH of solutions can be measured using *universal indicator* and a simpler indicator of acidity or alkalinity solutions can be made apparent by using pink or blue *litmus papers*.

Pink litmus paper used in alkali substances will turn mauve/blue. Conversely, blue litmus paper used in acid solutions will turn red.

If hairs are placed in an alkaline solution above pH 8.5 they swell and the cuticle lifts. In slightly acid solutions the cuticle is smooth and the hair is soft; in strong solutions of either acid or alkali the hair will break down and is destroyed.

Acids and alkalis are used in this way for high-lift colours. High-lift colours have added ammonia and this alkaline compound helps to swell the hair, enabling the colour to penetrate deep into the cortex of the hair.

Stronger alkaline compounds are available as hair-removing creams; these are applied to areas where the skin contains unwanted hair. The application is left for the prescribed time and is then wiped away, removing the hair with it. The skin is then rinsed and an acid-balancing skin conditioner is then applied.

pH Scale

Activity

Example questions and model answers

Q1 How long should it take to complete the shampoo and conditioning service at work?

A1 We are allowed to take up to X minutes for the whole process.

Q2 What is dermatitis and how do you avoid contracting it?

A2 Dermatitis is a skin condition that arises from direct contact with chemical substances. It has patchy red areas, often between the fingers or over the hands. In advanced stages, the areas are itchy and the surface of the skin can break. It can be avoided by wearing non-latex disposable gloves.

Q3 What types of protective wear are available for clients while they are in the salon?

A3. The salon provides gowns, towels and protective capes, which are worn whilst the services and treatments are carried out.

Q4 How would you advise your clients about choosing a shampoo?

A4 I would look at the hair and scalp before I took my client to the basin to see the natural condition.

Activity

Answer the following questions in the spaces provided:

Q1 Why is your posture important when you are shampooing and conditioning?

Q2 What safety considerations do you have to think about whilst the client is at the basin?

Q3 Why do you have to rinse the hair well after shampooing or conditioning?

Q4 Why do you need to keep the wash area clean and tidy?

EKU *statement*

GH8.45) The importance of removing conditioning products, when required

---

GH8.3   Condition and treat the hair and scalp

Why do we condition the client's hair?

One of our primary roles as hairdressers is to improve and maintain the condition of our client's hair. If the cuticle surface of the hair is roughened or damaged the

Remember

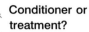 **Conditioner or treatment?**
If your client does not routinely condition their hair, then the problem of dull hair is made worse. In a case like this, deeper-acting and longer-lasting treatments will be needed.

The principle of seeing shine can be thought of like this.

If you walk down the street, stop outside a shop window and look in, you will see your own reflection in the glass. The image of yourself is bounced back to your eyes from the smooth, flat surface of the glass. If the surface was roughened and uneven the image would be distorted and you will not be able to see a clear reflected image.

Now think of this in hair terms. The smoother the surface of the hair the better the shine. The duller the hair, the more roughened the surface is.

EKU *statement*

GH8.44) When and how to apply conditioning products

appearance will be dull. Clients want their hair to shine, therefore, we have to improve the cuticle surface to make it as smooth as possible. We do this with the help from conditioners and that way their hair will be easier to manage, easier to comb and easier to brush.

Conditioning: what should you be doing?

Question	First of all ask the client what has been previously done and what has been used upon the hair. If this is a regular client in the salon, check out the treatment history on their records.
Look and feel	Examine the hair and scalp closely. What condition is the hair in now? Look at the tell-tale signs – porous lengths and ends; loss of natural moisture and elasticity; dry, split or damaged ends or cuticle. Test for elasticity as good conditioned hair should be able to stretch and return to its previous length.
Advise	From what you see and feel, what would be the best course of action? A simple surface conditioning treatment? A salon-based deep-acting treatment? A prescribed course of treatment at home? Or a combination?
Agree	From the course of action you advise, get your client to see the benefits too. Explain how long the process will take, and also the costs involved.
Reassurance	Tell the client when to expect to see any marked changes and improvements. Explain that maintenance at home is just as important.
Maintenance	Prescribe any follow-ups. Explain how the hair should be managed at home or if products are needed to support the whole process.

What are the benefits of using conditioners?

Professional products are formulated to protect and improve a range of different hair types and disorders. The main benefits of a good conditioner are that it:

- smoothes the cuticle edges
- improves the handling and combing when the hair is both wet and dry
- temporarily repairs and fills damaged sites along the hairshaft or missing areas of the cuticle or cortex
- provides shine, lustre and sheen
- creates flexibility and movement by locking in moisture
- balances the pH value of the hair back to a slightly acid 5.5.

Activity

What is your salon's procedure in respect of the following and what products would you use on each occasion?

1 Shampooing and conditioning hair prior to a cut and blow-dry?

2 Shampooing and conditioning hair prior to a perm?

3 Shampooing and conditioning hair after a highlighting service?

Applying conditioner

Step-by-step: Conditioning

Each conditioning treatment is specific to the task in hand. It is therefore extremely important to follow the manufacturer's instructions so that the product can do its job. Some (like a dandruff treatment) require the hair to be divided and lotions to be applied directly to the scalp. Others require heat assisted from hot towels or a *steamer* for deeper penetration into more damaged types of hair.

The following sequence provides guidelines for applying more general surface-type conditioners.

1 After shampooing, squeeze out excess moisture from the hair.

2 Apply a small amount of conditioner into the palm of the hand and gently rub your hands together, applying the conditioner evenly to a wider surface area.

3 On longer hair, apply the conditioner to mid-lengths and ends first, working through the hair with the fingers, separating the lengths, or

4 On short hair, evenly apply the conditioner to all of the hair.

5 Then start the *petrissage* movements over the scalp from the frontal area, over the top and down through to the nape. Repeat this circular process several times.

6 On longer hair that is in poorer condition, you may need to comb the conditioner through whilst still at the basin. Using a wide-toothed conditioning comb, start disentangling the hair, working at the points of the hair first, and then gradually working a little further up the hair, until the hair can be combed easily from roots to ends.

7 Finally rinse all traces of conditioner away from the hair and lightly squeeze out the excess water. If the entire product is not rinsed from the hair; it may act as a barrier to any following processes.

8 Place the towel around the hair, secure into place and move the client to a styling section.

9 Place another fresh towel around the client's shoulders and remove the damp one squeezing out the excess moisture from the lengths.

10 Disentangle the hair with a wide-toothed comb until all tangles are free from the hair.

EKU *statement*

GH8.33) How heat affects the hair during the conditioning treatment

GH8.37) The manufacturers' instructions relating to the use of shampooing and conditioning products in your salon

EKU *statement*

GH8.19) Why it is important to check electrical equipment used to aid conditioning and treatment processes

GH8.41) How to use and handle equipment used during conditioning and treatment processes

A hair spa

Types of heat used during conditioning treatments

Steamer

A steamer looks like a portable hood dryer with a water tank reservoir on the top. The water tank is removable and can be filled with tap water; the tank is replaced into the machine and a heating element boils the water when it is switched on. As the water boils within the machine the steam is transferred to the twin-walled, transparent hood part of the steamer. A series of small holes within the inner wall of the steamer allows steam to emerge and provide a hot, moist heat which is delivered to the person seated beneath.

The application of moist heat develops the treatment more quickly than if it were left at room temperature; it enables the product to penetrate more deeply into the hair, where, if it were left without heat, it might not work as well.

Precautions A steamer is an electrical piece of salon equipment, always check the condition of the plug and lead before turning it on.

When it is in use, keep an eye on the levels of water within the reservoir and always check with the client to make sure that the temperature is comfortable and not too hot.

Note The machine can be used for conditioning treatments and some lightening services, such as highlights and root-application oil bleach. When a steamer is used within a lightening service the moist heat principle develops the hair colour without extracting moisture from the hair and stops the product from drying out during the process.

Hot towels

We can see from above that heat is used within treatments to help the product to penetrate further into the hair. Hot towels can be used as another alternative for applying heat during the processing of a treatment.

A towel is folded in half length-ways and folded again to make a long, thick band shape. The towel is then immersed into a sink of hot water and left to soak for a few moments. As the towel is removed, it is wrung out by twisting so that all excess water is removed and it is then placed around the client's head and secured so that the hair is totally enveloped within the towel. It can be left to develop for a period of time (according to the product manufacturer's instructions) and the towel and residual product can be removed and rinsed from the hair.

Scalp massage

Massage is a therapeutic method of manipulating the skin and muscles by either hand or machine. The effects of this may be:

- improved blood flow and the removal of fatty or bodily waste
- stimulation, re-energising and invigoration
- soothing relaxation
- improved muscle tone.

Scalp massage has been a normal part of hairdressing services throughout history. It is common throughout Asia and has now become a beneficial supplement to the Western range of hairdressing services. There are several different types but the most popular used in Britain are Indian head massage and Oriental Shiatsu massage. Many salons view this as a major area for improvements to their service tariffs and offerings and there are several courses and texts available on the subject.

Contra-indications to scalp massage

Scalp massage can be a therapeutic and/or stimulating service to clients, but not every client will benefit from it, or like the sensation that massage provides. Look for signs to see if the service *can* be provided and *ask* the client if they have any reasons that they know of that would *not permit* the service to be conducted.

Do not provide massage when:

- there are signs of cuts, abrasions on the scalp
- there are signs of reddening from conditions like eczema or skin sensitivity or skin allergies
- the client feels unwell or has a headache
- the client's scalp is naturally oily, as massage will stimulate the sebaceous glands further and make the hair even greasier
- there are any other adverse symptoms such as infections or infestations.

If you have any doubts about symptoms and contra-indications, always ask a senior member of staff for their assistance. You may be putting the salon at risk from legal action or pursuance if you don't follow this process properly. If you do offer scalp massage services and have covered the above contra-indications, make sure that you keep a record of your consultation and the responses made by the client after the service, for future reference.

Pre-shampooing scalp massage

Scalp massage stimulates grease production and loosens dead skin cells and dirt from the pores. Given before shampooing, it provides a wonderful prelude to the other salon services. The time taken to do this depends really on you and the client. Some people can stand more stimulation than others. Older clients, for example, may have more sensitive scalps and will not benefit from ten minutes of manipulation. Conversely, other clients may find it more beneficial than the other services offered. It's a very personal thing.

Remember

 Effleurage is a smooth, soothing stroking action, performed with firm but gentle movements of the hands. You should use it before and after the more vigorous movements. It improves skin functions, soothes and stimulates nerves and relaxes tensed muscles.

Effleaurage

EKU statement

GH8.22) The importance of questioning clients to establish any contra-indications to hair and scalp treatment services

GH8.23) Why it is important to record client responses to questions

GH8.24) The legal significance of client questioning and the recording of client's responses to questioning

GH8.27) How and why the contra-indications in the range can effect the scalp massage service

Remember

 Petrissage is a deeper, circular, kneading movement. It assists the removal of waste build-up and promotes the flow of nutrients to the skin and is normally used in conditioning and hand scalp massage.

Petrissage

Providing hand massage

1 Seat your client comfortably, with a clean fresh towel and gown.

2 Using effleurage first, draw your fingertips firmly but not too hard over the head. Your hands should move from the front hairline in an even pressure down to the nape several times.

3 Next use petrissage. Apply this lightly but firmly. With the fingertips, feel through the hair to the scalp and gently rotate on the scalp all over the head. Maintain an even pressure and balance throughout the process, covering all areas, slowly but with the same rhythmic momentum without exerting too much pressure.

4 Finally, use effleurage again to release the pressure of blood stimulated around the scalp during the previous movements.

5 Allow the client to sit quietly for a while to enjoy the benefits of the massage process.

GH8.4 Provide aftercare advice

EKU statement

GH8.49) How to use combs and brushes and correctly comb hair from pant to root

GH8.50) How often to shampoo, condition and treat the hair according to the hair and scalp condition and lifestyle

GH8.51) Products for home use that will benefit the client end those to avoid and why

EKU statement

GH8.25) The direction in which the hair cuticle lies and its importance when disentangling wet hair

GH8.47) The importance of detangling the hair from point to root

Remember

 When disentangling long hair, always work from the points of the hair first, working backwards up the hair, towards the roots. This:
● makes combing far easier and quicker
● eliminates harsh, painful pulling
● reduces tearing and further damage to the hair
● minimises any discomfort to the client.

After completing the shampooing and conditioning treatments you should provide the client with some recommendations on how they can manage their hair themselves. This will ensure that:

✔ | the client is able to gain similar benefits at home from those gained by attending the salon

✔ | the client continues the care regimen of that provided by the salon.

Specifically, you need to tell them about

● the ways and reasons for combing and brushing their hair
● different sorts of products that would be beneficial to them
● how often they should use these products at home.

The ways in which the client should comb and brush their hair

You need to tell the client how they can make their hair easier to manage and maintain a good condition for a longer period of time. Many contemporary effects involve some sort of styling or finishing product and we have already explained that shampooing aims to remove this type of product build-up. But combing and brushing should occur at other times too. Many clients aren't aware that they should be brushing or combing their hair on a daily basis and that's regardless whether they are washing it or not. The action of styling and most finishing products on the hair will lock the cuticle together in some way and it is this principle which enables the hair to stay in style/place. But unless this is detangled in the morning after lying on it, it will start to damage those areas that are locked together by tearing layers of cuticle away from the hair.

So it is essential that the hair is detangled. Initially this is done by separating the main tangles with the fingers and then when roughly loosened, the hair can be brushed or combed.

If the client has longer hair; tell the client to start brushing near the ends of the hair first. If the hair is brushed from the root area first, all the locking points down the hair will be squeezed to the same point causing a large knotted area that will be really difficult to remove without damaging the hair. As the ends become free, the client can slowly work backwards, up the hair shaft to the mid-length and ends and then finally the roots.

Hair should always be combed or brushed downwards. If you have ever attempted to backcomb dry hair, you may have noticed some resistance. This is because the cuticles' free edges all point towards the ends of the hair. So when you push against them they will tangle together. But that makes combing hair out much simpler. When we comb through conditioners we always detangle the ends first, working back up the lengths. This helps the cuticle edges to slip over one another making the whole process far less painful.

The different sorts of products that would be beneficial to the client

Your recommendations for products are based upon what you decided to use during the shampooing and conditioning process. Salons want their clients to make the most of the services that they offer and that includes the retail ranges that it may offer too. Most forward thinking salons use the same products at the wash-point as those available within their retail items; this backs up the salon's services by giving the client the opportunity to have similar experiences at home as they do in the salon.

You should always make a point of telling the client what products you are using on their hair and more importantly why you are using them. This is a professional protocol that stimulates interest and can lead to important additional sales too.

(For more information on specific types of products see pages 150–157.)

How often the client should use these products at home

Finally, after providing the client with information about what products they should be using, you should also be giving them some idea of how frequently their product regimen should be used. Many people are locked into washing their hair on a daily basis and in most cases this is unnecessary. Very few people need to wash their hair every day but it becomes part of a habit, particularly if in having a shower everyday they find it's just as quick to wash their hair too. If their own particular needs point towards not washing everyday, then you should tell them. For example if the client has dry, porous and damaged hair, they certainly will not benefit from excessive washing, although the conditioning aspect will be particularly beneficial. Similarly, a client who has an excessively, oily scalp may have to shampoo every day, but then may not benefit from using a regular surface conditioner. As you can see each client must be considered on their own merits; they are individuals with individual needs. Your advice will go a long way to helping them counter their own particular problems.

ERROL DOUGLAS USING MATRIX

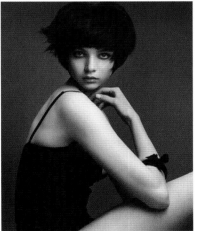

ERROL DOUGLAS USING MATRIX

Checkerboard

	I know how to prepare the client correctly for shampooing and conditioning treatments	I know how to check the stock levels of backwash products and how to refill them	I can always shampoo and condition any client's hair within ten minutes
I know the different massage techniques and when they are used	I know how contact dermatitis can occur and how it can be avoided	I understand the implications of backwash products in relation to personal health and safety	I always make sure that the client is comfortable throughout the process of shampooing and conditioning hair
I know how to communicate effectively with staff and customers	I understand the implications of poor posture, cleaning and personal hygiene	I know how to shampoo and condition a wide range of hair lengths correctly	I always follow the manufacturer's instructions
I know what surface conditioning is, the application techniques and the benefits to the client's hair	I know why the wastage of salon resources should be minimized	I know what deeper-acting conditioners are, their applications and their benefits to the client's hair	I know how to provide advice to the client and recommend products that suit their needs

Assessment of knowledge and understanding

Project

This project relates to the techniques of shampooing and conditioning and the differences between types of conditioner.

Describe in your own words when you would use the following techniques:

- rotary
- effleurage
- petrissage.

How would you adapt the techniques for clients with very long hair?

What is the purpose of the following types of conditioner:

- Surface-acting?
- Penetrating?

Write your answers in your portfolio.

Revision questions

A selection of different types of questions to check your knowledge.

Q1 Coarser, _____ hair takes longer to dampen than finer, oilier hair during shampooing.

Fill in the blank

Q2 Petrissage is commonly used during shampooing.

True or false

Q3 What factors should you consider during shampooing and conditioning (select all that apply)?

Multi selection

Water hardness	☐ 1
Water pressure	☐ 2
Water softness	☐ 3
Water temperature	☐ 4
Water wastage	☐ 5
Water wetness	☐ 6

Q4 Effleurage is a massage movement of circulatory movements.

True or false

Q5 The pH value of pH-balanced shampoos and conditioners is:

Multi choice

3.5–4.5	○ a
4.5–6.0	○ b
5.5–6.5	○ c
7.0–7.5	○ d

Q6 Dandruff is a condition of the scalp usually treated by shampoo.

True or false

Q7 Which of the following would take place after chemical processing (select all that apply)?

Multi selection

Pre-perm shampoo	☐ 1
Anti-oxidant conditioning	☐ 2
Medicated treatment	☐ 3
Conditioning rinse	☐ 4
Anti-dandruff shampoo	☐ 5
Pre-perm treatment	☐ 6

Q8 When conditioning long hair it is important to apply to the mid-lengths and _____ .

Fill in the blank

Q9 A shampoo for dry hair would typically contain?

Multi choice

Critical acids	○ a
Oils	○ b
Medicating agents	○ c
Anti-dandruff agents	○ d

Q10 During conditioning it is always necessary to leave the treatment on.

True or false

Preparing for assessment checklist

Remember to:

✔ prepare clients correctly for the services you are going to carry out

✔ shampoo and condition hair correctly, prior to all salon services

✔ 'brush up' on the science of how shampoos work on the hair to make it clean

✔ adhere to the safety factors when working on a client's hair

✔ wear *personal protective equipment* (PPE) to avoid contact dermatitis

✔ keep the work areas clean, hygienic and free from hazards

✔ work carefully and methodically through the processes of shampooing and conditioning the hair

✔ use positive body language as it plays such an important part in good customer service

✔ use only the correct shampooing and conditioning products appropriate to the task

✔ use good posture and avoid the consequences of poor posture.

ADAM HARRIS @ MG MARTIN GOLD

Chapter**eight**
Style and finish hair

GH10

GH10.1

GH10.2

GH10.3

GH10.4

GH10.5

More information

- Personal hygiene
  EKU GH10.14

- Physical effects on
  hair (alpha beta
  keratin) EKU
  GH10.20 page 184

- Contact dermatitis
  GH10.5

General salon hygiene see
**(Unit G20 Health and
Safety)** EKU GH10.15 EKU
GH10.16 EKU GB5.18

See also the appendices for
following relevant
legislation:

- COSHH EKU GB5.3

- Electricity at Work
  Regulations EKU
  GB5.4

Styling and finishing: quick overview

Unit title

GH10 Style and finish hair

This is a **mandatory** unit for students taking Hairdressing Level 2, it is made up of
five main outcomes

Main outcomes

GH10.1 Maintain effective and safe methods of working when styling and finishing hair

GH10.2 Blow-dry hair into shape

GH10.3 Finger-dry hair into shape

GH10.4 Finish hair

GH10.5 Provide aftercare advice

What do I need to do for GH10.1?

- Take adequate precautions in preparing yourself and the client before any setting
  or dressing procedure

- Work tidily, safely and effectively at all times

- Maintain standards of personal health and hygiene

- Use a range of tools and equipment suitable for drying hair

- Check the temperature of straighteners or tongs prior to use

What do I need to do for GH10.2?

- Confirm the agreed look with the client

- Use a range of techniques, products and styling tools to create the effects

- Work to a commercially acceptable/viable time

- Keep the hair damp and maintain the correct hair tension whilst styling

Keywords

Temporary bonds

The hydrogen bonds within the hair that are modified and fix the style into shape

Hygroscopic

Readily absorbing moisture from the atmosphere

Alpha keratin

Hair in its natural state

Beta keratin

Hair in its moulded shape, for example curly hair that has been dried straight. When the client enters a damp environment the hair reverts back to the alpha state

Information covered in this chapter

- The types of products you should use to style and finish hair and how they work
- The types of equipment to use when styling hair and how they are used
- A variety of styling techniques that you will use
- The basic science of the physical changes that take place during styling as well as the effect that heat and humidity have on the hair
- The advice you should give to clients in order to maintain their own hair

What do I need to do for GH10.3?

- Confirm the agreed look with the client
- Achieve a range of styles by finger-drying hair
- Keep the hair damp whilst styling

What do I need to do for GH10.4?

- Use heated styling equipment to finish the look
- Use back combing or back brushing where necessary
- Apply finishing products to the hair

What do I need to do for GH10.5?

- Give the client recommendations and advice for maintaining their own hair

What aspects do I need to cover for GH10.1, GH10.2, GH10.3, GH10.4 and GH10.5?

- A range of hair-styling products that will be used during styling
- A variety of tools and heated styling equipment
- Different hair lengths, tendencies and growth patterns

What do I need to know for GH10.1, GH10.2, GH10.3, GH10.4 and GH10.5?

- Your salon's requirements in relation to salon policies and current legislation
- How to work safely and hygienically when setting or dressing hair
- The basic science affecting the styling procedures
- How to use a range of styling tools and heated equipment and when they are applicable
- How to use a range of styling products and when they are applicable in achieving the desired effects
- How to use a range of blow-drying and finishing techniques to achieve the desired effects
- How to recommend or provide advice to the client on hair maintenance at home

Introduction

This chapter looks at the aspects of blow-drying and finger-drying hair. Blow-drying has been the most popular styling technique for several decades, its popularity has grown in the belief that effects can quickly be achieved and that hair maintenance is low. However, in the hands of professionals it seems so simple and that is because the client gets to see the creation of the final effect *before their very eyes*.

So this section gives you the information to spread a little magic with your clients too!

 GH10.1 Maintain effective and safe methods of working when styling and finishing hair

Client preparation

Styling and finishing will always follow other services, even if the earlier service was only shampooing. There is one thing that is common to all previous services and that is that your client is left with wet hair. You need to make sure that if the towel is taken away the client's hair will not drip. This is not a safety issue but a measure of your care and attention. It's bad enough when saturated short hair drips down on to the gown and soaks the client's clothes, but this becomes even worse and far more uncomfortable if the client has long hair.

If you can, the best way to tackle any service is with the client's hair in a slightly damp i.e. semi-dry state and this goes for cutting, perming or blow-drying. Working with damp hair is far more comfortable for the client and is the preferred option for busy stylists with little time to spare.

Why work with damp partially dried hair?

In blow-drying or setting the hairstyle is fixed as the alpha keratin changes to beta keratin. This takes place at the point where hair changes state from moist to dry. So when blow-drying, finger-drying and setting it is better to work with hair that is damp. It cuts down the time of drying and maximises the work efficiency and amount of time spent on each client. Hair that is saturated still has to be dried, and using the hood dryer on maximum heat (or in blow-drying at top speed) and scorching the hair dry is definitely not the solution:

- it is uncomfortable for the client
- it will probably cause damage to the client's hair
- it may even burn their scalp too.

Client positioning

Client positioning has a lot to do with your safety too. If a client is slouched in the chair, they are a danger not only to themselves but to you too. Client comfort should extend to the point where it makes the salon visit a welcome and pleasurable experience. But

EKU *statement*

GH10.10) The safety considerations which must be taken into account when styling and finishing hair

Remember

 Always dry the client's hair well to remove the excess water before combing, blow-drying or finger-drying

EKU *statement*

GH10.23) Why hair should be kept damp during the blow-drying and finger-drying processes

Remember

 Work with semi-dry hair During styling this enables the natural tendencies of the hair to be seen.

EKU statement

GH10.9) How the position of you and your client can affect the desired outcome and reduce fatigue and the risk of injury

EKU statement

GH10.6) The range of protective clothing that should be available to clients

GH10.7) Why it is important to use personal protective equipment

GH10.8) The type of personal protective equipment available

EKU statement

GH10.1) Your salon's requirements for client preparation

Remember

Look out for ways and things that can make your client's visit more comfortable and pleasurable. This is the first step in providing a better customer service.

EKU statement

GH10.9) How the position of your client and yourself can affect the desired outcome and reduce fatigue and the risk of injury

Remember

Tell the client that you are adjusting the chair height, they might be a little shocked in the belief that it's going to give way!

that's where it ends. The salon is not an extension of the client's own front room! They should not clutter the floor around the styling chair with bags, magazines and shopping. Anything that can safely be stored away should be: it is not only a distraction, it's a safety hazard too!

Salon chairs are designed with comfort and safety in mind; your client should be seated with their back flat against the back of the chair and the chair at a height at which it is comfortable for you to work. You need to be able to get to all parts of the head, so the chair's height should be adjusted to suit the particular height of the client. Don't be afraid of asking the client to sit up: it is in their best interest too!

Client protection

Make sure that the gown is still on and properly fastened around the neck. It should cover and protect the client's clothes and come up high enough to cover collars and necklines. Don't make the fastening too tight, but it should be close enough at least to stop things going down the back of the neck.

If you can style and dry hair with a towel around the client's shoulders, do so. But in some situations this is not possible as the length of the hair can get in the way of the styling or drying technique. Remember, apart from plastic capes; the towel and gown are the main pieces of personal protective equipment for the client and these are the only things guarding them from the things that you do.

(See Unit GH8, page 149, for more information on client preparation.)

Activity

Different salons have different ways of doing things. Find out what your salon's policy is in respect to:

1   Preparing the client prior to styling

2   Preparing tools and equipment ready for use

3   The use of styling products within the salon

4   Retail products and how they are communicated to the client

Write your answers to these points in your portfolio.

Your posture and work positioning

Hairdressing, as you already know, involves a lot of standing and because of this you need to be comfortable in your work. You should always adopt a comfortable but safe work position and sometimes comfortable and safe are not necessarily the same thing.

A naturally comfortable position for work should allow you to stand close enough to the styling chair without touching it. This should allow you to position your shoulders and body directly above your hips and feet and to distribute your weight evenly over them. You shouldn't have to twist at any point as you can easily work around the chair or get your client to turn their head slightly towards you. You should wear flat shoes, so that your body weight is comfortably supported on the widest parts of the feet. This will allow you to work for longer periods of time without risk of injury or fatigue.

Always make a point of lifting your arms to check the work height for your client. If you have to raise your arms anywhere near horizontal during your work, you will find that your arms will start to ache very quickly. Make your adjustments to the styling chair, either up or down to suit your needs. Don't forget to tell the client what you are doing, if only out of courtesy, as it might be a little shocking for them to find themselves being 'jacked' up to the ceiling!

EKU *statement*

GH10.13) Methods of working safely and hygienically and which minimise the risk of cross-infection and cross-infestation

GH10.14) The importance of personal hygiene

Your personal hygiene

You may have already covered this in Unit G20, but here is a quick check reminder.

Make sure that you always:

✔	Wash your hands before attending to any clients
✔	Wear the minimum of jewellery that can dangle or tangle in the client' hair
✔	Wear comfortable (flatter and not open-toed) footwear when on the salon floor
✔	Be aware of bad-breath–use breath fresheners if you do have a problem
✔	Take a shower daily before going to work
✔	Make sure your work-wear is clean and fresh everyday
✔	Think how you want to be seen by others – you are an advertisement for the service you offer, so make sure that your hair is clean and styled
✔	Minimise the risk of cross-infection to your colleagues and clients

EKU *statement*

GH10.2) Your salon's expected service times for setting services

GH10.11) The importance of positioning equipment for ease of use

GH10.12) Why it is important to keep your work area clean and tidy

GH10.17) The importance of using products economically

Working efficiently, safely and effectively

Working efficiently and maximising your time is essential so making the most of the resources available should occur naturally. But how can you do that? One way of making the most of the salon's resources is being careful in the way that you handle the equipment and the products that you use. Always treat the salon's materials in the same way that you would look after your own equipment. Always try to minimise waste, be careful for how much product you use; it's pointless using an amount of mousse the size of a football if a small orange will do! It only needs a bit of care and control when you dispense the products. Only use as much as you need, remember: the towels don't need excess styling products, it's just throwing money away.

Another factor to consider is tidiness. You need to work in an orderly environment; you should have the materials that you need at hand and the equipment that you want to use in position and ready for action. You need to be thinking about all of the things that you need *before* you need them. This is a good exercise in self-organisation and shows others that you are thinking about your work.

Keep an eye on the clock; you must remember that you need to be working to time and that means providing the service in a commercially acceptable time.

EKU statement

GH10.15) Why it is important to check electrical equipment used to aid the setting and dressing processes

Remember

Always wear non-latex disposable gloves when handling chemicals. This will reduce the risk of developing dermatitis.

EKU statement

GH10.4) Your responsibilities under the current Electricity at Work Regulations

EKU statement

GH10.34) How to carry out the styling techniques in the range

Remember

Safe use of electrical equipment – the Dos and Don'ts

Do

Do check the plugs and leads to make sure they are not loose or damaged before they are used.

Do replace equipment after every time it is used.

Do unravel and straighten the leads properly before use.

Do switch off electrical items when they are not in use.

Do check heated styling equipment such as straighteners and tongs before applying them to the client's hair.

Don't

Don't use electrical equipment with wet hands.

Don't use any piece of equipment for any purpose other than that for which it was intended.

Don't ravel up leads tightly around the equipment; it could work the connection loose.

Activity
Product knowledge

Complete the table below to show how the list of products is (a) applied and (b) suitable for different hair-styling methods.

Product	How is it applied/ used?	For what sort of styling methods is it suitable?
Mousse		
Setting lotion		
Styling glaze		
Serum		
Defining wax		
Heat protection		
Moulding crème		

This section covers the following topics:

- Consulting the client.
- Influencing factors affecting styling.
- Styling equipment.
- Styling and finishing products.
- Styling techniques.

Consultation

G7 Advise and consult with clients, in chapter 5, covers all of the considerations that you should make before carrying out any hairdressing service. If you haven't covered the consultation yet, read that chapter first. Otherwise see the checklist below to review the main points.

EKU *statement*

GH10.13) Methods of working safely and hygienically and which minimise the risk of cross-infection and cross-infestation (see Unit G20 pages 10–21)

GH10.29) How the factors in the range affect the styling process and the finished look

Consultation checklist

Things to look for	Things you could ask the client	Why ask this?
Look at the hair shape	How would you like your hair styled?	You can see if the style is achievable from the length and layering patterns as you brush through the hair and what sorts of products you will need to help style it.
Look for conditions of the scalp that will stop you from carrying on	Have you had any problems with your hair or scalp recently?	If the client has had problems it gives you a lead to investigate further.
Look at the type and tendency of the hair	Is your hair naturally wavy (or curly)?	If there is movement in the hair you need to find out if it is natural to get an idea of which brushes you need to use and whether you will need to use other heated styling equipment too.
Look at the amount and texture of the hair	Does your hair take long to dry and style?	Thicker hair and some hair textures take longer to dry. You need to find out if there are any condition issues first.
Look at the head and facial shape	Do you find that some styles suit you better than others?	Find out whether the client naturally chooses and wears styles that are aesthetically correct for them.
Look at the natural partings	Is this the way that your hair usually falls?	If the natural parting is not where the client wants it, you need to point out the pitfalls of working against the natural fall of the hair.
Look at the quality of the hair and the way that it lies	Do you normally use a finishing or defining product on your hair?	Will the final look be improved by definition, serums or other finishing products?
Likes and dislikes, visual aids/ pictures	Would you like something along these lines or do you prefer a simpler style?	You must get the client to confirm the desired effect before you start.

EKU *statement*

GH10.40) How lifestyle can influence their choice of style (e.g. active sports, career and job requirements)

Influencing factors affecting styling

The client's physical features and their lifestyle have an impact on the choice of styling. Their face and head shape may not be suitable for what they have in mind. Similarly, if their job or leisure activities constrain the options available to them, then you do need to point these aspects out.

The basic rules for styles and face shape suitability are:

- face shapes
- lifestyle (see Unit G7 Advise and consult clients pages 123–124)
- hair growth patterns (see Unit G7 Advise and consult clients page 121)

Face shapes

An oval-shaped face suits any hairstyle, so these facial types present the fewest problems and style selection limitations.

Oval face shape

Generally speaking, round face shapes need height to compensate for the width of the face. Hairstyles that are cut to a level just below the ears tend to draw a focus to that point and therefore longer lengths at the side are a better option.

Round face shape

Shorter profile lengths improve longer facial shapes with added width as opposed to added height.

Long facial shape

Squarer face shapes need rounder styled edges with texture on to the face to soften the corners or heavier jawlines. Longer lengths also are favourable; these tend to create a frame focus elsewhere.

Square face shape

The width of the face can be compensated for with height. However, the triangular face tends to be accompanied by a pointed chin. Avoid short perimeters with solid angles, as this will exacerbate the problem. Compensate with longer lengths at the sides with fullness and movement.

Triangular face shape

Styling equipment

Blow-dryers

The blow-dryer is one of the most commonly used items of equipment in the salon. There is a huge range of models available, with a variety of power outputs, speeds and heat settings. The latest ionic dryers can even reduce the 'flyaway' effect that is produced by static electricity when hair is heated in a colder environment.

A good professional hair blow-dryer should:

- have at least two speeds and two heat settings
- have different shaped nozzles to channel the heat onto the brush or comb
- have a lead long enough for it not to tangle around the chair or client
- be powerful enough to dry damp hair quickly (1300w–1500w)
- have a cool shot button – to enable hot hair to be fixed (set) into shape around a brush
- be not too long so that it is balanced in the hand and can be held away from the clients hair during drying
- be light enough so that it can be manipulated easily and used for long periods without fatigue
- be quiet enough so that it allows natural conversation with the client

Remember

Portable appliance testing (PAT)
All items of electrical equipment have to be tested and certified fit for use by a competent person. The items are tested, labelled and recorded and a compiled list is made available for inspection.

Activity
Give your answers to the following questions:

1 Why is hair always dried from roots to points?

2 When blow-drying why should the nozzle be parallel with the head?

3 Why is it important to keep the dryer moving during blow-drying?

4 What size mesh of hair should you work with when drying?

5 What effect does cold-shot have when blow-drying?

6 Why should you rough dry the hair before you start?

Remember

The cool-shot switch on a dryer is really useful for fixing in stronger volume or end movement into hair. After the hair has been heated, with the brush still in position, the cool shot immediately cools the hair fixing the 'set' hair into position (just as allowing set hair to cool down after the rollers have been carefully removed makes the set last longer).

There is no real value in choosing a dryer that is too powerful, as this may burn or scorch the client's hair during use. The dryer should be well balanced – so that when it's held it doesn't protrude too far forwards and become heavy to hold. You need to be able to work comfortably too and this means at a height and distance that doesn't impede your correct posture or cause shoulder fatigue. The dryer's lead should be long enough to work with comfortably around either side of the client so that you don't trail the lead over their lap!

EKU *statement*

GH10.25) The range of drying and finishing products, tools and equipment available for styling and finishing hair

GH10.27a) Why and how to use the different types of styling brushes when blow-drying

GH10.27b) Why and how to use the different types of attachments when blow-drying

When a dryer is not in use there should be a safe position to store it. In daily salon use this could be a metal (ring) dryer holder attached to the side of the workstation; in the evening this could be in a storeroom or cupboard upon a shelf.

Brushes

Choosing the right tools to get the desired effect is essential. Different brushes do different jobs; if you use the wrong type of brush it may have a detrimental effect on the finished look.

The length of the hair and the desired effect dictates the type of brush you need to use. The table below gives a quick overview of what types are available and how they are used.

Effects of humidity on hair

More information on the effects of humidity on hair and the physical changes that take place within the hair can be found in Unit GH11 Set and dress hair, page 226.

	Uses	Description	Technique	Cleaning and maintenance
Denman Classic Styling brush DENMAN	General brushing, detangling hair before: shampooing, styling and blow-drying straight hair of any length	A parallel, flat brush with removable cushioned bristles. Available in small (5), medium (7), and large (9) rows of plastic bristles	Blow-drying is achieved by placing the leading edge of the bristles against the mesh of hair then turning the brush to engage the hair across all of the width. The brush is used from roots to points with the drier blowing across the cushioned surface	Denman brushes can be dismantled by removing the rubber cushioned head from the brush handle and the bristle rows can be removed and washed in hot soapy water, then dried and replaced. Rows of bristles can be replaced if damaged or overheated. Brushes can be placed in a UV cabinet for 15 mins to complete the cleaning/sterilisation process
Vented brush DENHAM	General brushing, blow-drying straight short and mid-length hair	A parallel, flat brush with a double row of rigid plastic bristles (short and long) affixed to a brush head that is not solid. Allowing air to pass between the bristles	Blow-drying is achieved by placing the leading edge of the bristles against the mesh of hair then turning the brush to engage the hair across all of the width. The brush is used from roots to points with the dryer blowing across the surface	Vented brushes can be cleaned by raking out any loose or tangled hair from the bristles, then washing in hot soapy water. The brush is then dried before use. Brushes can be placed in a UV cabinet for 15 mins to complete the cleaning/sterilisation process

	Uses	Description	Technique	Cleaning and maintenance
Paddle (flat) brush DENHAM	General brushing, detangling hair and pre-dressing hair	A flat brush with a wide head usually with a cushioned head with wider teeth than a Denman. Sometimes the bristles are natural in composition, but generally they are plastic	Paddle brushes are generally too wide to use for blow-drying although sections can be dried by placing sections of hair upon the brush and drying by drawn down from the roots to the points of the hair.	Paddle brushes can be cleaned by raking out any loose or tangled hair from the bristles, then washing in hot soapy water. The brush is then dried before use. Brushes can be placed in a UV cabinet for 15 mins to complete the cleaning/sterilisation process
Radial brushes DENHAM	Blow-drying with volume, lift, wave and curl on shorter or longer length hair	Radial brushes are completely round in section and come in a wide variety of sizes. The bristles are usually made of plastic although pure bristle brushes are still available. The inner body of radial brushes are often made of metal allowing the brush to heat up; improving the drying speeds of the underneath hair within a section.	Blow-drying volume and movement is achieved by placing meshes of damp hair around the brush and drying the hair in position from both sides. When dry, the curl or movement can be affixed or set into position by applying a cool shot to increase the durability of the set	Radial brushes can be cleaned by raking out any loose or tangled hair from the bristles, then washing in hot soapy water. The brush is then dried before use. Brushes can be placed in a UV cabinet for 15 mins to complete the cleaning/sterilisation process
Diffuser (although not a brush it is a piece of equipment used to style the hair) IMAGE COURTESY OF BABYLISS PRO	Scrunch-drying and finger-drying hair to optimise the natural or permed movement within the hair	A diffuser is an attachment for a blow-dryer that suppresses the blast of hot air and turning it into a multidirectional diffused heat	The hair is styled with the fingers by either pressing into the cupped diffuser to dry or by working through the hair with the fingers until the hair is dried with the required amount of texture or definition	Diffusers are cleaned by spraying with an antibacterial spray then wiped with paper towels

Styling and finishing products

Choosing suitable products: you need to be aware of all the products that your salon uses and when and what effects they will achieve on different hair types and lengths.

Diversion Some of the EKUs you need for this unit may be found in other units. To save you from unnecessary duplication we have cross-referenced each unit to other areas. You may have already studied that unit in which case a revision of the information will help you apply that knowledge to this unit. If you have not studied that information before then this will help you when you do study that unit. Where you see this sign it will guide you to the unit in which you will find the information you need.

EKU *statement*

GH10.19) The effects of humidity on hair (also EKU GB5.19 and EKU GH11.19)

GH10.20) The physical effects of the blow-drying, finger-drying and heated styling processes on the hair structure

IMAGE COURTESY OF GOLDWELL UK

Activity
Brushes

What are the differences between using the following brushes during blow-drying?

Brush	What sort of style is it used for?	What effect does it give?
Denman		
Small diameter radial		
Large diameter radial		
Paddle		
Vented		

Activity
In your portfolio explain each of the following:

1   alpha keratin

2   beta keratin

3   why hair should be allowed to cool before brushing through or finishing

4   the effects of humidity on hair

5   the effects of excessive heat upon the hair

6   what advice on hair maintenance you could give to the client.

The table below shows the main ranges of styling products and what they do.

Product	What is it for?	How is it applied?	When do you use it?
Styling mousse	A general styling aid for adding volume and providing hold	Apply a blob the size of a small orange evenly to the lengths	Use on dampened hair before sectioning and drying

WELLA UK

Product	What is it for?	How is it applied?	When do you use it?
Root lift mousse 	A special mousse that has a directional nozzle allowing you to apply foam at or near to the roots	Lift and separate sections of dampened hair so that the root area is exposed. Hold the can so that the nozzle aims the foam near the root	On hair that needs body but doesn't require setting hold at the mid-lengths and points
Styling gel/glaze 	A wet look firm hold finish on shorter hair styles	Apply a small 'pea-size' amount from the fingertips all over evenly (You can always add more if necessary)	Not easy to blow-dry with but can be used in finger-drying and scrunch-dry techniques
Moulding clay 	A dual purpose product for styling or finishing that bonds the hair with firm hold	(On damp hair) apply a small 'pea-size' amount from the fingertips all over evenly (On dry hair) apply with fingertips to the points of the hair for texture and definition (You can always add more if necessary)	Used to give a firm textural bond on most lengths of hair
Defining crème 	A finishing product that provides control on unruly hair	(On dry hair) Apply small 'droplet' amounts a little at a time with fingertips (You can always add more if necessary)	Used throughout the lengths of the hair for smooth control and conditioning

IMAGE COURTESY OF GOLDWELL UK

WELLA

IMAGE COURTESY OF GOLDWELL UK

WELLA UK

EKU *statement*

GH10.3) Your own responsibilities under the current Control of Substances Hazardous to Health Regulations in relation to the use of styling and finishing products

GH10.26) The manufacturers' instructions for the use of the specific styling and finishing products in your salon

GH10.27d) Why and how to use the different types of products and when to apply them

Product	What is it for?	How is it applied?	When do you use it?
Defining wax WELLA UK	A slightly greasy finishing product that provides textural effects to short to longer hair	(On dry hair) apply small 'pea-size' amounts a little at a time with fingertips (You can always add more if necessary)	Used throughout the ends of the hair for style definition and/or textural effects
Serum IMAGE COURTESY OF GOLDWELL UK	A slightly oily finishing product that provides improved handling and shine	(On dry hair) apply small droplet amounts a little at a time with fingertips (You can always add more if necessary)	Used throughout the lengths of the hair for smooth control and better conditioning
Hairspray WELLA UK	A finishing product that is available in a variety of holds/ strengths from either a pump or aerosol spray	Apply mist to hair from about 30–40 cm away from the hair for a 'fixed' hold on dry hair	Used as a final fixative as an overall sealer or applied as a scrunching, textural finish
Dry wax WELLA UK	A non-greasy finishing product that provides textural effects on short, to longer hair	(On dry hair) apply small 'pea-size' amounts a little at a time with fingertips (you can always add more if necessary)	Used throughout the ends of the hair for style definition and/or textural effects

Note: always follow the manufacturer's instructions when handling styling and finishing products. See Unit G20 – COSHH Regulations, page 9.

EKU statement

GH10.21) How the
incorrect application of heat
can affect the hair and
scalp

GH10.28) Current
techniques for blow-drying,
finger-drying and finishing
hair

GH10.32) Why the hair
needs to be sectioned for
styling

Styling techniques

Blow-drying hair

Blow-drying is the most popular way of styling hair; it involves the tensioning, drying and positioning of hair into place with just a hand dryer and a brush. The technique requires a reasonable amount of dexterity and is quite difficult to pick up at first.

Prior to blow-drying the hand dryer is fitted with a heat- and air-focusing nozzle; this stops the dryer from randomly blasting the hair (and anything else) in a haphazard way. As the style is progressed, the nozzle can be moved around so that the client's scalp can be shielded from the potentially damaging, very hot blast and other sections of hair (awaiting styling) are not disturbed by the jet stream.

The idea is to start at the bottom or nape area and fasten any hair not being styled out of the way neatly. Then as each subsequent section is completed the stylist works upwards to the next section so that newly dried and styled hair is placed upon previously dried sections. This is the most methodical approach and ensures that the hairstyle is constructed in a logical efficient way.

When the client's hair is ready for styling the excess water must be removed so that:

- only damp and not saturated sections are worked upon
- the benefits of any styling products are not lost and diluted by excess water
- the client's hair is not unduly or excessively overheated
- the client remains comfortable and dry throughout the process rather than getting wet and cold.

Remember

 Clean the gauze filters out on the back of the hand dryer regularly. This will prolong the dryer's life and enable it to work more efficiently too.

Remember

Hairdryers only blow out what they suck in from the other end. Always make sure that the filter is attached to the back of the dryer, as this will prevent your client's hair from getting sucked in. This is not only embarrassing for you, it is dangerous and unpleasant for the client too.

EKU statement

GH10.30b) How the
finished result of blow-
drying is affected by size of
hair mesh

GH10.30c) How the
finished result of blow-
drying is affected by size of
brush

GH10.33) How the size of
the section and the angle at
which the hair is held during
drying influences the
volume and direction of the
hair movement

Apply the styling product

After consultation and preparation you should towel-dry the client's hair and then, with a wide-tooth comb, carefully find the parting and detangle the hair lengths. Remember if the hair is long you will need to work from the points through the lengths towards the roots.

You need to work upon hair that is damp rather than wet, so pre-dry any areas that need it first.

Then, select your product (depending upon your styling needs) and apply to the hair (see the styling product table on pages 185–186). Distribute the product evenly throughout the hair, trying not to overload any particular areas and work through the lengths so that the product is evenly distributed upon the hair.

Drying the hair – roots to points

You should only work on relatively small areas at any one time; ideally these sections should not be any larger that the 'footprint' area of any type of brush than you will be using. If the sections are too large you will not be able to dry each mesh of hair properly and this will affect the durability of the finished look.

Be careful not to overheat any sections of the hair while you are drying, the effects would be long term and very detrimental to the condition of the hair.

Start the blow-dry at the lower back by sectioning out of the way any surplus hair and securing it with a clip. Then, taking your dryer in one hand, offer the dryer across to the section so that you can see whether the angle of the nozzle will create a parallel jet stream of air to the angle of the hair. Then after any adjustments; take your brush in the other hand and introduce the bristles to the hair somewhere near to the root area. Pick and turn the brush so that the hair is caught across the bristles, turn on the dryer and now aiming across the brush, follow the brush downwards with the dryer holding it about 10–15 cm away.

Focusing the jet stream

The hair can only dry if the blast from the dryer is working over the surface of it. So bearing this in mind carefully aim the flat, jet stream of heated air across the surface of the brush, shielding the heat from the back (scalp side) side of the brush. As you move the brush down, move the dryer down so that it mirrors the position of the brush at always the same distance away. Blow-drying from root to point ensures that the cuticle lays flat therefore reducing fly-away frizz and smoothing the overall result.

Water moisture will naturally fall down the hair shaft with gravity, so starting near the root area will always quicken the drying process. After a couple of passes through the hair the section will be dry.

If you are using a radial type brush you will find that you need to take a section (like that of rollering) and wind the hair around the brush. Again, focus the jet stream over the curved surfaces of the brush, but this time from both sides. This will enable the hair to dry around the brush forming part of the wave. Then after drying and while still warm, use a cool shot from the dryer (or use blast only without heat settings) to 'freeze' the wave into place. (This fixes the style with more durability like in setting; when rollers are allowed to cool down before removal and final brushing and dressing out.) If you do not allow the meshes of hair to cool it will result in a less firm result and will not last as long.

Finally, with the section dry you can take down another mesh, ready for drying into position.

Working with tensioned hair

You have to maintain an even tension to the meshes of hair throughout the blow-drying service. This ensures that the hair will dry with a smooth, sleeker effect without frizzes or crimped areas. If you do create a kinked, uneven result, you can lightly spray down the

EKU statement

GH10.30d) How the finished result of blow-drying is affected by the angle at which the brush is held

GH10.31) Why the direction of air flow when drying is important to achieve the desired look

EKU statement

GH10.22) Why hair should be allowed to cool prior to finishing (also GB5.22)

GH10.30e) How the finished result of blow-drying is affected by not allowing the hair to cool before removing the hair mesh from the brush

EKU statement

GH10.30a) How the finished result of blow-drying is affected by tension

EKU statement

GH10.35) The effects that can be achieved by curling on and off base hair with water and start again. Look out for the hair in the sectioning clips waiting to be dried too: If the hair has a natural tendency to wave or curl it might disfigure it before you can style it. Again, lightly mist it down with water and start over.

Blow-dry styling dos and don'ts

Dos

Do dry off the hair well so that it's moist but not wet before starting the blow-dry.

Do take small enough sections that you can control and dry evenly throughout.

Do try to direct the flow of air away from the client.

Do adjust the chair height so you can reach the top of the client's head without overstretching.

Do ask the client to adjust their head position if you need to.

Do clip out of the way any sections that are not yet being worked on.

Don'ts

Don't leave damp towels around the client's shoulders.

Don't leave the dryer running whilst you resection the hair.

Don't use the top heat setting unless its really necessary.

Don't pass the brushes to the client for them to hold in between sectioning.

Don't try to use the same hand for brush work on both sides of the head.

Don't over-dry the hair as this will cause permanent damage.

Remember

Blow-drying with radial brushes is very similar to setting with rollers, if you dry the mesh of hair on base it will give you lift at the root area; whereas a section dried off base (dragging the roots) will keep the root area flatter.

Step-by-step: Blow-drying short hair

Step 1 Squeeze out sufficient mousse to blow-dry with.

Step 2 Sectioning to start.

Step 3 Creating lift and direction.

Step 4 Creating lift under the crown.

Step 5 Directing the hair back from the sides.

Step 6 Final effect.

Step-by-step: Blow-drying long hair

1 Apply a small amount of styling mousse to the hair.

2 Divide the hair at the back so that the nape can be blow-dried first.

3 Work up the back, finishing and drying each section before moving on to the next.

4 Continue up the back until all of the hair is completed. Section off the sides and start at the lower section again.

5 Finally, work forward from the crown towards the frontal/fringe area.

Step 1 Squeeze out sufficient mousse to blow-dry with.

Step 2 Sectioning to start.

Step 3 Smooth even tension.

Step 4 Directing the flow of air in line with the hair.

Step 5 Back complete, move on to the sides.

Step 6 Finishing around the face.

GH10.3 Finger-dry hair into shape

Finger- and scrunch-drying (see Unit GB5 Dry and finish men's hair)

These are mandatory techniques for both hairdressing and barbering at level 2. This particular section is covered on pages 211–212.

Activity
Dos and don'ts

Fill the table by indicating what the main dos and don'ts are for blow-drying.

Dos	Don'ts

Diversion The knowledge statements for Level 2 in both the hairdressing and barbering standards are often repeated in different outcomes within units elsewhere.

To save you from any unnecessary duplication, this book is cross-referenced to other areas. So wherever you see this sign it will direct you to another unit for the essential knowledge and understanding (EKU).

GH10.4 Finish hair

After blow-drying the client's hair, you will need to do something to finish the look if it is only to brush the final effect through. More often than not, there is a lot more to do. This could be to:

- apply finishing products to the hair
- use other heated equipment to finish the effect.

Applying finishing products to the hair

Choosing the correct finish really depends on the look you are trying to achieve. It would be easy to get it all wrong at this stage and choose something that works against you. Sometimes it's the right product but wrongly applied, but often it's the wrong product correctly applied. Confused?

Most styling products like mousse or setting lotion do not create an immediate build-up upon the hair. They might be a little tackier than you had expected, or they might give a firmer hold than you had wanted. But in either case, when the hair is dry, a little too much won't have a critical effect on the desired outcome. However, if you apply too much serum or wax on the hair you will find yourself having to wash and start all over again!

This is easily avoided if you add product to your final effect in small steps. In other words, you build up the desired effect slowly by adding a little more until the result is achieved. (For more information on finishing products see pages 196–197.)

How do styling products make hair last longer?

Hair and, more importantly, hairstyles are affected by moisture, and moisture is in the air around us at different levels of what we call *humidity*. We know that if we get our hair damp that the style won't last and this effect is something in salons that we try to avoid.

Styling products put an invisible barrier onto the hair so that the moisture is partially repelled; this plastic film effectively lasts until it is shampooed out of the hair. In cases

EKU *statement*

GH10.37) Products for home use that will benefit the client and those to avoid and why (see GH11.37)

GH10.38) How the continual use of heated equipment can affect the hair (see GH11.38)

GH10.39) How to recreate and maintain the agreed style (see GH11.39)

GH10.41) How to give effective advice and recommendations to clients

EKU *statement*

GH10.19) The effects of humidity on hair

where excesses of finishing products have been applied to the hair product 'build-up' can occur. This may happen when people re-apply product without washing in-between; this overloads the hair and is often difficult to remove.

If your client is unaware of the effects that product build-up has on the hair you should advise them on how to manage their hair with other alternatives.

How do heat protecting products work?

In the paragraph above you can see how products work to protect the hair from moisture in the atmosphere; well that's not the only thing they can do. Blow-dryers can get very hot, but heated styling equipment is another thing altogether. Straightening irons and tongs have been very popular and many clients have been in the habit of using them, not just when the hair is shampooed and conditioned.

Heat-protecting sprays will put a heat-resistant layer upon the hair by doing two things.

- They improve the surface of the hair by smoothing it and enabling the heated equipment to slip over the surface without grabbing in any areas (like Teflon coated cooking pans).
- They resist high temperatures from styling surfaces long enough for the hair bonds to be re-arranged in the new (temporary) shape (see alpha and beta keratin, page 175).

EKU *statement*

GH10.24) How heat protectors act to protect the hair (also EKU GB5 24 and EKU GH11 24)

Keeping the heated styling equipment clean

With prolonged use, the surfaces on tongs and straighteners can get product build-up themselves. This should always be looked out for as any residue of styling products such as wax, hair sprays, gels, serums etc. will impair the slippy, smooth surfaces and create roughened areas that will grab and stick to the hair when they are hot. This is potentially damaging as it may also burn the hair.

EKU *statement*

GH10.18) The reasons why tools and heated styling equipment should be kept free from excess oils and product build-up (also GB5 18)

Heated equipment: straightening irons and tongs

Using heated tongs, hot brushes and straightening and crimping irons

Electric curling tongs, heated brushes and straightening irons are a popular way of applying finish to a hairstyle. They are particularly useful in situations where:

- setting or blow-drying will not achieve the desired look
- the hair is not in a suitable condition to be dried into shape.

Sometimes you will not achieve the result that the client is expecting. When extra volume, movement or curl is needed on hair that lacks natural body, or is very fine, additional help is needed to create a lasting effect. Heated tongs and/or brushes provide a quick solution to do this. They can be bought in a variety of different sizes (i.e. diameters), which give different levels of movement.

Professional heated tongs (and many hair straighteners) usually have a thermostatic temperature control. This is particularly useful as you can *dial up* the heat setting

EKU *statement*

GH10.27c) Why and how to use the different types of heated styling equipment when styling and finishing required to achieve the desired effect for a particular hair type. This eliminates the chance of damage to the hair caused by excess heat.

Remember

 Some hair conditions are more suited to setting techniques. If the client's hair is too porous or bleached, dry setting or heated rollers would be a good alternative.

Step-by-step: curling using ceramic straighteners

Hair straighteners do a fantastic job of providing a smooth straight finish on most hair types. But, like curling a ribbon with scissors on Christmas presents, they can be used to create a variety of effects.

Step 1 Shampoo and dry the client's hair into shape, removing any tangles.

Step 2 Start by sectioning and then securing the hair at the lower back of the head.

Step 3 After allowing the straighteners to reach the correct operating temperature, take a small oblong section and offer up the straighteners to the hair in an almost vertical position.

Step 4 Grip the hair near to the root area (but not too close).

Step 5 Turn the straighteners so the hair extends around the handle.

Step 6 Draw the straighteners down the hair section in one smooth and controlled movement.

Step 7 Your should now have a row of spiraled curls.

Step 8 Continue this same action up through the back and into the sides.

Step 9 Carefully arrange and separate the curls with your fingers to create the final effect.

Straightening irons and particularly ceramic straightening irons have been a very popular way of calming unruly hair. They work by electrically heating two parallel plates so that the hair can be run between them in one movement from roots to ends, smoothing out the unwanted wave or frizz in the process.

EKU *statement*

GH10.24) How heat protectors act to protect the hair (also GB5.24, GH11.24)

Ceramic straighteners have been particularly successful as they heat up in just a few moments and have a higher operating temperature than metal irons (170°C). This alarmingly high temperature would initially be considered as damaging to hair but, because they have the ability to transfer heat quickly and smoothly to the hair without *grabbing*, they are very effective in creating smoother effects. But because of their temperature you must check them before you introduce them to the hair so that you don't permanently damage the client's hair.

EKU *statement*

GH10.15) Why it is important to check electrical equipment use to aid the drying and finishing processes (also GB5.15)

GH10.21) How the incorrect application of heat can affect the hair and scalp

Remember

 Very hot styling tools without a non-slip coating or ceramic surface, can often tend to stick when they are introduced to hair that has styling products on it.

This grabbing effect can cause damage as the hair will bond to the edges of the equipment until it is removed. Always check the temperature settings before you use heated equipment and where possible start at a lower temperatures. Remember, you can always turn the temperature *up*.

Remember

 Hot styling tools can make hair static and flyaway, heat protection sprays control this and protect the hair from being excessively overheated.

When straightening is needed to complement the look on longer hair, it is often better to straighten each section as the blow-dry proceeds. If you start underneath, each section is completely finished before you move on up the head. The hair will stay flatter from the outset and each section is totally dry, stopping the hair from reverting to its previous state (i.e. reverting to alpha keratin).

The use of crimping irons tends to go through phases of popularity at least once every decade or so. They too have parallel fixed plates but these are wavy and produce flat 'S' waves on longer hair. They are a great styling accessory for competition and stage work as crimped effects are visually striking and very unusual. In staged hairdressing shows models with crimped hair will often accompany the look with strong fashion colours.

Unlike tongs and straightening irons, crimpers are not turned, twisted or drawn through the hair.

1 Each mesh of hair is started near the head and works down to the points of the hair.

2 The meshes should be no wider than the crimping irons and are crimped across the width of the plates.

3 After a few moments of heating each section of the mesh the crimpers are moved to the last wave crest created and pressed again.

4 This is repeated down the lengths of the hair until all of the hair is crimped.

5 The final look is not combed out or brushed, but allowed to fall in waved sections.

Crimping is not advisable on shorter, layered hair unless a frizzy, fluffy look is wanted. The most successful results are on longer, one-length hair.

Electrical equipment health and safety checklist

✔	Never get too close to the client's head with hot styling equipment
✔	Never leave the styling equipment on one area of hair for more than a few moments
✔	Always replace the styling tools into their holder at the workstation when not in use
✔	Always check the filters on the back of hand dryers to make sure that they are not blocked (this will cause the dryer to overheat and possibly ignite)
✔	Look out for trailing flexes across the floor or around the back of styling chairs
✔	Let tools cool down before putting them back into storage
✔	Always check for deterioration in flexes or equipment damage
✔	Never use damaged equipment under any circumstances

Activity
Facial shapes

For consultation purposes, as hairdressers, we tend to group clients into categories that follow a range of basic facial shapes.
Look at the list below. What styling options or limitations does each facial shape provide?

Facial shape	Styling options/limitations
Round	
Oval	

Remember

Heated equipment – advice for the client
Heated styling equipment such as straightening irons and tongs work at very high temperatures. When you are ready to use them, tell your client to keep their head still as any sudden movement or twisting could draw the hot surfaces closer to the scalp or even burn them.

Remember

Care for tongs, straighteners and crimpers
When hairspray or styling products have been used on hair they can cause a build-up on the surface of electric tongs and straighteners. Over time, this will cause tacky or sticky points to develop upon the surface of the equipment when it is hot. Hair will stick to these areas and will cause damage. Sticky points on tongs and straighteners stop the equipment from gliding smoothly over the hair.

Facial shape	Styling options/limitations
Square	
Oblong	
Heart	
Triangular	

Styling and finishing products

Product ↓		Uses		
		on short hair	on medium-length hair	on longer hair
Mousse (styling product)	A useful setting aid available in different strengths. Needs to be applied evenly through the hair lengths. Can be applied with a brush on longer hair	Apply a blob the size of a golf ball evenly to the roots and ends on damp hair to give volume and texture	Apply a blob the size of a small orange evenly to the roots and ends on damp hair to give volume and texture	Apply a blob the size of an orange evenly to the ends for styling hold
Setting lotion (styling product)	Classic setting agent in liquid or semi-gel form. Needs to be applied evenly along the hair lengths	Apply half the contents of the bottle all over evenly for volume and styling hold	Apply the contents of a bottle all over evenly for volume and styling hold	
Styling gel/glaze (styling product)	A firm setting agent that will produce a wet-look finish after drying	Apply a small amount all over evenly for firmer styling hold	Apply a moderate amount all over evenly for firmer styling hold	

L'ORÉAL PROFESSIONNEL

IMAGE COURTESY OF GOLDWELL UK

L'ORÉAL PROFESSIONNEL

Product ↓		Uses		
		on short hair	on medium-length hair	on longer hair
Dressing cream (setting and finishing product)	A non-greasy control cream for eliminating static from hair. Needs careful application as it is easy to overload finer hair types	Apply a small amount to your fingertips. Work through before combing out to give control, reduce static and calm down strays	Apply a small amount to your fingertips. Work through before combing out to give control, reduce static and calm down strays	
Serum (setting finishing product)	An oil based control agent for eliminating static and improving texture. Needs careful application as it is easy to overload finer hair types	Apply a small amount to your fingertips. Work through to flatten and add shine	Apply a small amount to your fingertips. Work through to flatten and add shine	Apply a small amount to different areas with your fingertips. Work through to flatten and add shine
Wax (setting/ finishing product)	A grease-based control agent for defining texture	Apply a small amount to your fingertips. Work through to define and hold	Apply a small amount to your fingertips. Work through to define and hold	
Hairspray (setting finishing product)	A finishing product for fixing hair into place	Apply mist to hair from about 30–40 cm away from the hair for a 'fixed' hold	Apply mist to hair from about 30–40 cm away from the hair for a 'fixed' hold	Apply mist to hair from about 30–40 cm away from the hair for a 'fixed' hold
Heat protection spray	Use in conjunction with electrically heated styling tools. The product laminates the outer layer of the hair so that it is protected from damaging effects of heat		Apply to lengths after drying to provide protection from intense heat when using straightening irons	Apply to lengths after drying to provide protection from intense heat when using straightening irons

GH10.5 Provide aftercare advice

The outline framework of aftercare advice for clients in relation to blow-drying (what products they should use, the effects of long-term use of heated styling equipment and style maintenance) is covered elsewhere in this book. To find out more on the advice that you should be giving, see Unit GH11 Set and dress hair – section GH11.3 (pages 234–235) or Unit G7 Advise and consult with clients.

Checkerboard

Checkerboard	I know and understand the health, safety and hygiene aspects of styling, dressing and finishing hair ☐	I understand the physical properties and changes within the hair that take place during styling and dressing ☐	I always recognise the adverse hair and scalp problems when I analyse the client's hair ☐
I know how the effects of excessive heat can damage hair ☐	I know the ranges of products available and how they should be used on the hair ☐	I know how to create a range of blow-drying and finger-dried effects on short, medium and longer hair ☐	I know the principles of blow-drying and how they are applied to achieve a variety of different looks ☐
I can carry out a variety of blow-drying techniques on different lengths of hair ☐	I provide clients with home care advice about style maintenance and product use ☐	I know how heated equipment should be used on the hair to achieve different effects ☐	I know how to achieve different finished effects on longer hair ☐

Assessment of knowledge and understanding

Project

For this project you will need to gather information from a variety of sources.

Collect together photographs, digital images and magazine clippings about styling, blow-drying, setting and dressing techniques.

Include styles for long hair as well as short; for weddings, special occasions and casual wear.

In your portfolio describe:

- how the styles were achieved
- why each is suitable for its purpose
- the equipment (with examples) that was used to create the effects
- the products (with examples) used to help hold or define the effects.

Revision questions

A selection of different types of questions to check your styling and finishing hair knowledge.

Q1   A round brush is also known as a _____ brush.   Fill in the blank

Q2   Humidity in the atmosphere will make a blow-dried finish drop.   True or false

Q3   Which of the following items are examples of heated styling equipment?   Multi selection

Tongs	☐ 1
Vented brush	☐ 2
Crimpers	☐ 3
Thinners	☐ 4
Grips	☐ 5
Straighteners	☐ 6

Q4   The keratin bonds of stretched hair are said to be in the beta state.   True or false

Q5   Which chemical bonds within the hair are affected during heat styling?   Multi choice

Hydrogen bonds	○ a
Disulphide bonds	○ b
Sulphur bonds	○ c
Premium bonds	○ d

Q6   Ceramic straighteners can be used to curl hair.   True or false

Q7   Heated tongs will produce which of the following results and effects?   Multi selection

Increased body at the roots	☐ 1
No body at the roots	☐ 2
Curl at the ends	☐ 3
Straighter effects	☐ 4
Wavy effects	☐ 5
Same as straightening irons	☐ 6

Q8   A paddle brush is a type of _____ brush.   Fill in the blank

Q9   Which item of equipment would smooth and flatten frizzy, unruly hair best?   Multi choice

Curling tongs	○ a
Ceramic straighteners	○ b
Crimping irons	○ c
Blow-dryer	○ d

Q10   In blow-drying the hair should always be dried from root to points.   True or false

Preparing for assessment checklist

Remember to:

✔	prepare clients correctly for the services you are going to carry out
✔	put on the protective wear available for styling and dressing hair
✔	listen to the client's requirements and discuss suitable courses of action
✔	adhere to the safety factors when working on clients' hair
✔	keep the work areas clean, hygienic and free from hazards
✔	promote the range of services, products and treatments with the salon
✔	clean and sterilise the styling tools and equipment before they are used
✔	work carefully and methodically through the processes of blow-drying hair
✔	take care when using heated styling equipment
✔	communicate what you are doing to the client as well as your fellow staff members.

Chapter**nine**
Men's styling and finishing

GB5

GB5.1

GB5.2

GB5.3

More information See Unit GH10 Style and finish hair

- Personal hygiene EKU GB5.14
- Contact dermatitis EKU GB5.5
- General salon hygiene see (**Unit G20 Health and Safety**) EKU GB5.15 EKU GB5.16 EKU GB5.18
- See also the appendices for following relevant legislation:
  - COSHH EKU GB5.3
  - Electricity at Work Regulations EKU GB5.4

Dry and finish men's hair: quick overview

Unit title

GB5 Dry and finish men's hair

This is a mandatory unit for students taking **Barbering Level 2**, it is made up of three main outcomes

Main outcomes

GB5.1 Maintain effective and safe methods of working when drying hair

GB5.2 Dry and finish hair

GB5.3 Provide aftercare advice

What do I need to do for GB5.1?

- Take adequate precautions in preparing yourself and the client before any setting or dressing procedure
- Work tidily, safely and effectively at all times
- Maintain standards of personal health and hygiene
- Use a range of tools and equipment suitable for drying hair

What do I need to do for GB5.2?

- Use a range of techniques, products and styling tools to create the effects
- Create a range of current looks for men
- Work to a commercially acceptable time

What do I need to do for GB5.3?

- Give the client recommendations and advice for maintaining their own hair

What aspects do I need to cover for GB5.1, GB5.2 and GB5.3?

- A range of hair styling products that will be used during styling
- A variety of tools and equipment used during styling
- Different hair lengths, tendencies, and growth patterns

- Your salon's requirements in relation to salon policies and current legislation
- How to work safely and hygienically when styling hair
- The basic science affecting the styling procedures
- How to use a range of styling tools and equipment and when they are applicable
- How to use a range of styling products and when they are applicable in achieving the desired effects
- How to use blow-drying and finger-drying techniques to achieve the desired effects
- How to recommend or provide advice to the client on hair maintenance at home

Keywords

Temporary bonds

The hydrogen bonds within the hair that are modified and fix the style into shape

Alpha and beta keratin

The different states of hair that take place during setting and blow-drying

Information covered in this chapter

- The types of products used styling men's hair and how they work
- The types of equipment used when styling hair and how they are used
- A variety of styling techniques that you will use
- The basic science of the physical changes that take place during styling as well as the effect that heat and humidity have on the hair
- The advice you should give to clients in order to maintain their own hair

Introduction

During a long period of very short hair fashions for men, the male client has tried to create individuality out of just a handful of hairstyles. This has been a tall order as it's hard to look different when you have the same clippered effect as the next man in the street. One of the things that has changed this pattern and enabled men to show individual style and flair is that, men, aided by their barbers (and probably their partners too) discovered the benefits of using finishing products to sculpt their own personality out of their hairstyles.

This provided a huge range of options for them and once they had mastered the techniques of applying them evenly, they could produce a vast array of really cool effects. This defining moment in men's styling has sparked a new dimension in men's hair styling:

1 it has developed the new direction of longer looks for men
2 it has provided them with as many fashion options as it does women
3 it has created new business for barber shops and salons that didn't exist before.

Diversion Some of the EKUs you need for this unit may be found in other units. To save you from unnecessary duplication we have cross-referenced each unit to other areas. You may have already studied that unit in which case a revision of the information will help you apply that knowledge to this unit. If you have not studied that information before then this will help you when you do study that unit. Where you see this sign it will guide you to the unit in which you will find the information you need.

GB5.1 | Maintain effective and safe methods of working when drying hair

All the knowledge aspects that you need to know for this outcome are covered in Unit GH10 Style and finish hair and Unit G20 Make sure your actions reduce risks to health and safety.

The specific references are as follows:

Preparing, protecting and positioning the client

EKU statement

GB5.1) Your salon's requirements for client preparation (see EKU GH10.1 page 176)

GB5.6) The range of protective clothing that should be available for clients (see EKU GH10.6 page 176)

GB5.7) Why it is important to use personal protective equipment (see EKU GH10.7 page 176)

GB5.8) The type of personal protective equipment available (see EKU GH10.8 page 176)

GB5.9) How the position of you and your client can affect the desired outcome and reduce fatigue and the risk of injury (see EKU GH10.9 page 176)

Preparing and positioning the equipment ready for use

EKU statement

GB5.10) The importance of positioning equipment for ease of use (see EKU GH10.11 page 177)

GB5.12) Why it is important to keep your work area clean and tidy (see EKU GH10.12 page 177)

Working efficiently and effectively

EKU statement

GB5.2) Your salon's expected service times for setting services (see EKU GH10.2 page 177)

GB5.11) The safety considerations which must be taken into account when styling and finishing hair (see EKU GH10.10 page 175)

GB5.17) The importance of using products economically (see EKU GH10.17 page 177)

GB5.18) The reasons why tools and heated styling equipment should be kept free from excess oils and product build-up (see also EKU GH10.18 page 192)

Working safely and preventing infections

The essential aspects that you need to consider are covered in Chapter 1, Unit G20 Make sure your actions reduce risks to health and safety. See particularly:

Reducing risks – good salon safety and salon equipment (pages 10–15)

EKU *statement*

GB5.13) Methods of working safely and hygienically and which minimise the risk of cross-infection and cross-infestation

GB5.16) Methods of cleaning, disinfecting and/or sterilisation used in salons

Personal health and hygiene (pages 17–19)

EKU *statement*

GB5.14) The importance of personal hygiene

Reducing risks – contact dermatitis (page 14)

EKU *statement*

GB5.5) What is contact dermatitis and how to avoid contracting it whilst carrying out styling and finishing services

Reducing risks – handling chemicals (page 14)

EKU *statement*

GB5.3) Your own responsibilities under the current Control of Substances Hazardous to Health Regulations in relation to the use of styling and finishing products

Working with electricity

Reducing risks – working with electricity (page 15)

EKU *statement*

GB5.4) Your responsibilities under the current Electricity at Work Regulations

GB5.15) Why it is important to check electrical equipment use to aid the drying and finishing processes see EKU GH10.15

LEE MORAN@SANRIZZ

Main differences for drying and finishing men's hair

Most of the preparatory aspects for this outcome are similar to those of styling and finishing hair unit GH10, although it is worth noting that some products and tools are developed with men specifically in mind as their applications are not so complex and generally used on shorter effects.

With these facts in mind the modern man creates his fashionable looks from a toolkit of far fewer styling products; he wants to create finished effects that are individual but achieved from products that do specific jobs.

EKU *statement*

GB5.25) The range of drying and finishing products, tools and equipment available for drying and finishing men's hair

GB5.26) When and why the types of drying and finishing products should be used

Finishing products for men

Product	Application	Purpose	Suitability
Dry wax	Applied in small amounts by the fingertips into pre-dried hair	A moderately firm hold providing a non-wet look or greasy finish. Ideal for men who really don't like the look of product on the hair, but need the benefits of the control it provides	Suited to short- and medium-length hair; the effects need to be created carefully and slowly by adding more as needed. It is very easy to add too much and overload the hair, particularly on finer hair types
Normal (grease-based) wax	Applied in small amounts by the fingertips into pre-dried hair	A firm hold that provides high definition and texture with a moist or slightly greasy effect. Ideal for most types of hair providing a groomed or sculpted look	Suited to short- and medium-length hair; the effects need to be created carefully and slowly by adding more as needed. It is very easy to add too much and overload the hair, particularly on finer hair types
Hair varnish	Applied in small amounts by the fingertips into pre-dried hair. Care needs to be taken in applying the product evenly, throughout the hair	A high-gloss look with a greasy texture. The styles created are moisture repelling. Ideal for men who do like product effects on their hair	Suits short hair with long lasting low maintenance looks, suitable for sports etc. Again the effect needs to be created slowly; it is easy to overload the hair and these types of product do produce a build-up upon the hair
Hair gel	Applied by the fingertips or with a comb into wet or pre-dried hair. It is easy to see where it has been missed	A wet look effect with strong hold. Suitable for sculpted looks and ideal for men who do like product effects on their hair	You can't really overload the hair with gel as the look is based on 100 per cent coverage. The effects created are suited to short hair and are not moisture resistant and will start to drop if they get moist or wet
Styling glaze	Applied first to the hands and rubbed into wet or pre-dried hair all over. The hair is styled after and allowed to dry and fix into shape	A wet look effect with firm–strong hold. Suitable for controlled or groomed looks with a mild, wet look effect	Again like gel, you can't overload the hair as the look is based on 100 per cent coverage. The styles created are suited to short hair and are more resistant to moisture than gel but create less sculpted or high-hair effects than gel

L'ORÉAL PROFESSIONNEL

L'ORÉAL PROFESSIONNEL

WELLA UK

WELLA UK

L'ORÉAL PROFESSIONNEL

Product	Application	Purpose	Suitability
Hair clay/ putty WELLA UK	Applied in small amounts by the fingertips into pre-dried hair	A moderately firm hold providing a non-wet look or greasy finish with high definition, texture and control	Fairly easy to apply; these products are very versatile and create a wide range of effects on any hair texture generally on shorter hair lengths
Defining crème WELLA UK	Applied in small amounts by the fingertips into pre-dried hair	A firm hold that doesn't dry on the hair providing an invent/reinvent option as the hair can be reworked throughout the day or night	Suits long-lasting, low maintenance looks, on any hair length; suitable for sports, leisure and work. The effect needs to be created slowly and it is easy to overload the hair, these types of product do produce a build up upon the hair
Hairspray WELLA UK	Applied to pre-dried hair by directional spraying from 30 cm away	Provides mild, moderate and firm hold, can be used as a final fixative or as a styling product when scrunched in	Easy to apply providing a long lasting effects on any hair length

Note. Always follow the manufacturer's instructions and guidance for use when using any styling or finishing products

Activity

Different salons have different ways of doing things. Find out what your salon's policy is in respect to:

1 preparing the client prior styling

2 preparing tools and equipment ready for use

3 the use of styling products within the salon

4 retail products and how they are communicated to the client.

EKU *statement*

GB5.27) The manufacturers' instructions for the use of the specific styling and finishing products in your salon

LEE MORAN@SANRIZZ

LEONARDO RIZZO@SANRIZZ

GB5.2   Dry and finish hair

EKU statement

GB5.13) Methods of working safely and hygienically and which minimise the risk of cross-infection and cross-infestation (see Unit G20 pages 10–15)

GB5.30) How the factors in the range affect the styling process and the finished look

This section covers the following topics:

● consulting the client
● influencing factors that affect styling
● styling and finishing products
● styling techniques.

Consultation

G7 Advise and consult with clients (in Chapter 5) covers all of the considerations that you should make before carrying out any hairdressing service. If you haven't covered the consultation chapter yet, read that section first otherwise this checklist below will help you to review the main points.

Consultation checklist

Things to look for	Things you could ask the client	Why ask this?
Look at the hair shape	How would you like your hair styled?	You can see if the style is achievable from the lengths and layering patterns as you brush through the hair and what sorts of products you will need to help style it
Look for infections or infestations that will stop you from carrying on	Have you had any scalp problems recently?	If the client has had problems it gives you a lead to investigate further
Look at the type and tendency of the hair	Is your hair naturally wavy (or curly)?	If there is movement in the hair you need to find out if it is natural to get an idea of which brushes you need to use and whether you will need to use other heated styling equipment too
Look at the amount and texture of the hair	Does your hair take long to dry and style?	Thicker hair and some hair textures take longer to dry. You need to find out if there are any condition issues first
Look at the head and facial shape (see Unit GH10 page 180)	Do you find that some styles suit you better than others?	Find out whether the client naturally chooses and wears styles that are aesthetically correct for them
Look at the natural partings	Is this the way that your hair usually falls?	If the natural parting is not where the client wants it, you need to point out the pitfalls of working against the natural fall of the hair
Look at the quality of the hair and the way that it lies	Do you normally use a finishing or defining product on your hair?	Will the final look be improved by definition, serums or other finishing products?
Likes and dislikes, visual aids/pictures	Would you like something along these lines or do you prefer a simpler style?	You must get the client to confirm the desired effect before you start

Choose the right equipment

EKU *statement*

GB5.28 and 29) Why and how to use the different types of styling brushes and combs and attachments when blow-drying and blow-waving

Men's hair styles tend to rely upon simpler effects. Admittedly, some men do dry their hair in a more formal blow-dried way but the vast majority tends to create their desired effects from finger-drying or scrunch-drying, with the backup of products to achieve the effects they want.

After making the correct choices on the effects that can be achieved by the products that you can use, you should be thinking about the sorts of equipment that you could use.

Styling tools and applications

	Uses	Description	Technique	Cleaning and maintenance
Denman Classic Styling brush	General brushing, detangling hair before: shampooing, styling and blow-drying straight hair of any length	A parallel, flat brush with removable cushioned bristles. Available in small (5), medium (7), and large (9) rows of plastic bristles	Blow-drying is achieved by placing the leading edge of the bristles against the mesh of hair then turning the brush to engage the hair across all of the width. The brush is used from roots to points with the dryer blowing across the cushioned surface.	Denman brushes can be dismantled by removing the rubber cushioned head from the brush handle and the bristle rows can be removed and washed in hot soapy water, then dried and replaced. Rows of bristles can be replaced if damaged or overheated.
Vented brush	General brushing, blow-drying straight short and mid-length hair	A parallel, flat brush with a double row of rigid plastic bristles (short and long) affixed to a brush head that is not solid. Allowing air to pass between the bristles	Blow-drying is achieved by placing the leading edge of the bristles against the mesh of hair then turning the brush to engage the hair across all of the width. The brush is used from roots to points with the dryer blowing across the surface.	Vented brushes can be cleaned by raking out any loose or tangled hair from the bristles, then washing in hot soapy water. The brush is then dried before use.
Paddle (flat) brush	General brushing, detangling hair and pre-dressing hair	A flat brush with a wide head usually with a cushioned head with wider teeth than a Denman. Sometimes the bristles are natural in composition, but generally plastic	Paddle brushes are generally too wide to use for blow-drying although sections can be dried by placing sections of hair upon the brush and drying by drawing down from the roots to the points of the hair.	Paddle brushes can be cleaned by raking out any loose or tangled hair from the bristles, then washing in hot soapy water. The brush is then dried before use.
Radial brushes	Blow-drying with volume, lift, wave and curl on shorter or longer length hair	Radial brushes are completely round in section and come in a wide variety of sizes. The bristles are usually made of plastic although pure bristle brushes are still	Blow-drying volume and movement is achieved by placing meshes of damp hair around the brush and drying the hair in position from both	Radial brushes can be cleaned by raking out any loose or tangled hair from the bristles, then washing in hot soapy water.

	Uses	Description	Technique	Cleaning and maintenance
		available. The inner body of radial brushes are often made of metal allowing the brush to heat up, improving the drying speeds of the underneath hair within a section	sides. When dry, the curl or movement can be affixed or set into position by applying a cool shot to increase the durability of the set.	The brush is then dried before use.
Diffuser (although not a brush it is a piece of equipment used to style the hair)	Scrunch-drying and finger-drying hair to optimise the natural or permed movement within the hair	A diffuser is an attachment for a blow-dryer that suppresses the blast of hot air and turning it into a multidirectional diffused heat	The hair is styled with the fingers by either pressing into the cupped diffuser to dry or by working through the hair with the fingers until the hair is dried with the required amount of texture or definition.	Diffusers are cleaned by spraying with an antibacterial spray then wiped with paper towels.

IMAGE COURTESY OF BABYLISS PRO

Activity

Product knowledge

For each of the products listed below, indicate for which styles and what hair lengths they are most appropriate.

Product:	Suitable styles and lengths
Soft wax	
Gel	
Moulding clay	
Pomade	
Mousse	
Hard wax	

IMAGE COURTESY OF BABYLISS PRO

Blow-drying

Believe it or not, the blow-dry using a hand-held dryer was historically a technique that was created for men's hairstyling.

In a time where ladies' hairdressing salons were made up of cubicles or partitioned areas, the client would be consulted and attended to in virtual privacy by their stylist. Conversely, the men in barber shops would be seated in open, communal styling areas where communications between barber and client and client to other clients was commonplace.

In front of the seated male would be a front wash basin with a shelf and styling mirror above. On one side of the shelf a leather strop would hang down for sharpening razors and on the other side there would be a heavy, retro-looking, chromed metal and Bakelite hand dryer.

Over the past 50 years some things have changed dramatically, but others have not. The history of the hand dryer is one, as in so many areas of life, in which an initial idea was taken from one particular environment, and then re-worked and re-invented to be supplanted in another.

Things you need to know about the basic science of drying and finishing hair:

1 The effects of humidity on hair (GB5.19 and GH11.19; see Unit GH11 page 226)

2 The physical effects of heated styling equipment on the hair structure (GB5.20 see Unit GH10, GH10.20)

3 How the incorrect application of heat can affect the hair and scalp (GB5.21 GH10.21 and GH11.21; see Unit GH10 pages 181, 194–195)

4 Why hair should be allowed to cool prior to finishing (GB5.22 and GH10.22; see Unit GH10 page 188)

5 Why hair should be kept damp before drying (GB5.23; see Unit GH10.23 page 187)

6 How heat protectors act to protect the hair (GB5.24, GH10.24 and GH11.24; see Unit GH10 page 192)

The techniques of blow-drying and the results achieved from blow-drying are covered in-depth in Unit GH10 pages 187–190.

Finger-drying

Finger-drying is a fast and more natural way of drying hair into style. After removing excess moisture from the hair some mousse can be applied to provide some body and texture to work with.

 Diversion There are a number of things that you need to know in relation to the basic science surrounding the drying and styling of hair. These aspects shown below are cross-referenced to other areas within this book to avoid any unnecessary duplication.

EKU *statement*

GB5.32) How the size of the section and the angle at which the hair is held during drying influences the volume and direction of the hair movement

Step 1 After applying a little mousse to the hair, section the back so you can start to finger dry the nape area first.

Step 2 With the nape area dry you can continue up the back.

Step 3 With the back dried you can work on the lower areas of the side.

Step 4 Readjust the balance and texture of the final shape.

Step 5 A little spray wax is applied to define the final effect.

The main idea of finger-drying is to use a blow-dryer with the fingers in a directional drying process, on generally shorter hair. Using the fingers provides three main benefits for this technique:

1 It allows a style to be moulded on hair that would normally be too short to dry with brushes.

2 It enables the stylist/barber to keep a check on the dryer heat as the fingers act as a temperature gauge for the client's head.

3 It provides stylist/barbers with a non-fussy styling option for the male client.

The checklist below covers the main considerations for finger-drying men's hair.

Finger-drying men's hair:

- Always work with damp and not saturated hair – rough–dry if necessary
- Work on small areas/sections of hair
- Try to dry the hair in the direction of roots to points – it will dry more quickly and keep the cuticle layer smoother, making it look healthier and shinier
- Avoid burning the scalp – angle your dryer away from the head
- Move the position of your client's head in order to get around and cover all areas of the head
- Use both hands to dry the hair, so swap the dryer around; this allows you to work on both sides of the head effectively

EKU *statement*

GB5.33) Methods of handling and controlling hair sections during the drying process

EKU *statement*

GB5.31) Why the direction of air flow when drying is important to achieve the desired look

EKU *statement*

GB5.29) Current techniques of drying and finishing hair

Activity
Blow-drying v finger-drying
Complete this activity by answering this question within your portfolio.

In what circumstances is blow-drying more suitable than finger-drying as a way of finishing a client's hair?

GB5.3   Provide aftercare advice

The outline framework of aftercare advice for clients in relation to blow-drying or finger-drying hair, such as what products they should use, the effects of long-term use of heated styling equipment and style maintenance, is covered elsewhere in this book.

To find out more on the advice that you should give your clients, see Unit GH11 Set and dress hair – section GH11.3 pages 247–248.

EKU *statement*

GB5.34) Products for home use that will benefit the client and those to avoid and why

GB5.35) How the continual use of heated equipment can affect the hair

GB5.36) How to recreate and maintain the agreed style

GB5.37) How lifestyle can influence their choice of style (e.g. active sports, career and job requirements)

GB5.38) How to give effective advice and recommendations to clients

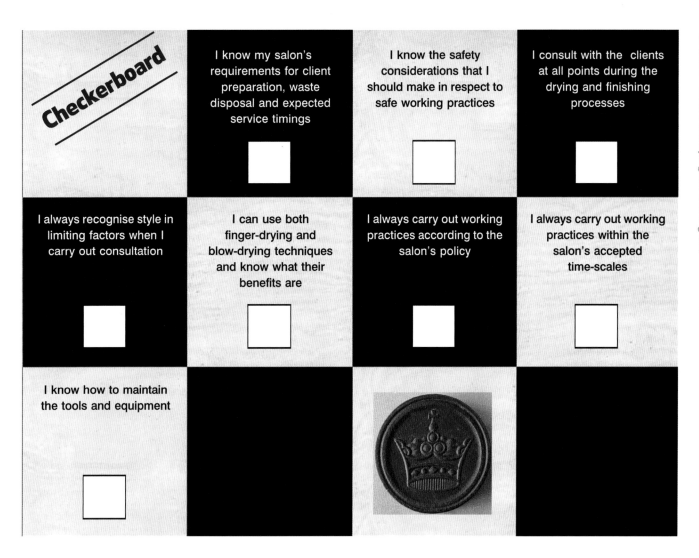

Checkerboard

I know my salon's requirements for client preparation, waste disposal and expected service timings ☐

I know the safety considerations that I should make in respect to safe working practices ☐

I consult with the clients at all points during the drying and finishing processes ☐

I always recognise style in limiting factors when I carry out consultation ☐

I can use both finger-drying and blow-drying techniques and know what their benefits are ☐

I always carry out working practices according to the salon's policy ☐

I always carry out working practices within the salon's accepted time-scales ☐

I know how to maintain the tools and equipment ☐

Assessment of knowledge and understanding

Project

For this project you will need to select two of your clients.

A Client 1 should have short hair.

B Client 2 should have longer hair.

For each of these clients:

1 Describe what your client's hair was like before you started.

2 Describe what techniques and tools were used to complete the look.

3 Explain what products you used and how they helped to achieve the look.

4 Take a photograph (perhaps with your mobile) of the finished effect.

Revision questions

A selection of different types of questions to check your men's styling knowledge.

Q1 The common name for drying hair with just the hands is called _____ drying.   Fill in the blank

Q2 Humidity in the atmosphere will cause a finished style to drop.   True or false

Q3   Which of the following are finishing products?   Multi selection

Mousse   ☐ 1
Wax   ☐ 2
Gel   ☐ 3
Setting lotion   ☐ 4
Hairspray   ☐ 5
Conditioner   ☐ 6

Q4   The keratin bonds of stretched hair are said to be in the beta state.   True or false

Q5   Which of the following is the odd one out?   Multi choice

Vented brush   ○ a
Denman brush   ○ b
Round brush   ○ c
Paddle brush   ○ d

Q6   Finger-drying is similar to scrunch-drying.   True or false

Q7   Which of the following are better sterilised in a UV cabinet rather than   Multi selection
in Barbicide™?

Cutting comb   ☐ 1
Conditioning comb   ☐ 2
A Denman brush   ☐ 3
A vented brush   ☐ 4
Plastic sectioning clips   ☐ 5
Metal sectioning clips   ☐ 6

Q8   A _____ is an attachment for a blow-dryer which reduces the hot hair blast.   Fill in the blank

Q9   Which item of equipment is best for smoothing and flattening frizzy, unruly hair?   Multi choice

Curling tongs   ○ a
Ceramic straighteners   ○ b
Crimping irons   ○ c
Blow-dryer   ○ d

Q10   Hair should be rough-dried before styling.   True or false

Preparing for assessment checklist

Remember to:

✔	prepare clients correctly for the services you are going to carry out
✔	put on the protective wear available for styling and dressing hair
✔	listen to the client's requirements and discuss suitable courses of action
✔	adhere to the safety factors when working on clients' hair
✔	keep the work areas clean, hygienic and free from hazards
✔	promote the range of services, products and treatments within the salon
✔	clean and sterilise the styling tools and equipment before they are used
✔	work carefully and methodically through the processes of blow-drying or finger-drying hair
✔	take care when using heated styling equipment
✔	communicate what you are doing to the client as well as your fellow staff members

FELLOWSHIP FOR BRITISH HAIRDRESSING F.A.M.E. TEAM 2008

Chapter**ten**
Setting and dressing hair

GH11

GH11.1

GH11.2

GH11.3

GH11.4

Set and dress hair: quick overview

Unit title

GH11 Set and dress the hair

This is a **mandatory** unit for students taking Hairdressing Level 2. It is made up of four main outcomes

Main outcomes

GH11.1 Maintain effective and safe methods of working when setting and dressing hair

GH11.2 Set hair

GH11.3 Dress Hair

GH11.4 Provide aftercare advice

GH13

GH13.1

GH13.2

GH13.3

Plaiting and twisting hair: quick overview

Unit title

GH13 Plait and twist hair

This is an **optional** unit for students taking Hairdressing Level 2. It is made up of three main outcomes

Main outcomes

GH13.1 Maintain effective and safe methods of working when plaiting and twisting

GH13.2 Plaiting and twisting hair

GH13.3 Provide aftercare advice

What do I need to do for GH11.1?

- Take adequate precautions in preparing yourself and the client before any setting or dressing procedure

- Work tidily, safely and effectively at all times

- Maintain standards of personal health and hygiene

Keywords

Temporary bonds

The hydrogen bonds within the hair that are modified and fix the style into shape

Hygroscopic

Readily absorbing moisture from the atmosphere

Alpha keratin

Hair in its natural state

Beta keratin

Hair in its moulded shape: i.e. curly hair that has been dried straight. When the client enters a damp environment the hair reverts back to the alpha state

Traction alopecia

A condition that is caused by the excessive pulling of hair at the root. It is often associated with longer hair worn in plaits, twists and hair-ups

Information covered in this chapter

- The types of products used when styling hair and how they work
- The types of equipment used when styling hair and how they are used
- How to set and dress hair into a style
- How to plait and twist hair into style
- A variety of styling techniques that you will use for both units

- Use a range of tools and equipment suitable for setting and dressing
- Work to a commercially acceptable time

What do I need to do for GH11.2?

- Confirm and agree the techniques and style requirements with the client
- Work in a controlled and methodical way when setting
- Apply suitable products to help form or control the desired effect

What do I need to do for GH11.3?

- Know how and when to use backcombing and backbrushing
- Brush out the roller marks from the hair

What do I need to do for GH11.4?

- Give the client recommendations and advice for maintaining their own hair

What aspects do I need to cover for GH11.1, GH11.2, GH11.3 and GH11.4?

- A range of setting products that will be used during styling or dressing the hair
- A variety of tools and equipment used during styling or dressing the hair
- The techniques of rollering, spiral curling and pin curling in, on and off base positions
- Hair that is both above and below shoulder length

What do I need to know for GH11.1, GH11.2, GH11.3 and GH11.4?

- Your salon's requirements in relation to salon policies and current legislation
- How to work safely and hygienically when setting or dressing hair
- The basic science affecting setting and dressing procedures
- How to use a range of setting and dressing tools and equipment and when they are applicable in achieving the desired effects
- How to use a range of setting and dressing styling products and when they are applicable in achieving the desired effects
- How to use a range of setting and dressing techniques and when they are applicable in achieving the desired effects
- How to recommend or provide advice to the client on hair maintenance at home

What do I need to do for GH13.1?

- Take adequate precautions in preparing yourself and the client before any setting or dressing procedure
- Work tidily, safely and effectively at all times
- Maintain standards of personal health and hygiene
- Use a range of tools and equipment suitable for setting and dressing
- Work to a commercially acceptable time

What do I need to do for GH13.2?

- Confirm and agree the techniques and style requirements with the client
- Maintain even tension when plaiting or twisting sections of hair
- Ensure that direction of the plaits or twists move in the desired direction
- Secure the ends of the plait or twist design securely
- Apply suitable products to help form or control the desired effect

What do I need to do for GH13.3?

- Give the client recommendations and advice for maintaining their own hair

What aspects do I need to cover for GH13.1, GH13.2 and GH13.3?

- A variety of tools and equipment used during styling or dressing the hair
- The techniques of fishtail plaits, French plaits, cornrows, two-stem twists and flat twists
- Removal of plaits and twists

What do I need to know for GH13.1, GH13.2 and GH13.3?

- Your salon's requirements in relation to salon policies and current legislation
- How to work safely and hygienically when plaiting or twisting hair
- The effects on the hair from plaiting and twisting
- How to use a range of styling products and when they are applicable in achieving the desired effects
- How to use a range of plaiting and twisting techniques and when they are applicable in achieving the desired effects
- How to recommend or provide advice to the client on hair maintenance at home

Information covered in this chapter (cont.)

- The basic science of the physical changes that take place during setting as well as the effect that heat and humidity have on the hair
- How to remove plaits and twists from hair
- The advice you should give to clients in order to maintain their own hair

More information

- Personal hygiene
  EKU GH11.14
- Contact Dermatitis
  EKU GH11.5

General salon hygiene, see Unit G20 Health and Safety
EKU GH11.15 EKU GH11.16 EKU GH11.18

See also the appendices for following relevant legislation:

- COSHH EKU GH11.3
- Electricity at Work Regulations EKU GH11.4

More information

- Personal hygiene
  EKU GH11.14
- Contact dermatitis
  EKU GH13.3

General salon hygiene see Unit G20 Health and Safety
EKU GH11.15 EKU GH11.16 EKU GH11.18

See also the appendices for following relevant legislation:

- COSHH EKU GH13.2
- Electricity at Work Regulations EKU GH11.4

Diversion Some of the EKUs you need for this unit may be found in other units. To save you from unnecessary duplication we have cross-referenced each unit to other areas. You may have already studied that unit in which case a revision of the information will help you apply that knowledge to this unit. If you have not studied that information before then it will help you when you do study that unit.

Where you see this sign it will guide you to the unit in which you will find the information you need.

Introduction

Setting and dressing hair have been frowned upon in recent years. Students didn't want to do them because they seemed old fashioned and boring; the clients that were available for training in this skill didn't really stretch the imagination or the technical abilities of the learner either. But don't dismiss this important and vital skill set out of hand; the techniques used within setting and dressing underpin virtually all the hairstyling disciplines.

This chapter combines *two* units to show you the techniques of folding, shaping, smoothing, fixing, curling, plaiting and twisting. Learn now, at the beginning, and a lot of the difficulties that your colleagues in training will have later in their career will be a 'walk in the park' for you.

GH11.1 Maintain effective and safe methods of working when setting and dressing hair

GH13.1 Maintain effective and safe methods of working when plaiting and twisting

Remember

Always look after your brushes, combs and other tools. Make sure they are washed, dried and hygienically clean before you start your work.

Although Unit G20 covers much of the general aspects that you need to know about health, safety and hygiene within the salon environment, each technical procedure you carry out has particular things that are relevant to health and safety. Styling and dressing hair are always carried out at the styling units and therefore the main health and safety concerns should relate to the client's comfort, positioning and protection as well as your posture, accessibility and care.

Information for the following topics can be found at the page references next to the essential knowledge and understanding statements below:

Preparing, protecting and positioning the client

EKU statement

EKU GH11.1 and GH13.1) Your salon's requirements for client preparation (see EKU GH10.1 page 175)

EKU GH11.6 and GH13.4) The range of protective clothing that should be available for clients (see EKU GH10.6 page 176)

EKU GH11.7 and GH13.5) Why it is important to use personal protective equipment (see EKU GH10.7 page 175)

EKU GH11.8 and GH13.6) The type of personal protective equipment available (see EKU GH10.8 page 175)

EKU GH11.9 and GH13.7) How the position of your client and yourself can affect the desired outcome and reduce fatigue and the risk of injury (see EKU GH10.9 page 175)

Preparing and positioning the equipment ready for use

EKU statement

EKU GH11.11 and GH13.8) The importance of positioning equipment for ease of use (see EKU GH10.11 page 177)

EKU GH11.12 and GH13.9) Why it is important to keep your work area clean and tidy (see EKU GH10.12 page 177)

Working safely and preventing infections

This area of work is covered in Unit GH10 Style and finish hair (Chapter 8) and in Unit G20 (Chapter 1). See also:

Reducing risks – good salon safety and salon equipment (pages 10-15)

EKU statement

EKU GH11.10) The safety considerations which must be taken into account when setting and dressing hair

EKU GH11.13 and GH13.10) Methods of working safely and hygienically and which minimise the risk of cross-infection and cross-infestation (see GH10.13 page 177)

EKU GH11.16 and GH13.12) Methods of cleaning, disinfecting and/or sterilisation used in salons

Personal health and hygiene (page 17)

EKU statement

EKU GH11.14 and GH13.11) The importance of personal hygiene (see GH10.14 page 17)

Reducing risks – contact dermatitis (page 14)

EKU statement

EKU GH11.5 and GH13.3) What is contact dermatitis and how to avoid developing it whilst carrying out styling and finishing (OR plaiting and twisting) services

Reducing risks – handling chemicals (page 14)

EKU statement

EKU GH11.3 and GH13.2) Your own responsibilities under the current Control of Substances Hazardous to Health Regulations in relation to the use of styling and finishing products

Reducing risks – working with electricity (page 15)

EKU statement

EKU GH11.4) Your responsibilities under the current Electricity at Work Regulations

Remember

Always dry the client's hair well to remove the excess water before combing, cutting, setting or curling.

Remember

Why work with semi-dry hair?
During cutting and styling services it enables the natural tendencies of the hair to be seen. This is extremely important as the hair's wave, movement and hair growth patterns are all being considered as the style is developed.

ISTOCKPHOTO.COM/ TOM TOMCZYK

EKU statement

GH11.16) Methods of cleaning, disinfecting and or sterilisation used in salons

GH11.25) The range of tools and equipment available for setting and dressing

EKU statement

GH11.24) How heat protectors act to protect the hair (see GH10.24 page 192)

GH11.26) The range of products available for setting and dressing

GH11.28a) Why and how to use the different types of tools and equipment for setting and dressing

Preparing the tools and equipment for setting and dressing hair

Make sure that you have prepared the area. Get everything that you need together beforehand, this includes the equipment that you need, as well as the products. You should have your trolley prepared with all the materials you will need. Rollers for setting should have been previously prepared by thorough washing and combs, brushes, sectioning clips etc. should be all cleaned, sterilised and made ready for use. (For more information on cleaning, sterilisation and general hygiene see Unit G20.)

Remember

Make sure that you always:

✔ Wash your hands before attending to any clients

✔ Wear the minimum of jewellery that can dangle or tangle in the client's hair

✔ Wear comfortable (flatter) footwear when on the salon floor

✔ Be aware of bad breath – use breath fresheners if you do have a problem

✔ Take a shower daily before going to work

✔ Make sure your workwear is clean and fresh everyday

✔ Think how you want to be seen by others – is the image you portray one you are proud of?

✔ Minimise the risk of cross-infection to your colleagues and clients

Tools and equipment

Equipment	Used for	Effects achieved	Precautions	Cleaning
Setting rollers IMAGE COURTESY OF BABYLISS PRO	Wet or dry setting hair	Provides a long-lasting effect on wet/damp hair or softer result on dry hair	Poor quality rollers have moulding flaws, these can catch on the client's hair during removal. Damaged rollers should be thrown away	Washed with hot soapy water and scrubbed clean, then dried and put back in trolleys/trays in sized order ready for future use
Velcro rollers DENMAN	Dry setting only	Provides a soft and not as durable curl effect as wet setting rollers	Self-clinging rollers tend to lock onto finer hair types. Be careful when removing as they will not only pull the hair but damage it too.	Washed with hot soapy water and scrubbed clean, then dried and put back in trolleys/trays in sized order ready for future use

Equipment	Used for	Effects achieved	Precautions	Cleaning
Heated rollers IMAGE COURTESY OF BABYLISS PRO	Dry setting only	Provides a soft but longer-lasting, more durable effect than Velcro rollers	These are very hot when they are first put into the client's hair. Use cotton neck-wool as an insulating base between the bottom of the curler and the client's scalp	Washed with hot soapy water and scrubbed clean, then dried and put back on to their appropriate heating stems ready for future use
Heated tongs KINDLY SUPPLIED BY WAHL (UK) LTD	Dry curling only. Used for adding more movement during comb-out	Provides a long-lasting effect on dry hair	Electrical item: Remember to check the condition of the lead before use. Very hot when in use: be careful not to burn the client or yourself	Spray cleaner and dried thoroughly after. Remove hairstyling product build-up from the curling surfaces
Tail or pin comb DENMAN	Sectioning hair into workable sizes dependent on the setting, plaiting or twisting technique used	They will provide tension when combing through sections and help to manage the hair	The point ends of tail combs can be metal or plastic, but both types are sharp. Be careful in sectioning or combing that you don't scratch the client's scalp	Washed in hot soapy water then kept in Barbicide™ until needed. When needed for setting they should be rinsed and dried first
Straight combs DENMAN	Dressing out hair; enabling the hair to be backcombed and smoothed	They will provide tension when combing through sections and help to manage the hair	Be careful during combing or backcombing that you don't scratch the client's scalp	Washed in hot soapy water then kept in Barbicide™ until needed. When needed for setting they should be rinsed and dried first
Flat brushes DENMAN	Flat, paddle-type brushes are used initially on wet hair to work setting agents through and to detangle	Used during dressing to remove roller/setting marks, smooth or shape the hair or introduce backbrushing into the hair	Be careful not to brush to vigorously as it can make hair static or be painful to the client	Washed in hot soapy water and scrubbed clean to remove hair and particles. They should be dried thoroughly and put away for future use
Grips and hair pins	Fixing hair into position as part of the finished hairstyle	Hair ups, partial hair up/back effects,	Grips and pins are metal with sharp points; care should be used when putting them in and when removing them to avoid tugging snatching the hair	Washed and dried and put into trolleys or trays
Pin clips	Wet or dry setting hair	Provides a narrow curl stem that can be positioned either flat against the skin or standing away	Pin clips tend to have fairly strong durable springs. These can pull the hair if not careful	Washed with hot soapy water and scrubbed clean, then dried and put back in trolleys/trays

Other equipment and the effects on different length of hair

Equipment	Short hair	Medium-length layered	Medium to long, one-length	Long layers
Lift pick comb	Dressing/back-combing	Dressing/back-combing	Dressing/back-combing	Dressing/back-combing
'Jumbo' wide-tooth combs	Conditioning, detangling and dressing	Conditioning, detangling and dressing	Conditioning, detangling and dressing	Conditioning, detangling and dressing
Denman Classic Styling brush	General brushing, pre-dressing and blow-drying straight	General brushing Pre-dressing and blow-drying straight	General brushing Blow-drying straight	General brushing Blow-drying straight
Vented brush	Disentangling and blow-drying straight	Disentangling and blow-drying straight	Disentangling, pre-dressing and blow-drying straight	Disentangling, pre-dressing and blow-drying straight
Paddle brush	General brushing, disentangling and pre-dressing	General brushing, disentangling and pre-dressing	General brushing, disentangling	General brushing, disentangling and pre-dressing
Radial brushes	Blow-drying with firm wave, volume or curl	Blow-drying with firm wave, volume or curl	Blow-drying with firm wave	Blow-drying with firm wave, volume or curl
Diffuser	Scrunch-drying with movement or texture	Scrunch-drying with movement or texture		Scrunch-drying with movement or texture

Brushes

Brushes come in a wide variety and they are vitally important. Each has different applications and uses. Good-quality, general-purpose brushes should have flexible and comfortable bristles. The handles should be designed to fit comfortably in the hand enabling you to get a good grip. The typical salon brushes like this are either vented, to allow good airflow when drying hair, or similar to Denman brushes, which have cushioned removable teeth.

(More information about brushes is covered in GH10 Style and finish hair, pages 182–183.)

Remember

Root direction will determine hair flow within a style.

Remember

Scrunch-drying is a way of drying hair more naturally with a diffuser. It uses the natural body or movement within the hair to create tousled and casual effects.

Remember

Portable appliance testing (PAT)

All items of electrical equipment have to be tested and certified fit for use by a competent person. The items are tested, labelled and recorded and a compiled list is made available for inspection.

Activity

Collect information on the range of different styling products available in the salon. Now set out a table to describe:

1 each product by name

2 how it is used

3 what it does

4 which hair type it is for.

Styling products

There is an ever-growing range of styling and finishing products available to the profession. As this has been the major growth area, careful market research and product

Activity
Tools and equipment

Write down what each of the items listed below is used for and how it is maintained.

Tool	What is it used for?	How is it maintained?
Pin clips		
Tail comb		
Velcro roller		
Paddle brush		
Hair grips		
Lift pick comb		

EKU *statement*

GH11.27) The manufacturers' instructions on the use of the specific setting and dressing products in your salon

DENMAN

development have ensured that each one is specifically designed to do a particular job. As a result the huge range is confusing and is driven by successful advertising and brand awareness. If you look closely at each manufacturer's range you will find that the brand leaders all have similar and competing products. The more these numbers of similar products increase, the more confused the purchaser becomes. At this stage the only factor that can help someone to make a choice between one product and another is a reputable and recognisable name.

Styling products contain plasticisers as a fixative to hold and support the hair in its shape. Apart from hold, they often have other agents and additives within the products that can retain or repel moisture, provide protective sunscreens, add shine and lustre or add definition and shape.

EKU *statement*

GH11.28) Why and how to use the different types of products for setting and dressing and when to apply them

- *Setting lotions* – such as mousses protect the hair from excessive heat. They increase the time that the hair is held in shape and the volume and/or movement created, all whilst being exposed to the blast from the dryer's nozzle. They can be in a variety of different strengths for differing hair types and holds.

- *Finishing products* – are products that enhance the hair by adding shine or gloss and improve handling and control by removing static, fluffiness or frizziness from the hair. Certain finishing products like waxes will define the movement in hair, giving texture or spikiness that could not otherwise be achieved.

- *Heat protection* – many products provide protection from heat styling. Regular use of straightening irons could damage the hair so there are a number of products that can be applied to eliminate any long-term effects. Other products provide protection from harsh UVA in sunlight in a variety of 'leave-in' treatments that can be used at any time. They are put on before exposure to harsh sunlight and can be removed after by washing. This is particularly useful for clients who have coloured hair, as the bleaching effects of sunlight will quickly remove colour. Other products have the ability to resist or remove the effects of minerals on the hair such as chlorine from swimming pools. This is particularly useful as blonde hair that is regularly subjected to chlorine tends to look green!

(More information on styling products can be found in GH10 Style and finish hair, pages 184–186.)

Activity
Equipment and their uses

When you would use the different styling equipment on different lengths of hair?

	Short hair	Medium-length hair	Long hair
Denman brush			
Vented brush			
Tail comb			
Setting rollers			
Velcro rollers			
Heated rollers			

GH11.2 Set hair

Consultation

Consultation is an essential part of every hairdressing process; you will always need to find out information before you start.

(For more, in-depth and specific information about consultation see Unit G7 Advise and consult with clients, pages 98–103.)

If you have already reviewed this information or covered it previously within your training, here is a quick checklist to cover the applicable aspects for setting and dressing hair.

Consultation checklist before setting hair

✔	What is the texture, type, tendency and condition of the hair like?
✔	How much hair is there, how long is the hair?
✔	Are there any limiting factors or adverse hair or scalp conditions?
✔	What type of effect does the client want?
✔	Does the hair type/texture/tendency/amount and length support the client's ideas?
✔	What tools and equipment do you need?
✔	What lifestyle limitations are there?
✔	How much time will it take?
✔	How much will it cost?
✔	Do you need to use any products to achieve the effect?
✔	Will the client benefit from using these products too?
✔	Agree and confirm desired effects with the client prior to starting the service

EKU *statement*

GH11.2) Your salon's expected service times for setting services

GH11.21) How the incorrect application of heat can affect the hair and scalp (see GH10.21 page 187)

GH11.22) Why hair should be allowed to cool prior to dressing (see GH10.22 page 188)

Preparing and positioning the equipment ready for use

EKU statement

EKU GH11.11 and GH13.8) The importance of positioning equipment for ease of use (see EKU GH10.11 page 177)

EKU GH11.12 and GH13.9) Why it is important to keep your work area clean and tidy (see EKU GH10.12 page 177)

Working safely and preventing infections

This area of work is covered in Unit GH10 Style and finish hair (Chapter 8) and in Unit G20 (Chapter 1). See also:

Reducing risks – good salon safety and salon equipment (pages 10-15)

EKU statement

EKU GH11.10) The safety considerations which must be taken into account when setting and dressing hair

EKU GH11.13 and GH13.10) Methods of working safely and hygienically and which minimise the risk of cross-infection and cross-infestation (see GH10.13 page 177)

EKU GH11.16 and GH13.12) Methods of cleaning, disinfecting and/or sterilisation used in salons

Personal health and hygiene (page 17)

EKU statement

EKU GH11.14 and GH13.11) The importance of personal hygiene (see GH10.14 page 17)

Reducing risks – contact dermatitis (page 14)

EKU statement

EKU GH11.5 and GH13.3) What is contact dermatitis and how to avoid developing it whilst carrying out styling and finishing (OR plaiting and twisting) services

Reducing risks – handling chemicals (page 14)

EKU statement

EKU GH11.3 and GH13.2) Your own responsibilities under the current Control of Substances Hazardous to Health Regulations in relation to the use of styling and finishing products

Reducing risks – working with electricity (page 15)

EKU statement

EKU GH11.4) Your responsibilities under the current Electricity at Work Regulations

Remember

Always dry the client's hair well to remove the excess water before combing, cutting, setting or curling.

Remember

Why work with semi-dry hair?

During cutting and styling services it enables the natural tendencies of the hair to be seen. This is extremely important as the hair's wave, movement and hair growth patterns are all being considered as the style is developed.

ISTOCKPHOTO.COM/
TOM TOMCZYK

EKU statement

GH11.16) Methods of cleaning, disinfecting and or sterilisation used in salons

GH11.25) The range of tools and equipment available for setting and dressing

EKU statement

GH11.24) How heat protectors act to protect the hair (see GH10.24 page 192)

GH11.26) The range of products available for setting and dressing

GH11.28a) Why and how to use the different types of tools and equipment for setting and dressing

Preparing the tools and equipment for setting and dressing hair

Make sure that you have prepared the area. Get everything that you need together beforehand, this includes the equipment that you need, as well as the products. You should have your trolley prepared with all the materials you will need. Rollers for setting should have been previously prepared by thorough washing and combs, brushes, sectioning clips etc. should be all cleaned, sterilised and made ready for use. (For more information on cleaning, sterilisation and general hygiene see Unit G20.)

Remember

Make sure that you always:

✔ Wash your hands before attending to any clients

✔ Wear the minimum of jewellery that can dangle or tangle in the client's hair

✔ Wear comfortable (flatter) footwear when on the salon floor

✔ Be aware of bad breath – use breath fresheners if you do have a problem

✔ Take a shower daily before going to work

✔ Make sure your workwear is clean and fresh everyday

✔ Think how you want to be seen by others – is the image you portray one you are proud of?

✔ Minimise the risk of cross-infection to your colleagues and clients

Tools and equipment

Equipment	Used for	Effects achieved	Precautions	Cleaning
Setting rollers IMAGE COURTESY OF BABYLISS PRO	Wet or dry setting hair	Provides a long-lasting effect on wet/damp hair or softer result on dry hair	Poor quality rollers have moulding flaws, these can catch on the client's hair during removal. Damaged rollers should be thrown away	Washed with hot soapy water and scrubbed clean, then dried and put back in trolleys/trays in sized order ready for future use
Velcro rollers DENMAN	Dry setting only	Provides a soft and not as durable curl effect as wet setting rollers	Self-clinging rollers tend to lock onto finer hair types. Be careful when removing as they will not only pull the hair but damage it too.	Washed with hot soapy water and scrubbed clean, then dried and put back in trolleys/trays in sized order ready for future use

Equipment	Used for	Effects achieved	Precautions	Cleaning
Heated rollers	Dry setting only	Provides a soft but longer-lasting, more durable effect than Velcro rollers	These are very hot when they are first put into the client's hair. Use cotton neck-wool as an insulating base between the bottom of the curler and the client's scalp	Washed with hot soapy water and scrubbed clean, then dried and put back on to their appropriate heating stems ready for future use
Heated tongs	Dry curling only. Used for adding more movement during comb-out	Provides a long-lasting effect on dry hair	Electrical item: Remember to check the condition of the lead before use. Very hot when in use: be careful not to burn the client or yourself	Spray cleaner and dried thoroughly after. Remove hairstyling product build-up from the curling surfaces
Tail or pin comb	Sectioning hair into workable sizes dependent on the setting, plaiting or twisting technique used	They will provide tension when combing through sections and help to manage the hair	The point ends of tail combs can be metal or plastic, but both types are sharp. Be careful in sectioning or combing that you don't scratch the client's scalp	Washed in hot soapy water then kept in Barbicide™ until needed. When needed for setting they should be rinsed and dried first
Straight combs	Dressing out hair; enabling the hair to be backcombed and smoothed	They will provide tension when combing through sections and help to manage the hair	Be careful during combing or backcombing that you don't scratch the client's scalp	Washed in hot soapy water then kept in Barbicide™ until needed. When needed for setting they should be rinsed and dried first
Flat brushes	Flat, paddle-type brushes are used initially on wet hair to work setting agents through and to detangle	Used during dressing to remove roller/setting marks, smooth or shape the hair or introduce backbrushing into the hair	Be careful not to brush to vigorously as it can make hair static or be painful to the client	Washed in hot soapy water and scrubbed clean to remove hair and particles. They should be dried thoroughly and put away for future use
Grips and hair pins	Fixing hair into position as part of the finished hairstyle	Hair ups, partial hair up/back effects,	Grips and pins are metal with sharp points; care should be used when putting them in and when removing them to avoid tugging snatching the hair	Washed and dried and put into trolleys or trays
Pin clips	Wet or dry setting hair	Provides a narrow curl stem that can be positioned either flat against the skin or standing away	Pin clips tend to have fairly strong durable springs. These can pull the hair if not careful	Washed with hot soapy water and scrubbed clean, then dried and put back in trolleys/trays

Other equipment and the effects on different length of hair

Equipment	Short hair	Medium-length layered	Medium to long, one-length	Long layers
Lift pick comb	Dressing/back-combing	Dressing/back-combing	Dressing/back-combing	Dressing/back-combing
'Jumbo' wide-tooth combs	Conditioning, detangling and dressing	Conditioning, detangling and dressing	Conditioning, detangling and dressing	Conditioning, detangling and dressing
Denman Classic Styling brush	General brushing, pre-dressing and blow-drying straight	General brushing Pre-dressing and blow-drying straight	General brushing Blow-drying straight	General brushing Blow-drying straight
Vented brush	Disentangling and blow-drying straight	Disentangling and blow-drying straight	Disentangling, pre-dressing and blow-drying straight	Disentangling, pre-dressing and blow-drying straight
Paddle brush	General brushing, disentangling and pre-dressing	General brushing, disentangling and pre-dressing	General brushing, disentangling	General brushing, disentangling and pre-dressing
Radial brushes	Blow-drying with firm wave, volume or curl	Blow-drying with firm wave, volume or curl	Blow-drying with firm wave	Blow-drying with firm wave, volume or curl
Diffuser	Scrunch-drying with movement or texture	Scrunch-drying with movement or texture		Scrunch-drying with movement or texture

Brushes

Brushes come in a wide variety and they are vitally important. Each has different applications and uses. Good-quality, general-purpose brushes should have flexible and comfortable bristles. The handles should be designed to fit comfortably in the hand enabling you to get a good grip. The typical salon brushes like this are either vented, to allow good airflow when drying hair, or similar to Denman brushes, which have cushioned removable teeth.

(More information about brushes is covered in GH10 Style and finish hair, pages 182–183.)

Remember

 Root direction will determine hair flow within a style.

Remember

Scrunch-drying is a way of drying hair more naturally with a diffuser. It uses the natural body or movement within the hair to create tousled and casual effects.

Remember

Portable appliance testing (PAT)
All items of electrical equipment have to be tested and certified fit for use by a competent person. The items are tested, labelled and recorded and a compiled list is made available for inspection.

Activity
Collect information on the range of different styling products available in the salon. Now set out a table to describe:

1 each product by name

2 how it is used

3 what it does

4 which hair type it is for.

Styling products

There is an ever-growing range of styling and finishing products available to the profession. As this has been the major growth area, careful market research and product

Activity
Tools and equipment

Write down what each of the items listed below is used for and how it is maintained.

Tool	What is it used for?	How is it maintained?
Pin clips		
Tail comb		
Velcro roller		
Paddle brush		
Hair grips		
Lift pick comb		

Remember

Always follow the manufacturer's instructions for using setting and dressing products within the salon.

EKU *statement*

GH11.27) The manufacturers' instructions on the use of the specific setting and dressing products in your salon

DENMAN

development have ensured that each one is specifically designed to do a particular job. As a result the huge range is confusing and is driven by successful advertising and brand awareness. If you look closely at each manufacturer's range you will find that the brand leaders all have similar and competing products. The more these numbers of similar products increase, the more confused the purchaser becomes. At this stage the only factor that can help someone to make a choice between one product and another is a reputable and recognisable name.

Styling products contain plasticisers as a fixative to hold and support the hair in its shape. Apart from hold, they often have other agents and additives within the products that can retain or repel moisture, provide protective sunscreens, add shine and lustre or add definition and shape.

- *Setting lotions* – such as mousses protect the hair from excessive heat. They increase the time that the hair is held in shape and the volume and/or movement created, all whilst being exposed to the blast from the dryer's nozzle. They can be in a variety of different strengths for differing hair types and holds.

- *Finishing products* – are products that enhance the hair by adding shine or gloss and improve handling and control by removing static, fluffiness or frizziness from the hair. Certain finishing products like waxes will define the movement in hair, giving texture or spikiness that could not otherwise be achieved.

- *Heat protection* – many products provide protection from heat styling. Regular use of straightening irons could damage the hair so there are a number of products that can be applied to eliminate any long-term effects. Other products provide protection from harsh UVA in sunlight in a variety of 'leave-in' treatments that can be used at any time. They are put on before exposure to harsh sunlight and can be removed after by washing. This is particularly useful for clients who have coloured hair, as the bleaching effects of sunlight will quickly remove colour. Other products have the ability to resist or remove the effects of minerals on the hair such as chlorine from swimming pools. This is particularly useful as blonde hair that is regularly subjected to chlorine tends to look green!

EKU *statement*

GH11.28) Why and how to use the different types of products for setting and dressing and when to apply them

Remember

Moisture is the enemy of any finished set; It weakens the hold and therefore how long the overall effect will last.

(More information on styling products can be found in GH10 Style and finish hair, pages 184–186.)

Activity
Equipment and their uses

When you would use the different styling equipment on different lengths of hair?

	Short hair	Medium-length hair	Long hair
Denman brush			
Vented brush			
Tail comb			
Setting rollers			
Velcro rollers			
Heated rollers			

GH11.2 Set hair

Consultation

Consultation is an essential part of every hairdressing process; you will always need to find out information before you start.

(For more, in-depth and specific information about consultation see Unit G7 Advise and consult with clients, pages 98–103.)

If you have already reviewed this information or covered it previously within your training, here is a quick checklist to cover the applicable aspects for setting and dressing hair.

EKU statement

GH11.2) Your salon's expected service times for setting services

GH11.21) How the incorrect application of heat can affect the hair and scalp (see GH10.21 page 187)

GH11.22) Why hair should be allowed to cool prior to dressing (see GH10.22 page 188)

Consultation checklist before setting hair

✔	What is the texture, type, tendency and condition of the hair like?
✔	How much hair is there, how long is the hair?
✔	Are there any limiting factors or adverse hair or scalp conditions?
✔	What type of effect does the client want?
✔	Does the hair type/texture/tendency/amount and length support the client's ideas?
✔	What tools and equipment do you need?
✔	What lifestyle limitations are there?
✔	How much time will it take?
✔	How much will it cost?
✔	Do you need to use any products to achieve the effect?
✔	Will the client benefit from using these products too?
✔	Agree and confirm desired effects with the client prior to starting the service

The principles of heat styling

Setting (and blow-drying) is a method of forming wet or damp hair into shape and then fixing it; with the aid of heat, to create a finished look. These methods of styling and dressing hair are temporary and the looks can be either classic or fashionable. You can make hair straighter, curlier, fuller, flatter or wavier.

Setting involves placing and positioning wet hair in to selected positions, and fixing the movement in to it, while it is dried into shape. You may roll the hair round curlers, secure it with clips or pins, or simply use your fingers. Once dry, you complete the process by dressing the hair with brushes and combs.

The hair should never be excessively heated otherwise permanent damage will result, so always keep an eye on the time that the client is seated under the dryer so that they don't get too hot or that longer-term damage doesn't occur.

Before removing the rollers allow them to cool down in position after taking out of the dryer. The cooling allows the hair set to fix into position as hot hair can 'relax' back to its previous state. (Remember it's the same as using a cool shot when blow-drying, this helps to fix the curl in after using a round brush.)

The dressing part involves the manipulation of the hair in a planned and controlled way. It starts with the removal of the setting marks by brushing and then continues as the hair is combed-out. The level of finish achieved during the comb-out relies upon the dexterity and skill of the stylist.

HAIR BY MOSKO, WISHAW PHOTOGRAPHY BY JOHN RAWSON@TRP

Activity
Using electrical equipment

A lot of the equipment safety issues are more to do with common sense. What things come to your mind when you handle salon electrical equipment?

List at least six safety precautions that should be considered when handling electrical equipment.

1
2
3
4
5
6

HAIR BY MOSKO, WISHAW PHOTOGRAPHY BY JOHN RAWSON@TRP

Before styling checklist

✔	Prepare the client by carefully gowning them and making sure that they are comfortable
✔	Remove any damp towels and loose clippings, then replace towel with a fresh dry one
✔	Look at the hair you are working with. Would the hair benefit from any styling aids?
✔	Are there any other limiting factors that need to be considered: physical features, growth patterns or density for example?
✔	Confirm the style, its purpose and what you are about to do next. If further explanation is required use pictures or style magazines as a visual aid
✔	After further discussion, agree with the client exactly what is to be done

During styling checklist

✔	Is the heat from the dryer comfortable?
✔	Is the body or volume OK?
✔	Is the parting or division of hair in the right place?
✔	Is the finished hairstyle OK? If not what aspect needs to be changed?

The effects of humidity on the hair

As with other techniques, setting produces only a temporary change in hair structure (and this is covered below). The fixed or set effect is soon lost if/when moisture is absorbed or introduced to the hair. You have probably already discovered this yourself: if, after having your hair done, you take a bath in a steamy bathroom, what happens to the hairstyle?

Moisture is all around us though and, in more extremes of humidity, it is seen as mist and fog. To help prevent style deterioration from happening, a wide variety of setting aids are available to slow down the 'collapsing' process and therefore hold the shape longer.

Different effects can be produced by different techniques:

- *increasing volume* – adding height, width and fullness, by lifting and positioning 'on base' when rollering or curling
- *decreasing volume* – producing a close, smooth, contained or flat style by pincurl stem direction, or by dragged or angled rollering 'off base'
- *movement* – varying line waves and curls by using differently sized rollers, pincurls or finger-waving.

Relaxed hair effects can be produced by wrapping hair or by using large rollers. Different techniques are used for hair of different lengths:

- *Longer hair* (below the shoulders) requires large rollers, or alternating large and small rollers, depending on the amount of movement required.
- *Shorter hair* (above the shoulders) requires smaller rollers to achieve movement for full or sleek effects.
- *Hair of one length* is ideal for smooth, bob effects.
- *Hair of layered lengths* is ideal for full, bouncy, curly effects achieved by, say, barrel or clockspring curls.

Different techniques can also be used to improve the appearance of hair of different textures:

- Fine, lifeless hair can be given increased body and movement. Lank hair can be given increased volume and movement.
- Coarse thick hair requires firmer control.
- Very curly hair can be made smoother and its direction changed.

Setting hair techniques

Curling techniques

Curls are series of shapes or movements in the hair. They may occur naturally, or be created by hairdressing – this could be chemically by perming or physically by setting. Curls add 'bounce' or lift to the hair, and determine the direction in which the hair lies.

EKU *statement*

GH11.19) The effects of humidity on hair

Each curl has a root, a stem, a body and a point. The curl base – the foundation shape produced between parted sections of hair – may be oblong, square, triangular and so on. The shape depends on the size of the curl, the stem direction and the curl type. Different curl types produce different movements.

You can choose the shape, size and direction of the individual curls: your choice will affect how satisfying the finished effect is and how long it lasts. The type of curl you choose depends on the style you're aiming for–a high, lifted movement needs a raised curl stem; a low, smooth shape needs a flat curl. You may need to use a combination of curl types and curling methods to achieve the desired style–for example, you might lift the hair on top of the head using large rollers, but keep the sides flatter using pincurls.

Curl parts

Rollering hair

There are various sizes and shapes of roller. In using rollers you need to decide on the size and shape, how you will curl the hair on to them and the position in which you will attach them to the base.

- Small rollers produce tight curls, giving hair more movement. Large rollers produce loose curls making hair wavy as opposed to curly.
- Rollers pinned on or above their bases so that the roots are upright, produce more volume than rollers placed below their bases.
- The direction of the hair wound on the roller will affect the final style.

Securing rollers

Securing rollers

Pinning rollers

Pinning rollers

Step-by-step: Rollering

1 Comb through to remove any tangles and apply the setting lotion evenly to the hair.

2 Start by taking a clean, smooth section of hair – that is no longer or wider than the 'footprint' (size of the basal section) of the roller being used – straight out, but slightly forwards from the head.

3 Place the hair points centrally on to the roller. Use both hands to retain the hair section angle and keep the hair points in position.

EKU *statement*

GH11.29) Current techniques for setting and dressing hair

GH11.30) How the factors in the range affect the setting and dressing processes and finished look

GH11.31) The types of setting techniques and why and when they are used

GH11.32) Why and how to use the different types of sectioning and winding techniques in the range

GH11.34) How the angle of winding on and off base influences the volume and direction of the hair movement

Remember

Evenly tensioned curls produce even movements. Twisted curl stems or ones where the tension *sags* produce movement that is difficult to style.

Remember

If you are not sure which size roller to use, go for the smaller. If necessary you can brush out and stretch too tightly curled hair later. Loosely curled hair will drop more readily, so you may not achieve the style you were aiming for.

Remember

Common rollering problems

✔ Rollers not secured properly on base either dragged or flattened will not produce lift and volume in the final style.

✔ Too large a hair section will produce reduced movement in the final effect.

✔ Too small a hair section will produce increased movement or curl in the final effect.

✔ Longer hair requires larger rollers unless tighter effects are wanted.

✔ Poorly positioned hair over-falling the sides of the roller will have reduced/impaired movement in the final effect.

✔ Incorrectly wound hair around the roller will create 'fish hook' ends.

✔ Twisted hair around the roller will distort the final movement of the style.

4 As you turn the roller 'lock' the hair points against the body of the roller. Then continue winding down with an even tension until you reach the base of the section.

5 As you work make sure that any shorter or wispy flyaway ends are included in the wound roller.

6 Place the wound roller centrally on to the sectioned base (i.e. 'on base') to achieve full height/volume from the set.

7 Secure the roller by pinning through to stop it unravelling. Make sure that the pins are comfortable and link through to other rollers and not on to the client's scalp.

Pincurling

Pincurling is the technique of winding hair into a series of curls or flat waves which are pinned in place with pin clips while drying. The two most common types of curl produced in this way are the barrel curl and the clockspring.

● The barrel curl has an open centre and produces a soft effect. When formed, each loop is the same size as the previous one. It produces an even wave shape and may be used for reverse curling, which forms waves in modern hairstyles. In this, one row of pincurls lies in one direction, the next in the opposite direction. When dry and dressed, this produces a wave shape. When used in just the perimeter outline of a short hairstyle they can control the shape and stop the ends (that could otherwise be set on rollers) from buckling.

● The clockspring curl has a closed centre and produces a tight, springy effect. When formed each loop is slightly smaller than the previous one. It produces an uneven wave shape throughout its length. It can be suitable for hair that is difficult to hold in place.

Activity
Styling and finishing products

List the products that your salon uses and for each one complete the information in the table below.

Product name	How is it used?	What hair type is it for?	Benefits to the hair

Step-by-step: Pincurling

1 Neatly section the hair and comb through any setting lotion – the size of the section will relate to the degree of movement achieved.

2 Hold the hair in the direction it will lie after drying.

3 Hold the hair at the midpoint in one hand using the thumb and first finger, with the thumb uppermost. Using the thumb and first finger of your other hand and thumb underneath, hold the hair a little way down from the hair points.

4 Turn the second hand to form the first curl loop. The hand should turn right round at the wrist.

5 On completion of the first loop, transfer the hair to the finger and thumb of the other hand.

6 Form a series of loops until the curl base is reached. The last loop is formed by turning the curl body into the curl base. The rounded curl body should fit into the curl base.

7 Secure the curl with a clip without disturbing the curl formed in the process.

Clockspring curl

Remember

Common pincurl faults

✔ Tangled hair is difficult to control. Comb well before starting.

✔ If the base is too large curling will be difficult.

✔ If you hold the curl stem in one direction but place it in another the curl will be misshapen and lift.

✔ If you don't turn your hand far enough it will be difficult to form concentric loops.

Barrelspring curl

Curl body directions

A flat curl may turn either clockwise or anti-clockwise. The clockwise curl has a body that moves around to the right and the anti-clockwise a body that moves around to the left. Reverse curls are rows of alternating clockwise and anti-clockwise pincurls; these will produce a finish that has continuous 's' waves, similar to the effect of finger-waves throughout the style. Stand-up pincurls, like rollers, have a body that lifts away from the scalp.

Stand-up pin curls

Remember

✔ Never place grips or pins in your mouth – this is unhygienic and could cross-infect.

✔ Never place tailcombs in your pocket – you could injure yourself and pierce your body.

✔ Never work on wet slippery floors and always clear up loose clippings of hair.

✔ Never use any items of personal equipment that have not been cleaned or sterilised.

Step-by-step: Drying the set

Wet setting is normally dried under a fixed or manoeuverable hood dryer. You need to do the following:

1 Make sure that the client is comfortable.

2 Set the dryer to a temperature that suits the client. Most dryers have an adjustment for the client so that if the dryer becomes too hot they can turn it down themselves.

Curl body directions

Remember

The elbow and arm should be held above the hand when it is placed on the head. Only the index finger should touch the head. This gives the required control and pressure. A comb which has sections of both widely and closely spaced teeth is the most suitable for this.

EKU *statement*

GH11.20) The physical effects of setting on the hair structure

Remember

If too much heat is applied to the hair it will sustain permanent, unrepairable damage.

EKU *statement*

GH11.21) How the incorrect application of heat can affect the hair and scalp

3 Set the timer for drying. You should allow around 15 minutes for short fine hair, and up to 45 minutes for long thick hair. The average is around 25–30 minutes.

4 Always check the client from time to time during the process.

5 After drying has finished, remove the hood dryer and let the hair cool down for a short while.

6 Then check to see if the hair is dry by carefully removing one roller from the crown area, one from the nape and one from the front; if they are all dry carry on carefully removing all the pins and rollers, leaving the set curl carefully in its position without dragging or distorting the formed curl.

The physical changes taking place in the hair

Hair in good condition is flexible and elastic. As hair is curled or waved, it is bent under tension into curved shapes. The hair is stretched on the outer side of the curve and compressed on the inner side. If it is dried in this new position, the curl will be retained. This happens because when hair is set the hydrogen bonds and salt bonds between the keratin chains of the hair are broken. The linking system is moved into a new temporary position. (The stronger disulphide links remain unbroken.)

Hair, however, is *hygroscopic* it is able to absorb and retain moisture. It does so by capillary action: water spreads through minute spaces in the hair structure, like ink spreading in blotting paper. Wet hair expands and contracts more than dry hair does, because water acts as a lubricant and allows the link structure to be repositioned more easily. So the amount of moisture in hair affects the curl's durability. As the hair picks up moisture the rearranged beta keratin chains loosen or relax into their previous alpha keratin shape and position. This is why the humidity – the moisture content of air – determines how long the curled shape is retained.

The condition and the porosity of hair affect its elasticity. If the cuticle is damaged, or open, the hair will retain little moisture, because of normal evaporation. The hair will therefore have poor elasticity. If too much tension is applied when curling hair of this type it may become limp, overstretched and lacking in spring. Very dry hair is likely to break.

Remember

The temporary bonds *(beta keratin state)* within the hair are only formed when the hair is completely dry.

However, they will revert to their former *(alpha keratin state)* if moisture or water is introduced to the hair.

Remember

Alpha and beta keratin
The keratin bonds of unstretched hair are in alpha keratin state and the keratin bonds of stretched hair are in beta keratin state. This is the basis of cohesive or temporary setting.

Activity

How are the following items made safe and hygienic and prepared for salon use?

1   Heated curling tongs

2   Crimpers

3   Ceramic straighteners

4   Hot brushes

5   Heated rollers

6   Hand dryers

GH11.3   Dress hair

Dressing out

Dressing is the process of achieving finish to previously set hair. Setting gives movement to hair in the form of curls or waves. Dressing blends and binds these movements into an overall flowing shape, the style you set out to achieve. It produces an overall form that flows, lightening the head and face and removing dull, flat or odd shapes.

Dressing uses brushing and combing techniques, and dressing aids such as hairspray to keep the hair in place. If you have constructed the set carefully and accurately only the minimum of dressing will be required.

Step-by-step: Brushing

Brushing blends the waves or curls, removes the partings or set marks, left at the curl bases during rollering and gets rid of any stiffness caused by setting aids.

1   One way of achieving the finished dressing is with a brush and your hand. The thicker the hair, the stiffer the brush bristles need to be. Choose a brush that will flow through the hair comfortably.

2   Apply the brush to the hair ends. Use firm but gentle strokes.

3   Work up the head, starting from the back of the neck.

4   Brush through the waves or curls you have set, gradually moulding the hair into shape.

5   As you brush, pat the hair with your hand to guide the hair into shape. Remember, though, that overdressing and over-handling can ruin the set.

The technique of double brushing uses two brushes, applied one after the other in a rolling action; this will remove setting marks better and quicker than a single brushing technique.

Remember

Always let the hair cool before removing all the rollers. Hot hair may seem dry when you first check it, but when it cools it may actually be damp.

EKU *statement*

GH11.35) Why set hair sections need to be brushed out thoroughly

EKU *statement*

GH11.33) Why and how to use smoothing, backcombing and backbrushing

Backcombed hair

Remember

Backcombing is applied to the underside of the hair section. Don't let the comb penetrate too deeply otherwise the final dressing and smoothing out will remove the support you have put in.

Backbrushing

Back-brushing is a technique used to give more height and volume to hair. By brushing backwards from the points to the roots, you roughen the cuticle of the hair. Hairs will now tangle slightly and bind together to hold a fuller shape. The amount of hair backbrushed determines the fullness of the finished style.

Tapered hair, with shorter lengths distributed throughout, is more easily pushed back by brushing. Most textures of hair can be backbrushed; because it adds bulk, the technique is especially useful with fine hair.

Step-by-step: Backbrushing

1 Hold a section of hair out from the head; for maximum lift, hold the section straight out from the head and apply the backbrushing close to the roots.

2 Place the brush on the top of the held section at an angle slightly dipping in to the held section of hair.

3 Now, with a slight turn outwards with the wrist, turn and push down a small amount of hair towards the scalp.

4 Repeat this in a few adjacent sections of hair.

5 Smooth out the longer lengths in the direction required, covering the tangled backbrushed hair beneath.

Note: The more the hair is backbrushed the greater the volume and support will be.

Backcombing

This technique is similar to backbrushing above; however, in this situation a comb is used rather than a brush to turn back the shorter hairs within a section to provide greater support and volume. Backcombing is applied deeper toward the scalp than backbrushing and therefore provides a stronger result.

Activity
Answer these questions in your portfolio:

1 What difference would there be from setting with rollers on base as opposed to off base?

2 What type of effect do you get from clockspring pincurls?

3 What type of effect do you get from barrel curls?

4 Why do you need to brush the hair first when combing out?

5 What is the difference between backcombing and backbrushing?

Use the styling mirror

As you work keep using the mirror to check the shape that you are creating. If you find that the outer contour is misshaped or lacking volume, don't be afraid to go back to resection and backbrush/comb again.

When you have finished the look hold a back mirror at an angle to maximise what the client can see of their hairstyle.

All these styling aspects create the basis for creating a variety of effects. The next part of this chapter looks at how this is applied to long hair dressings.

SCOTT SMURTHWAITE @ CREAM

Heated styling equipment: tongs and straightening irons

See Unit GH10 Style and finish hair: GH10.4 Finish hair pages 191–197.

Electrical accessories health and safety checklist

✔	Never get too close to the client's head with hot styling equipment
✔	Never leave the styling equipment on one area of hair for more than a few moments
✔	Always replace the styling tools into their holder at the workstation when not in use
✔	Always check the filters on the back of hand dryers to make sure that they are not blocked (this will cause the dryer to overheat and possibly ignite)
✔	Look out for trailing flexes across the floor or around the back of styling chairs
✔	Let tools cool down before putting them back into storage
✔	Always check for deterioration in flexes or equipment damages
✔	Never use damaged equipment under any circumstances

HAIR BY CIENTE@BERKHAMSTED PHOTOGRAPHY BY JOHN RAWSON@TRP

Activity

In your portfolio explain each of the following:

1 alpha keratin

2 beta keratin

3 why hair should be allowed to cool before it is brushed out

4 the effects of humidity on hair

5 the effects of excessive heat upon the hair

6 what advice on hair maintenance you could give to the client.

Dressing and styling longer hair

Many people find working with longer hair or doing non-routine services quite daunting, but they needn't be. The main reason why someone finds any part of hairdressing difficult is because they are not doing that particular aspect or discipline regularly.

EKU *statement*

GH11.36) Methods of handling, controlling and securing hair to achieve curls and rolls

The most important things to remember with long hair-ups are:

- assessing whether a particular look or effect is going to suit the client
- agreeing the effect before you start
- having a plan of what you are trying to achieve
- building enough structure to support the look.

It may seem like this list states the obvious, but each one is vital and this is why:

Assess the style's suitability

This is the first aspect that you should consider. In most cases, non-routine hairdos are for special situations. It's not a quick, casual throw-up that the client does to get their hair out of the way. They come to the salon for the things that they can't achieve themselves: that's what hairstyles for special occasions are.

The problem from a suitability point of view is, how will the client know if they are going to like their hair up if they seldom have it styled that way? For people who don't normally wear their hair in plaits, pleats or twists, there is always underlying reasons and these could be:

- their hair is too thick
- they don't like the shape of their ears
- they feel that 'head-hugging' shapes make them more conspicuous
- it makes their nose bigger
- they prefer their hair to have volume so they don't like it scraped back
- their hair isn't really long enough.

The table below provides a quick look up for the physical limiting/influencing factors

EKU *statement*

GH13.24) How the factors in the range influence the choice and direction of plaited or twisted style

Physical features – style suitability

Physical features	Head shapes					Protruding ears	Prominent nose	Short neck
Hair style	Oval	Round	Heart	Triangular	Square			
Vertical roll/ pleat	✔	with height to compensate	✔	with height to compensate	with height and width to compensate	Volume at the sides to cover	Volume at the sides	Needs to be sleek
Barrel curls	✔	✔	✔	✔	✔	Volume at the sides to cover (not triangular)	Volume at the sides	Needs to be sleek
Low knot or chignon	✔	✔ with height	✔	✗	with height	Volume at sides except triangular	✗	✗
High knot	✔	✔	✔	✔	✔	Volume at sides except triangular	✗	Needs to be sleek
Plaits	✔	✔ with height	✔	✔	✗	Volume at sides except triangular	✔	Needs to be sleek
Twists and cornrows	✔	✔ with height	✔	✔	✔ use designs that involve curves and not straight lines/ linear effects	Volume at sides except triangular	✔	Needs to be sleek

Agree the effect before you start

When you have selected a suitable look you need to find examples of how this would look on the client. Visualisation and, more importantly, self-visualisation from the client's point of view is very difficult. You need to try to rearrange the hair loosely, so they can get an idea of the weight distribution, height and width. If you can convey to them roughly what it will look like when their face is exposed, and they like what they see, you are halfway there. It will save lots of time later and save you having to unpick everything that you have done.

Have a plan – get organised

If the client likes the effect in principle then you can set out a plan of how you will achieve it. You need to work out where you need to start, the midpoint in the styling and what the final touches will be. The starting point will be a position that you will be unlikely to get at and change later on, so it's a bit like making a cake.

- You start with a recipe – the style you want to create.
- You gather the ingredients – all the pins, grips, bands and accessories.
- Get out tools – get all the equipment you need together.
- Start preparing the mix – start the process.
- Place in the oven – mould and spray.
- Take out and ice the cake – finish off with the decoration/accessories.

Building a base structure for vertical rolls/pleats

Some styles need support; they cannot last and stay in without it. It needs to be secure as well as creative in its effect. It can only be secure if you use backcombing, grips, bands etc. Do not be afraid to backcomb the hair. It may look as if the whole thing is getting too big, but don't forget you can take out as much as you like when you smooth the dressing. Backcombing provides you with a solid base that you can grip without the fear of the grips dropping out. As you become more experienced in handling long hair, you will find that you won't need to use much spray in the styling stage, but only later in the finishing off.

The other main tool for giving structure and support is grips. Kirby grips have one leg with a serrated profile; this helps them to stay in the hair much better.

Wherever possible ensure that you interlock (criss-cross) your grips, whether the patterning is in a straight line (e.g. in supporting and fixing a pleat) or whether it is placed in a complete interlocking circlet (e.g. in hair dressed in knots, chignons or any other centrally positioned dressings).

Vertical roll (French pleat)

The vertical roll is a formal classic dressing that suits many special occasions. The hair can be enhanced further by the additions of accessories or fresh flowers. If you review the planning stages for putting hair up you will see under 'building the support' that backcombing is an essential aspect for creating a solid foundation. This should be your starting point for the step-by-step procedure.

Interlocking grips

Step-by-step: vertical roll (French pleat)

Step 1. Section and backbrush the bulk of the hair

Step 2. After smoothing the hair, interlock a row of grips to secure the base of the pleat

Step 3. Sweep the hair over and tuck the free edges inwards

Step 4. Secure the smooth pleat with fine pins

Step 5. Style and finish the remainder into position

Activity
Setting techniques

The list below covers a range of setting techniques. what are they for and when are they used?

Technique	What does it do?	When is it used?
Backbrushing		
Backcombing		
Barrel curls		
Off-base setting		
On-base setting		

Step-by-step: Asymmetric chignon (courtesy Patrick Cameron)

This simple but very effective hair-up is an ideal quick option for either party or formal wear.

Step 1. Brush through well and smooth down the side opposite to where the chignon will be.

Step 2. Divide the hair down to the ear. Fix one section with a band low to the hairline at the nape behind the ear.

Step 3. Twist the remainder down to meet the hair secured with the band.

Step 4. Now twist the hair in the covered band too.

Step 5. Twist this section underneath the other and continue through to the ends with both sections.

Step 6. Secure the sections together with a band at the ends.

Step 7. Now feather the effect by pulling out some loose ends.

Step 8. Loop around and fix in position.

Step 9. Continue to twist and secure with grips.

Step 10. Finally smooth out the front area and fix down into position.

Extracted from *Dressing Long Hair 4* by Patrick Cameron, www.patrick-cameron.com tel: 020 7923 0599

| GH13.2 | Plait and twist hair |

Plaiting hair

Remember

The tension used in plaiting can exert exceptional pressure on the hair follicle and scalp-type plaits/corn rows create more vulnerability than free-hanging plaits. In extreme cases hair loss may be caused by this continued pulling action; areas of hair become thin and even baldness may be result!

This condition is called *traction alopecia* and is particularly obvious at the temples of younger girls with long hair who regularly wear their hair up for school, sport or dancing.

Plaiting is a method of intertwining three or more strands of hair to create a variety of woven hairstyles. When this work is done for specific occasions, it is often accompanied by ornamentation: fresh flowers, glass or plastic beads, coloured silks and added hair are also popular.

The numerous options for plaited effects are determined by the following factors:

- number of plaits or twists used
- positioning of the plait or twist across the scalp or around the head
- the way in which the plaits are made (under or over)
- any ornamentation/decoration or added hair applied.

'Plaits' usually refers to a free-hanging stem(s) of hair that is left to show hair length. This length can be natural or can be extended by adding hair during the plaiting process; an example is the 'French' or 'fish-tail' plait.

Step-by-step: Loose plaiting – three-stem (loose) plait

The three-stem plait is easily achieved and demonstrates the basic principle of plaiting hair.

1 Divide the hair to be plaited into three equal sections.
2 Hold the hair with both hands, using your fingers to separate the sections.

3 Starting from either the left or the right, place the outside section over the centre one. Repeat this from the other side.

4 Continue placing the outside sections of hair over the centre ones until you reach the ends of the stems.

5 Secure the free ends with ribbon, thread or covered band.

EKU *statement*

GH13.28) The manufacturers' instructions relating to the use of the products in the range

Step-by-step: Three-stem 'French' plaiting

1 Brush the hair to remove all tangles.

2 With the hair tilted backwards, divide the foremost hair into three equal sections.

3 Starting from either the left or the right, cross an outside stem over the centre stem. Repeat this action with the opposite outer stem.

4 Section a fourth stem (smaller in thickness than the initial three stems) and incorporate this with the next outside stem you are going to cross.

5 Cross this thickened stem over the centre, and repeat this step with the opposite outer stem.

6 Continue this sequence of adding hair to the outer stem before crossing it over the centre.

7 When there is no more hair to be added, continue plaiting down to the ends and secure them.

Step 1. Section the hair from the hairline into three stems.

Step 2. Plait the sections in with the main stem.

Step 3. Continue to plait.

Step 4. The completed plait.

EKU *statement*

GH11.17) The importance of using products economically

EKU *statement*

GH13.14) The potential consequences of excessive tension on the hair

EKU *statement*

GH13.15) What is traction alopecia

GH13.16) How to identify the signs of traction alopecia

GH13.17) The physical effects on the hair structure of plaiting and twisting

Longer-lasting plaits and twists

Introduction

There is another type of plaiting technique that has gained great popularity because of its impact, durability and easy-to-manage effects. It's called cornrowing. The cornrow is another type of three-stem plait that is secured close to the scalp to create head-hugging patterned designs.

'Cane rows', otherwise known as 'corn rows', are a technique that originated in Africa. Its ethnic origins have been a unique way of displaying hair art and design and have often incorporated complex patterns that historically indicated status or tribal connection. In fact, as this art form has been passed down by subsequent generations for thousands of years, it is quite probable that the very first hairdressers worked on these elaborate techniques, as it is unlikely that people could do these themselves.

Cane rows create design patterns across the scalp by working along predefined channels of hair. These channels are secured to the scalp by interlocking each of the three subdivided stems as the plaiting technique progresses.

Short or even layered hair can be made to look longer still if hair is added, via extensions, during the process. The added hair is plaited into the style along each of the sections that create the plaited effect.

When cane rows have been applied to the hair the effect can last for up to six weeks or more before they should be removed. Advice should be given on handling and maintaining the hair although regular shampooing can still be carefully achieved.

Preparation for corn rows and twists

Unlike loose plaits designed to last for just a day or so; the closer, tighter technique of plaiting lasts up to several weeks. Because of this you need to make sure that you cover all the aspects of durability, maintenance and expected results, with the client; from the outset. This type of work takes a lot longer than basic loose plaits, so make sure that you also give the client a good idea of the costs involved.

A thorough consultation for this type of work is essential. All of these intricately designed effects take a lot of time and you need to have a clear idea of what you are trying to achieve before you start. Plaiting and twisting involves some additional tension on the hair and this can put the client's hair roots under considerable excess stress. Our clients want their hair designs to be neat, controlled and easy to manage and to last for as long as possible; because of this it is very easy to cause traction alopecia.

As we noted earlier, traction alopecia is caused by the excessive and continuous strain put on the roots by hair styled effects such as plaits and twists. You need to make sure that you ask the client throughout the service that the work that you are doing is comfortable and not pulling at different areas across the scalp.

You need to be able to recognise during consultation any previous signs of traction alopecia. The first indications of traction alopecia can be seen around the front hairline, often around the temples. This shows as an area of thinned or missing hair and if the condition is recent, it will be sore and tender.

Before any plaiting, twisting or weaved effects can be applied to the hair, you need to assess the suitability of this form of styling for the client.

Other factors affecting the service of plaited or twisted hairstyle The following list provides you with a quick checklist of things that you should consider in addition to the normal consultation covered previously in this chapter

✔	Style terminology
✔	Style suitability
✔	Hair condition
✔	Hair length
✔	Removal of previous plaits or braids.

Style terminology This is an important aspect for client consultation. It is all too easy for the client to understand a technical term as meaning one thing, while you know it to mean something completely different. This communication aspect may seem rather basic, but it is still the single main reason why clients end up being dissatisfied with a service. It is always better to get down to basics; try to refrain from using clever technical terms. It might be appropriate with your colleagues as you speak the same language. But often the terms used by clients (wrongly) are words picked up from magazines, TV and other people, such as friends or work colleagues. Different people have different ways of saying things; a corn row to one person could mean a Senegalese twist to another.

Activity
Create a portfolio of work

Finding ways to describe effects to clients is very difficult. You may have a clear idea of what you are trying to achieve, but can you convey that to your client before you start?

Complex work takes a lot of time and you can save yourself from dealing with a surprised, shocked or dissatisfied client by collecting a portfolio of elaborate work. When you see examples of different or complex effects, make sure that you keep them for a visual aid that you can use in consultation.

What will take you five minutes to cut and paste into a style book could save you a lot of time if you finish and have to start again.

These complex ways of styling hair involve a lot of work and take a lot of time. In most cases they would take considerable time to unravel and redress. So make sure that you both have a clear idea of what you are trying to achieve. Use visual aids; examples of pictures communicate effects that often cannot be put easily into words.

Style suitability This is an important aspect of consultation. Any work that you are planning to do should be really thought through beforehand. If you were to do a full head of scalp plaits, would they suit the client's head and face shape? It may look elaborate when it's finished, it may impress other people, but you do need to ask yourself whether the style enhances the client and is an improvement on what she looked like before. All of this type of work takes a lot of time and when it's done well, the final effects are long-lasting too.

For more information on style suitability see Unit G7 Advise and consult with clients, pages 98–103.

Remember

Traction alopecia is a problem caused by hair tensioning.

Hair is capable of sustaining its own weight and, within reason, a certain amount of mechanical wear and tear, such as brushing, combing and detangling knots. Any added hair is an extra weight or mass upon the hair roots and where extensions have been attached to small areas of the hair, thinning or baldness can occur!

EKU *statement*

GH13.18) How hair texture affects the plaiting process and styling possibilities

GH13.24) How the factors in the range influence the choice and direction of plaited or twisted style

EKU statement

GH13.31) The removal requirements for plaits and twists

Remember

 Previous plaiting is difficult to remove. Make sure that you are careful and patient when you disentangle the hair

When plaits are removed you may also find that the scalp sheds a lot of dead skin cells. This is quite normal and shouldn't be mistaken for something more sinister. Scalp plaits can be washed, but the wearer seldom rubs them too much as they don't want to spoil the effects. This means that dead cells are locked in and cannot be shed in the normal way, over time. This is easily remedied when you cleanse and condition the hair thoroughly.

EKU statement

GH13.19) How to create corn rows, a French plait, two strand twists, fish-tail plaits and flat twists

GH13.20) The importance of sectioning hair accurately when plaiting and twisting

GH13.21) Methods of securing the completed plaits and twists

GH13.22) How to handle the hair when plaiting and twisting to maintain a correct and even tension

GH13.23) How to adjust the tension of plaits and twists

Hair condition   Test the hair for poor elasticity, look for damage or over-porous hair. Hair that is weakened for any reason is a contra-indication for plaiting or twisting. If the client is definitely intent on having some form of plait or twisted hair design work, think about recommending a course of restructurants or hair strengtheners beforehand.

Hair texture   is also a major consideration: if the hair is curly it will need smoothing or straightening first, so that the hair is easier to handle and to improve the final look of the designed work. Remember, hair curl patterns can vary across the scalp; some areas such as the lower nape may be tighter than other areas, so make sure that you check the hair and scalp all over.

Hair Length   This is an obvious consideration. Make sure that the hair is long enough to produce the effect that you want to achieve. If not, would the hair benefit from added hair extensions?

Removal of previous plaiting

If the client needs her previous design work removed you should dissuade her from having a new set of plaits or twists put in straight after.

Extra care should always be taken when removing the old plaits, as the scalp may be quite tender, sensitive or even sore. Over time, products can build up around the scalp and this can bond the hair together making detangling quite difficult. In any event you will need patience and care to disentangle or unravel the hair, so that it is not weakened, broken or damaged any further.

Shampoo and condition the hair

The hair must be shampooed and conditioned thoroughly before any plaiting or twisting service is done. You need to make sure that any traces of product – moisturisers, gels, sheens and oils – are removed from the hair first.

Drying into shape

Both plaiting and twisting techniques tend to make the hair appear shorter, as with plaits, much of this length is used laterally (across and around the head) as decoration. So you would need to blow-dry the hair first, to make the most of its overall length. This is necessary anyway, as the hair needs to be dried and made smoother before any other work can take place. After blow-drying, the hair and scalp can be prepared with hair oils or dressings. Any moisturising will be beneficial to the hair, making it more elastic, improving its brittleness and making it more pliable.

The design that you create is based on a sort of graphical layout. Regardless of whether you are doing scalp plaits, singles or twists, the direction in which they flow is related to their starting position on the scalp and accurate sectioning creates this.

Cane/corn rows

Cane rows are a type of scalp plait that creates linear designs across the head. They will last anything from one week to a couple of months; although with washing and general wear and tear they tend to look a little untidy after a couple of weeks. Cane rows create design patterns across the scalp by working along pre-defined channels of hair. These channels are secured to the scalp by interlocking each of the subdivided stems as the plaiting technique progresses.

Short or even layered hair can be made to look longer still by adding hair extensions to the client's hair during the process. The added hair is plaited into the style along each of the sections that create the braided effect.

Advice should be given on handling and maintaining the hair although regular shampooing can still be carefully achieved. This type of work is ideal for natural hair as it can be worn with or without added hair extensions, even making short hair look long. They are easily removed although the smaller the plait stems and sections the more difficult and fiddly it becomes.

Method of cane rowing

1 Wash, condition and pre-dry the hair smooth.

2 Section out a channel of hair with a tail comb to create the direction of the design required.

3 Use a sectioning clip to secure the other parts of the remainder hair out of the way.

4 For cane rows without added hair, subdivide the client's hair from the front of the channeled section into three stems.

5 Holding the front, first section between the middle and third finger of the left hand and the next, middle section between the index finger and thumb. Now take the last or third section, between the middle and third finger of the right hand.

6 Pass the middle section with the index finger of the left hand under the last outer section of the right hand and pass the new middle section under the outer section of the left hand.

7 Pick up a little hair along the channel with the fourth finger and incorporate into the outer third stem.

8 Repeat 6 and 7 until you have worked along the complete channel of hair until the point where the plait leaves the scalp to hang freely.

9 Then continue plaiting the single, three stems until all of the hair is plaited.

10 Secure the ends with a covered professional band and start steps 2–10 again on the next cane row.

Method for adding hair into the cane row

The method for adding or extending the hair is similar to the above except that narrow strands of hair extensions are taken and added to take the place of the two outer sections, i.e. it is looped across the client's natural hair to create the first and third stem of the braid. Then as each time the outer braid introduces part of the client's hair, the added hair is secured down to the scalp.

Added hair or extension hair can be made from a variety of materials that can be natural or synthetic. They come in a variety of different textures, types and colours and can be added to the client's natural hair for a variety of different styling reasons. Subtle, harmonising tones and textures can be added to make the client's own hair appear longer than it is. Conversely, bright fashion colour extensions can be added to create dramatic, contrasting effects.

Single plaits

Single plaits are a popular method of styling for men or women. They can be done on natural or chemically processed hair although the effects are more dramatic on longer

EKU statement

GH13.13) The importance of using bands for professional use

Remember

Added hair/extensions
There are many ways that you can incorporate added hair into a hairstyle:

1 It can be worked into the style during plaiting.

2 It can be knotted onto a single stem of a plait and form other stems of the plait as you work through the hair.

3 It can be twisted around natural hair and secured at the ends by tying with thread.

EKU *statement*

GH13.25) The types of products available for use with plaits and twists

GH13.26) When and why you would use the types of products in the range

GH13.27) The importance of using products economically

hair. This doesn't mean that people with shorter hair can't have plaits; they are obvious candidates for extensions and added hair. Single plaits are quite durable and typically they will last for up to three months, but, like cane rows, their appearance deteriorates after a few weeks. The ends of the plaits should be secured with professional rubber bands.

Method for single plaits

1 Wash, condition and pre-dry the hair straight.
2 Starting at the nape section the hair horizontally and secure the remainder.
3 Subdivide the horizontal section into small 1 cm by 1 cm square sections and separate into three equal stems.
4 Hold the first section between the middle and third finger of the left hand and the next, middle section between the index finger and thumb. Now take the last or third section between the middle and third finger of the right hand.
5 Continue to cross the outer stem on the left, over the centre stem, and then pass the outer stem on the right over what is now the centre stem.
6 Repeat this down to the ends of the hair and secure with a professional band.
7 Move to the next square section of hair and repeat steps 4–6.
8 Continue this by working up the back of the head, then to the lower sides and again up to the top of the head.

If added hair extensions are required, do the above steps 1 and 2 then at:

3 Subdivide the horizontal section into smaller square sections, then attach extension hair to each of the stems of the client's hair and plait as normal as a three-stem plait above.

Twisting techniques

Twists are an alternative to plaited styles; they will last for up to a month before they become untidy. Unlike plaits they don't involve any interlocking of hair, so they usually require an application of pomade or light styling gel to bond the hair while the twists are being formed.

Remember to use products sparingly though, as it would be easy to apply too much product and then that would make the hair feel greasy or dirty and then it would have to be washed again.

Twisting is achieved by using the fingers or a comb to twist the hair into strands. This can be done in linear patterns along the scalp such as flat twists, or off the scalp as with single twists or two stem twists.

Method for creating a flat twist

Flat twists have a similar appearance at a distance to corn rows, but when you look more closely you can see that the hair isn't interlocked in the same way. The durability of the effects depends upon the type of hair, but as a rule of thumb, twists don't last as long as corn rows. But on a positive note they don't take anything like the same amount of time to put in as tight, three-stem scalp plaits.

Step 1. Shampoo, condition and dry the hair roughly into shape.

Step 2. After brushing the hair to remove any tangles, start the style at the front by dividing the hair with a tail-comb.

Step 3. Twist the section of hair firmly but not too tightly back towards the crown area.

Step 4. Grip the twisted section into place before starting the next channel.

Step 5. Continue with the same technique on each of the channels.

Step 6. Twist the sections at the back from the nape up to the crown in the same way.

Step 7. Leave a section at the front to soften the hairline profile. Lightly backcomb the remaining hair to finish.

Method for creating single twists

1 Wash, condition and towel dry the hair.

2 Divide the hair into four quadrants and secure with sectioning clips.

3 Section off horizontally at the nape and secure the remainder out of the way.

4 Subdivide the horizontal sections into smaller areas of just a few millimetres across. (The smaller the sections the tidier the twist will look.)

5 Apply the gel or pomade throughout the length of the twist stem.

6 Place a tailcomb into the stem close to the root and start to turn in either a continuous clockwise (or anti-clockwise) movement. Work down the section of hair to the end.

7 Continue on to the next twist in the horizontal section and repeat steps 5 and 6.

8 Continue working up the head.

9 When all of the twists have been completed, arrange them neatly in the direction of the desired style and place under a dryer for 20–30 minutes.

10 When completely dry, apply product; either a spray fixative or sheen to complete the look.

Method for creating two-stem twists

1 Wash, condition and towel dry the hair.

2 Divide the hair into four quadrants and secure with sectioning clips.

3 Section off horizontally at the nape and secure the remainder out of the way.

4 Subdivide the horizontal sections into smaller areas of just a few millimetres across. (The smaller the sections the tidier the twist will look.)

5 Apply the gel or pomade throughout the length of the twist stem.

6 Subdivide the single stem, making two stems and start twisting left over right (or vice versa) and continue through the length of the hair.

7 Continue on to the next twist in the horizontal section and repeat steps 5 and 6.

8 Continue working up the head.

9 When all of the twists have been completed, arrange them neatly in the direction of the desired style and place under a dryer for 20–30 minutes.

10 When completely dry, apply product – either a spray fixative or sheen – to complete the look.

Senegalese twists

Senegalese twists are a scalp twist effect; they consist of stems of hair that are always twisted in the same direction with hair crossing over and creating a rope effect.

1 Wash, condition and pre-dry the hair smooth.

2 Section out a channel of hair with a tail comb to create the direction and the design required.

3 Using the fingers, start close to the root, take a small section of hair and twist it in a clockwise movement.

4 As you work along the channel pick up and work in more sections of hair to create the scalp twist effect.

5 When the channel of twisted hair is finished, secure until all of the others are finished.

6 The free ends of the twists can be interlocked together, and then after they have been dried under a dryer the effect can be thermally styled to complete the total effect.

GH11.4 and GH13.3   Provide aftercare advice

Good service is supported through good advice and recommendation. The work that you do in the salon needs to be cared for at home by the client too. What would be the point of creating something if the client doesn't know how to achieve and/or maintain the same effects at home?

Home- and aftercare checklist

✔	Talk through the style as you work; that way the client sees how you handle different aspects of the look.
✔	Show and recommend the products/equipment that you use so that the client gets the right things to enable them to get the same effects.
✔	Explain how routine styling with tongs or straighteners can have detrimental effects.
✔	Demonstrate the techniques that you use so they can achieve that salon hair look too.
✔	When you have put the client's hair up, or provided a plaited or twisted effect, give them advice on how to take the style down/remove the plaits or twists.

Talk through the style as you work

It's very difficult to do two things at the same time and you have probably found this yourself at work. Have you noticed how a senior stylist chats with the client whilst they are working? On the other hand, have you noticed the difference when a junior stylist is trying to do a similar technical piece of work? It seems to go very quiet!

The client probably notices this too; that's because a less confident stylist will always divert their attentions to the job in hand.

It's far easier to talk about the things that you are doing with the hair than to talk about the client's children at school, who may be taking their exams. Make a point of talking through your technique as you go. The benefits are twofold:

1 it eliminates long periods of silence whilst you are working and, more importantly,

2 it is really useful to the client as they get useful advice on how to recreate a similar effect at home.

Show and recommend the products/ equipment that you use

As you talk about the ways in which you have styled the hair, make a point of talking through the products that you have used as well.

So when you use a particular product, why not hand it to them so they can have a closer look. This way they get to see, smell and feel the product too and subconsciously this has a very powerful effect on them. By doing this you are involving the client in what you are doing by giving them a greater experience of the service. They will be able to see a direct link between what you are doing and the effects that you are achieving on their hair, with the added benefit of knowing that buying those particular products will help them to recreate a similar effect.

Explain how routine styling tools can have detrimental effects

Only hair in good condition is easy to maintain. You know how difficult it is to make dry, damaged hair look good. It tends to be lifeless, dull and sits there just like a

EKU *statement*

GH11.40 and GH13.30)
How lifestyle can influence their choice of style (e.g. active sports, career and job requirements)

 Diversion For more information on how to provide advice to clients see Unit G7 Advise and consult clients

EKU *statement*

GH11.42 and GH13.32)
How to give effective advice and recommendations to clients (this also covers GB5.38, GH10.41 and GH4.47)

EKU *statement*

GH11.31) The removal requirements for plaits and twists

EKU *statement*

GH11.37 and GH13.29)
Products for home use that will benefit the client and those to avoid and why (this also covers GB5.34, GH10.37 and GH4.46)

Remember

In shops, people are more likely to buy things that they have handled, so make a point of passing the products that you use to the client so that it initiates interest and discussion.

EKU *statement*

GH11.38) How the continual use of heated equipment can affect the hair (this also covers GH10.38 and GB5.35)

Remember

The condition of the client's hair is directly proportional to the amount of heat applied to it, i.e. the greater the temperature the worse the hair will be.

EKU *statement*

GH11.39) How to recreate and maintain the agreed style (this also covers GH10.39 and GB5.36)

EKU *statement*

GH11.41) The removal and or take-down requirements for the hairstyle

wig! Your clients can recognise the difference between good and poor condition and given the choice, they will always choose hair that has lustre, shine, flexibility and strength.

With these known facts, you would be doing an injustice to your clients if you didn't warn them of the pitfalls of repeatedly using hot styling equipment, so make a point in asking them if they use them at home too. If they say that they use straighteners or tongs on a daily basis then tell them about the benefits of using heat protection sprays. Remember, the condition of their hair is directly proportional to the amount of heat applied to it. So if they are locked into using these styling tools their hair is going to need all the help it can get.

Demonstrate the techniques that you use

Clients want to be able to recreate the effects that you achieve in the salon and this is your chance to show them how to do it. Clients haven't had the benefit of your training; they don't know the little tricks and techniques that make it seem so simple. Show them how to do things; correct brushing, backcombing, twists or rolls. We have all seen the effects when these are not done properly, so make a point of giving them a few tips on how they can achieve a similar result.

Advise on how to take the style down

Damage occurs when the hair is mistreated and this is a simple fact that we all know. When hair is put up, it tends to use a lot of *scaffolding* in support. All that metal work in pins, grips, ornaments and accessories or even rubber hair bands can have a damaging effect on the hair if they are not handled and removed in the proper way.

Tell your clients where they need to start; most people try to feel around the back and take out the first grip or pin that they come to. That's not the way to do it. You know that if the innermost hair sections are pulled out first then it creates a big knot and then everything just tangles together. If you were taking it down, you would start at the last area that was secured into place. Tell clients where they should start and the negative, damaging effects on their hair if they just pull the style apart.

Finally, tell your client about the things that they may need help with too. If you are doing a bridal hair-up, then it might involve a headdress too. Many brides will wear one through the ceremony and the reception after, but want to remove this at some point later in the evening. You know that if it isn't done carefully it could pull the whole hairstyle out of shape! Explain how the combs or accessories are positioned into the hair and the ways that they can be removed carefully without destroying the hairstyle.

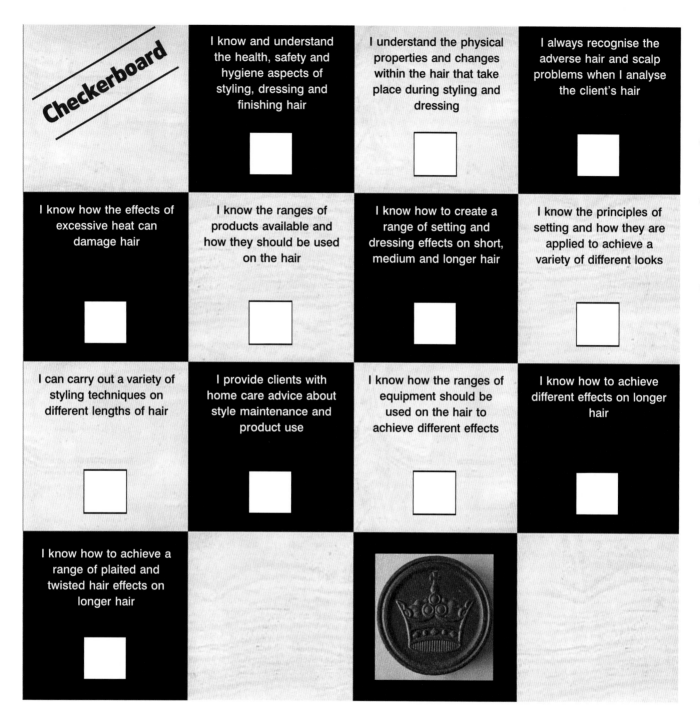

Checkerboard

I know and understand the health, safety and hygiene aspects of styling, dressing and finishing hair

I understand the physical properties and changes within the hair that take place during styling and dressing

I always recognise the adverse hair and scalp problems when I analyse the client's hair

I know how the effects of excessive heat can damage hair

I know the ranges of products available and how they should be used on the hair

I know how to create a range of setting and dressing effects on short, medium and longer hair

I know the principles of setting and how they are applied to achieve a variety of different looks

I can carry out a variety of styling techniques on different lengths of hair

I provide clients with home care advice about style maintenance and product use

I know how the ranges of equipment should be used on the hair to achieve different effects

I know how to achieve different effects on longer hair

I know how to achieve a range of plaited and twisted hair effects on longer hair

Assessment of knowledge and understanding

Project

For this project you will need to gather information from a variety of sources.

Collect together photographs, digital images and magazine clippings about styling, blow-drying, setting and dressing techniques.

Include styles for long hair as well as short; for weddings, special occasions and casual wear.

In your portfolio describe:

- how the styles were achieved
- why each is suitable for its purpose
- the equipment (with examples) that was used to create the effects
- the products (with examples) used to help hold or define the effects.

Revision questions

A selection of different types of questions to check your knowledge.

Q1 Self-cling rollers are commonly known as _____ rollers. Fill in the blank

Q2 Humidity in the atmosphere will help to retain set hairstyles. True or false

Q3 Which of the following dressings are traditionally long 'hair-up' styles? Multi selection

Plaits	☐ 1
Knots	☐ 2
Weaves	☐ 3
Rolls	☐ 4
Braids	☐ 5
Pleats	☐ 6

Q4 The keratin bonds of stretched hair are said to be in the beta state. True or false

Q5 Which chemical bonds within the hair are *not* affected during setting? Multi choice

Hydrogen bonds	○ a
Disulphide bonds	○ b
Salt bonds	○ c
Oxygen bonds	○ d

Q6 Heated rollers are a quick way of setting wet or dry hair in to style. True or false

Q7 Hair set on rollers produces which of the following results and effects? Multi selection

Increased body at the roots	☐ 1
No body at the roots	☐ 2
No movement at the ends	☐ 3
Straighter effects	☐ 4
Wavy effects	☐ 5
Same as blow dried effects	☐ 6

Q8 On long hair, a _____ is a vertical fold, placed centrally at the back. Fill in the blank

Q9 Which item of equipment would smooth and flatten frizzy, unruly hair best? Multi choice

Curling tongs	○ a
Ceramic straighteners	○ b
Crimping irons	○ c
Blow dryer	○ d

Q10 'Hair-ups' are easier to perform on hair that has just been washed, conditioned and dried off. True or false

Preparing for assessment checklist

Remember to:

✔	prepare clients correctly for the services you are going to carry out
✔	put on the protective wear available for styling and dressing hair
✔	listen to the client's requirements and discuss suitable courses of action
✔	adhere to the safety factors when working on clients' hair
✔	keep the work areas clean, hygienic and free from hazards
✔	promote the range of services, products and treatments with the salon
✔	clean and sterilise the tools and equipment before they are used
✔	work carefully and methodically through the processes of setting and blow-drying hair
✔	place, position and direct the hair appropriately to the achieve desired effect
✔	communicate what you are doing to the client as well as your fellow staff members.

Chapter**eleven**
Adding/extending hair

GH15

GH15.1

GH15.2

GH15.3

GH15.4

GH15.5

 More Information

- Personal hygiene
  EKU GH15.14

- Contact Dermatitis
  EKU GH15.5

- General salon
  hygiene see
  Unit G20 Health
  and Safety

See also the appendices for
following relevant
legislation:

- Electricity at Work
  Regulations
  EKU GH15.4

Hair extensions: quick overview

Unit title

GH15 Attach hair to enhance a style

This is an **optional** unit for students taking Hairdressing Level 2, it is made up of
five main outcomes

Main outcomes

GH15.1 Maintain effective and safe methods of working when attaching hair

GH15.2 Plan and prepare to attach hair

GH15.3 Attach and blend pieces of hair

GH15.4 Remove pieces of hair

GH15.5 Provide aftercare advice

What do I need to do for GH15.1?

- Take adequate precautions in preparing yourself and the client before any setting or
  dressing procedure

- Work tidily, safely and effectively at all times

- Maintain standards of personal health and hygiene

- Use a range of tools and equipment suitable for hair extension services

- Work to a commercially acceptable time

What do I need to do for GH15.2?

- Look for contra-indications to hair extension services

- Ask the client questions to help identify any unseen contra-indications and record the
  client's responses

- Carry out tests to establish the suitability of hair extension services

- Prepare suitable extensions to compliment the client's hair

What do I need to do for GH15.3?

- Confirm and agree the required effect with the client before starting

- Work with and apply extensions in a controlled and methodical way

- Check that the client remains comfortable through the process

- Identify any problems and report them to the appropriate person

What do I need to do for GH15.4?

- Follow the manufacturer's instructions for the safe removal of hair extensions

- Carefully remove hair extensions and product build-up from the client's hair

- Clean and prepare the client's hair ready for the next service

What do I need to do for GH15.5?

- Give the client recommendations and advice for maintaining their own hair

What aspects do I need to cover for GH15.1, GH15.2, GH15.3 and GH15.4?

- Hair extensions that are designed to last for a day or those designed to last for several weeks

- A variety of products, tools and equipment used during extension services

- The techniques of affixing different types of hair extensions

- A range of contra-indications to hair extension services

- The types of tests that you should perform prior to extending the client's hair

What do I need to know for GH15.1, GH15.2, GH15.3 and GH15.4?

- Your salon's requirements in relation to salon policies and current legislation

- How to work safely and hygienically when extending hair

- The basic science affecting hair extensions and extension procedures

- How to use and adapt a variety of hair extension types and techniques to achieve the client's desired effect

- The range of tests that you need to carry out prior to delivering any extension service and the courses of action you should take based upon the findings of those tests

- The signs and effects of traction alopecia

- How to cut and style the extensions after they have been applied

- What sorts of advice you should recommend to the client on hair maintenance at home

---

Keywords

Traction alopecia
A condition that is caused by the excessive pulling of hair at the root. It is often associated with longer hair worn in plaits, twists and hair-ups

Cold and hot bonded hair extensions
Cold bonding systems are used at Level 2 to add hair to enhance a hair style. Hot bonding systems are used at Level 3 in different ways and incorporate the use of heat to affix the hair extension to the hair

Clip-on extensions
Pre-coloured wefts of hair that have clips or combs attached to them so that they can be affixed to the hair

Self-adhesive extensions
Pre-coloured wefts of hair that have self-cling, peel-off strips that reveal a sticky tape that attaches the extension to the client's hair

Contra-indications
Signs from tests, visual inspection and client questioning that indicate that a hair extension service is not suitable and therefore cannot be carried out

Hair tests
Pull tests, elasticity tests, and skin tests, which are used to determine contra-indications to hair extension services

Keywords (cont.)

Wefts
Long continuous strands of pre-coloured, pre-bonded hair that create a 'curtain' of hair that can be used to add to, or extend a client's own natural hair

Information covered in this chapter

- The types of products used when extending hair and how they are used
- The types of equipment used when extending hair and how they are used
- How to apply hair extensions
- The things that you should look out for before conducting hair extension services
- How to safely remove extensions from the hair
- The advice you should give to clients in order to maintain their own hair

Introduction

Why are extension services so popular? The answer is pretty obvious: people choose hair extensions to make their hair longer than it already is; and in a world where people no longer want to wait for hair to grow, it provides a relatively quick, temporary solution to their needs.

The term *hair extensions* now covers a wide variety of natural and synthetic pre-formed and post-formed hair additions. They can be applied as single pieces that can be woven or bonded to the client's natural hair, as wefts that can be stitched, clipped or stuck to the client's hair or as added fibres that are introduced to the client's hair, making the hair fuller and longer and providing a long-lasting effect.

 Diversion Some of the EKUs you need for this unit may be found in other units. To save you from unnecessary duplication we have cross-referenced each unit to other areas. You may have already studied that unit in which case a revision of the information will help you apply that knowledge to this unit. If you have not studied that information before then it will help you when you do study that unit.

Where you see this sign it will guide you to the unit in which you will find the information you need.

Note

There are so many different types of hair extension services that, in an attempt to clarify what you will be doing and working with, please note the following differences.

A Level 3 student will be working with all types of hair extensions services. They are required to apply hot and cold, pre-bonded and unbonded hair fibres to natural hair. They will also be blending fibre to match, highlight or introduce other colouring effects whilst attaching hair extensions to the client's own hair.

A Level 2 student will be working with pre-coloured clip-on, stitched, woven and (cold bonded) self-adhesive systems to provide hair extension effects. The student should be able to match the hair extension to either the client's own natural hair or the type of extended effect that client desires.

GH15.1 Maintain effective and safe methods of working when attaching hair

You will be using two different types of hair extension at Level 2:

1. The first, a clip-on extension that is a quick and simple way of adding pre-coloured hair to create a new, generally longer hairstyle effect that will last for an event or an evening out.

2. The second, a self-adhesive extension that is pre-coloured with wefts of hair that have a sticky, peel-back strip, on double sided tape. These are positioned so that they stick to the hair, close to the scalp. The effects created will last longer

(up to several weeks) but need careful removal by trained people using chemicals that unstick the wefts before they move too far away from the scalp as the hair continues to grow out.

Although Unit G20 covers much of the general aspects that you need to know about health, safety and hygiene within the salon environment, each technical hairdressing procedure you do has particular things that are relevant to health and safety.

A full head of hair extensions (even temporary ones) takes a long time to apply, so the main health and safety concerns should relate to the client's comfort, their positioning and their protection. Your posture, work accessibility and personal hygiene are equally important.

Therefore, many of the preparations that you should make regarding these issues are covered elsewhere, so in an attempt to reduce duplication and repetition, please note that some essential knowledge components are diverted to other locations.

Client preparation and protection

See GH10.1 Maintain effective and safe methods of working when styling and finishing hair (page 176)

See GH12.1 Maintain effective and safe methods of working when cutting hair (pages 273–275)

Your preparation, protection and working position

See GH10.1 Maintain effective and safe methods of working when styling and finishing hair (page 176)

See GH20 Make sure your own actions reduce risks to health and safety (pages 10–15)

Service timings

Different extension services take differing lengths of time; you need to be clear in your own mind how long these services take. For example, a partial head of clip-on wefts is going to take less time than a whole head of self-adhesive extensions. So therefore the cost implications in relation to materials used, cost of labour and profit margin required by the salon will all vary considerably. You need to find out how much your salon charges for each type of service so that you can inform clients about the range of options available to them, prior to any consultation/examination taking place.

How long will it take?

To get a rough idea of how long a hair extension service will take, you could time how long it takes to apply one extension then multiply that by the total amount that you will use to create the whole effect. (See Select your material and prepare the hair for extensions on page 260 for more information.)

Synthetic hair wefts

Most temporary hair extensions are made of 'manmade' fibres (acrylic and nylon) and need special care and handling. These

GREAT LENGTHS

EKU statement

GH15.1) Your salon's requirements for client preparation (see page 175)

GH15.6) The range of protective clothing that should be available for clients (see page 20)

EKU statement

GH15.9) Why it is important to protect clients from hair clippings (see page 285)

GH15.12) Why it is important to avoid cross-infection and infestation (see page 276)

EKU statement

GH15.7) The type of personal protective equipment that should be available and used by yourself (see page 20)

GH15.8) Why it is important to use personal protective equipment (see page 17)

GH15.10) How the position of your client and yourself can affect the desired outcome (see pages 175–176)

GH15.13) Why it is important to keep your work area clean and tidy (see page 19)

GH15.17) The importance of personal hygiene (see page 17)

EKU statement

GH15.3) Your salon's and legal requirements for disposal of waste materials

GH15.5) What is contact dermatitis and how to avoid developing it whilst carrying out hair-attachment services

Remember

 If they are looked after, some hair extensions such as clip-ons can be used again, whereas self-adhesive types can only be used once.

types of extension have specific advantages and disadvantages which are highlighted below and at the typical problems table at the end of this chapter.

Hair extension type	Advantages	Disadvantages
Clip-on synthetic wefts CONNECT-2-HAIR LTD	Very easy and relatively quick to apply. Colours don't fade; they are pre-coloured in a variety of single or multi-toned effects. Can be shaped and cut easily to suit or achieve the desired effect. Bulk up fine hair, or hair that lacks volume. Can provide a quick cost effective solution to people who want longer hair. Can be removed at home with care providing the right advice has been given.	Needs careful handling, tends to get matted very easily. Needs to be brushed regularly when applied to avoid tangling Avoid heat styling as all synthetic extensions are very susceptible to becoming misshapen or damaged when excess heat is applied. Can cause traction alopecia if incorrectly applied.
Self-adhesive wefts CONNECT-2-HAIR LTD	Last for a long time with care and attention. Provide a cost-effective solution to the need for longer-lasting hair extensions. Far quicker to apply than single, pre-bonded hot extension systems. Colours don't fade; they are pre-coloured in a variety of single or multi-toned effects. Can be shaped and cut easily to suit or achieve the desired effect. Bulk up fine hair, or hair that lacks volume.	Need careful home maintenance so advice/ products are essential to maintain the look. Need to be removed at the salon by trained staff. Avoid heat styling as all synthetic extensions are very susceptible to becoming misshapen or damaged after excess heat has been applied. Can cause traction alopecia if incorrectly applied.

GH15.2 Plan and prepare to attach hair

It's not a positive thing to look for why *not* to do something; but with hair extensions you really do have to find out if your client is a suitable candidate for the service.

Your client may be very keen to have them, but you need to safeguard the salon's good name and remove the possibility of legal action being taken at some later time, by making sure that you:

● conduct a thorough consultation with the client

● correctly identify any contra-indications to the extension service

● carry out the necessary tests upon the client

● ask the client the right sorts of questions

● record the responses that the client makes in answer to your questions

● clean and prepare the hair.

Consultation

You need to consider many things before you venture into the process of adding hair. It may be an exciting piece of work for you to do and make a long day much shorter; but remember that's not the point. It's not worth doing unless it 'ticks all the boxes' for the client too. Wanting hair extensions is not enough; they have to be suitable, appropriate and achievable.

Style suitability This is an important aspect of consultation. Any work that you are planning to do should be really thought through beforehand. When you add hair to the client's existing hair it will change the appearance dramatically, by making the roots a lot fuller than they were to start with. You need to make this clear to the client beforehand as it is very difficult for anyone to visualise what the difference will be after the service is finished.

Similarly, if you were to do a full head of hair extensions, will they still suit the client's head and face shape after? It may be a very professional application when it's finished, it may impress many other people, but you do need to ask yourself whether the style enhances the client and is it an improvement on what she looked like before.

Hair condition Test the hair for elasticity strength and sustainability (see tests on page 259) to look for damage or over-porous hair. Hair that is weakened for any reason is a contra-indication for hair extensions. If the client is definitely intent on having extensions, think about recommending a course of restructurants or hair strengtheners beforehand.

Hair tendency This is also a major consideration: if the hair is curly it may need smoothing or straightening first, but remember when the hair is washed it will revert back to its natural state and this may look very strange if the hair extensions don't match the rest of the natural tendency.

Hair density The amount of natural hair will affect the choice of extension and the amount needed to provide an overall balanced result.

Hair styling It is unlikely that new wefts of hair can be applied without any form of styling or cutting post-application. The wefts are not the hairstyle themselves; they are the material that you add in order to create a new style afterwards.

BALMAIN

Remember

Any hair extensions work takes a lot of time and when it's done well, the final effects can be long-lasting too.

Make this clear to the client from the outset; you will need to adapt the newly applied lengths to suit both the natural fall and abundance of their hair as well as the client.

Cutting into newly applied lengths of hair can be quite shocking to clients as they see this as the core of what they are paying for. You need to be reassuring in the course of action that you take; if you need to do a lot of cutting after, explain why.

Face and head shapes Style suitability is about balance and proportion, so you need to take the client's physical features into consideration during the consultation. The basic principles of how these apply is covered in Unit G7 Advise and consult with clients and a further aesthetic evaluation can be seen in Unit GH11 Physical features – style suitability, on page 241. The principles applied to hair-ups can be used here although the considerations applicable to hair extensions are more to do with adding width and height.

Activity

Preparing for hair extensions

Complete this table by filling in the missing information. Review this chapter again if you need to find out more.

Preparation	What do you need to do?	What things do you need to look out for?
Styling tools		
The client		
Yourself		
Clip-on extensions		
Self-adhesive extensions		

EKU statement

GH15.18) The importance of questioning clients to establish any contra-indications to hairdressing services

GH15.26) Potential consequences of failing to carry out tests

GH15.27) The courses of action to take in the event of adverse reactions to tests (e.g. what type of reactions you must report to other, more senior people)

GH15.32) How to identify the signs of traction alopecia

GH15.33) How the contra-indications in the range can affect the provision of the service (e.g. hair loss and excessive thinning, eczema, psoriasis, allergies etc.)

Remember

Traction alopecia is a problem caused by hair tensioning.

Hair is capable of sustaining its own weight and, within reason, a certain amount of mechanical wear and tear, such as brushing, combing and detangling knots. Any added hair is an extra weight or mass upon the hair roots and where extensions have been attached to small areas of the hair, thinning or baldness can occur!

You should explain this to the client during your consultation.

Looking for contra-indications to hair extension services

One of the more serious after-effects of wearing hair extensions is traction alopecia. This occurs when a constant pressure, resulting from wearing hair tied up or adding weight from hair extensions, is exerted upon the roots of the hair. This can result in hair loss in patches upon the scalp showing as baldness and is particularly obvious in areas of weaker hair such as the temples or hairlines.

If your client hasn't had hair extensions before, they could still suffer with traction alopecia, as this is the result of any hair tensioning styling effect. But make a point of visually inspecting the scalp to look for the signs.

Skin sensitivity This is another consideration. You should ask the client if they have any sensitivity issues relating to product intolerances or to synthetic materials. Not everyone is comfortable with wearing hair attachments; some people don't like the added weight caused by added hair pieces and headaches can be caused by the constant pressure formed at the roots by wearing extensions. Similarly, the amount of added synthetic material can slow down the ventilation to the scalp causing the head to get hotter and sweat or simply feel generally uncomfortable. This effect is similar to that of wearing synthetic fabrics over the body; not everyone can do this and many people, given the choice, prefer to wear natural fibres.

Allergies This is not to be mixed up with skin sensitivities. Someone may have a sensitivity to certain things but it doesn't mean that they are allergic to them, the allergic reaction is something quite different and, potentially, far more dangerous. It is unlikely that a client would be allergic to synthetic hair; but it is quite possible that they might be allergic to the chemicals that you would use to maintain the looks or to remove long-lasting hair extensions at some later time.

Again ask the client if they have any known allergies to certain products or chemicals.

Hair and scalp disorders Look for the obvious signs that something is wrong. Hair loss, general thinning, hair damage, weakened hair, infestations and scalp infections are all contra-indications. If you are not sure, then ask someone in authority with more experience for a second opinion.

Medical advice If you are unsure of any indicators that you see, or hear of, from asking the client questions, then the service must be postponed at least until the client has sought medical advice.

Carry out the necessary tests

Even if you have no reasons so far not to carry out the extensions service, you must still do a few tests before carrying out the service. First of all think about the type of extension service that you are going to offer.

Clip-on hair extensions You need to check the hair's strength and elasticity to make sure that the added weight to the hair doesn't create a pressure and tension that the hair will not be able to sustain and hence cause damage or breakage.

Self-stick extensions In addition to a pull test and an elasticity test you should also do a skin test with the removal chemicals that you will be using in several weeks' time. There is no point in applying the extensions if they cannot safely be removed at some later time.

See Unit G7 Advise and consult with clients for more information about conducting tests and testing (pages 113–114).

Asking the client the right questions

You cannot find out enough information about the client by examination alone. In addition to the questions you should ask covering the previous aspects, you need to find out whether the client has had an extensions service before and whether they had any problems with them.

EKU statement

GH15.21) The types and purposes of tests

GH15.22) The importance of following manufacturers' instructions for testing

GH15.24) When and how tests should be carried out and the expected results

GH15.31) The potential consequences of excessive tension on the hair

Remember

 Too much weight upon the hair will result in traction alopecia, hair damage or breakage!

EKU statement

GH15.23) The methods of and reasons for conducting pull tests

GH15.25) How the results of tests can influence all aspects of the service

EKU statement

GH15.19) Why it is important to record client responses to questioning

GH15.20) The legal significance of client questioning and of recording the client's responses

GH15.28) Why it is important to record test results

Ask the client how they intend to manage their hair themselves, if they have had extensions before, they may have covered many of the pitfalls that others tend to find difficult. Most of the difficulties that the clients encounter are to do with having more hair than they have been used to before. People don't like to change their habits; the ways in which they use products and equipment have to change if they want to maintain their hair in looking its best and you have an obligation to give them the benefit of your professional opinion.

Record the client's responses

Make sure that you record the responses to the questions that you ask as well as the details of the tests that you perform. Update the client's record card in full and immediately after you have done the test. Don't leave it until later, you might forget! These records are essential information that will be needed again and help to show that a competent service has been provided at that time.

This would be vitally important if there was a problem at some later stage, particularly if something went wrong and it involved any legal action taken against the salon.

Remember

Record the client's responses to your questions and the comments about how the results of any tests affected their hair and skin.

If you are not sure about the results of any tests that you perform, ask a senior member of staff for their second opinion.

EKU statement

GH15.16) The correct use and maintenance of tools and equipment

GH15.34) The manufacturer's instructions for preparation of added hair

EKU statement

GH15.35) How the client's hair should be prepared for each of the hair attachment systems in the range

GH15.39) How the attachment systems in the range secure added hair into the client's hair

GH15.41) Tools and equipment necessary for each attachment system in the range and how these are used

Activity

Hair tests for extensions

Complete this activity by filling in the missing information in the spaces provided

Type of test	What is the purpose of the test?	How is the test carried out?
Elasticity test		
Pull test		
Skin test		

Prepare the hair for extensions

After conducting your consultation you need to select the appropriate extensions.

Both clip-on and self-adhesive wefts are available in a range of natural and vivid fashion shades. You will have found out during your consultation what result the client is expecting. Do they want strong colour contrasting effects that will obviously stand out from their own hair, or do they want it to match their natural hair to give a new longer effect? After selecting your colour, you need to work out how much material you will need.

Hair extensions are applied to a point that will create a horseshoe section around the head at the temples. If you continue further up than this they will stick out from the head too much and show.

So, generally speaking for a complete head of self-adhering extensions you would need three or four wefts on both sides and five to seven at the back. This, making a total of around 11–15, would be enough although some thicker densities could take even more. As clip-on extensions can be more bulky because of the comb/clip attachments you may need fewer as they will stick out at the sides.

Remember

Always follow the manufacturer's instructions for preparing, handling and applying hair extensions to hair.

Remember

Handle the synthetic wefts of hair with care, they can become easily matted or tangled; always hold them by the bonded end, allowing the free hair ends to fall naturally. Comb or brush carefully to keep them smooth.

Before continuing with the application you should wash, condition and dry the hair into style. This is particularly important for longer-lasting extensions as this could be the last time the scalp would get a good rubbing to remove dead skin cells for some time.

When hair extensions have been left in for some time it is quite normal to see dandruff forming at or near the scalp. This is because it is very difficult to remove the shedding layers of the epidermis when the extensions attachments are so close to the scalp. This is easily removed by washing after the extensions have been removed. (Explain this to the client so that any shocks later are avoided and they know that this is a normal expectation for this type of service.)

GREAT LENGTHS

Activity
Practise the techniques

You will not be able to jump straight in and complete a full head of self-adhesive extensions without having seen how they work and can be adapted to different hair types and lengths.

Get used to working with extensions before carrying out the service on your clients; practise the tensioning and application on training blocks beforehand. This will get you up to speed with the placement, timings and dressing of the hair, well before trying it out live!

Remember

Hair extensions will often need some form of trimming or styling too, so practise this part of the service after you have applied them.

EKU *statement*

GH15.55) How to help relieve client anxieties in a reassuring way

EKU *statement*

GH15.42) The generally accepted sequences of working for the hair attachment systems in the range

GH15.43) Why it is important to maintain a correct and even tension when attaching hair

Step-by-step: Technique for adding clip-on extensions

1 Starting at the lower nape; section off the hair into neat areas, securing the lengths out of the way.

2 Backcomb the section near the root to provide an area for the clip-on extension to bond to. Apply a little hairspray to help fix the hair.

3 Select your extension, making sure that the hair is free from tangles and that the snap-in clips are open and ready to use.

4 Clip-on the extension along the weft and into the backcombed section of hair. Snap the clips closed to lock into place.

5 Continue the steps 2–4 around the head until you reach a point near to the temple area.

6 Drop the upper section over the extensions and style to create the finished effect.

Step 3 Select your extension.

Step 4 Clip the extension into the section of hair.

Step 5 Continue until you reach a point near to the temple area.

IMAGES COURTESY OF WWW.HEADKANDY.COM

Step-by-step: Adding self-adhesive hair extensions

Step 1 Preparing the natural hair Taper the hair using thinning scissors to soften the edges and use a finger razor to flat taper the fringe area and remove any straight blunt cut lines so that the fibre will blend with the natural hair.

Step 2 Preparing the natural hair.

Step 3 Mega-mixing the extension hair colours together.

Step 4 The wefts are applied. The practitioner uses a Mclau on her finger to help take straight clean sections of hair. The weft is measured to the same width as the hair section and cut to size using an old pair of hairdressing scissors.

Step 5 Apply the weft directly onto the natural hair.

Step 6 Applying the extension hair.

Step 7 Take a fine section of natural hair (about ¼ cm) above the tape and drop it down over the tape, pressing the natural hair to the topside of the tape to ensure that the weft is secure and that the tape is undetectable. Follow the same procedure in areas 2, 3 and 4, before placing the titian highlights into areas 5 and 6.

Step 8 The titian fibre is applied by cutting 1 cm square sections of the tape and placing it visually.

Final effect

EKU *statement*

GH15.44) Why and how freehand blending cutting techniques should be adapted when hair extensions are present

Remember

You can't cut hair extensions into layered effects very easily as the sections are difficult to hold. If you do need to cut the added hair after, always finish off the effects by freehand cutting.

Remember

Before you do any cutting after the extensions have been applied, show the client the different types of perimeter shapes that can be achieved, so that they can choose between solid or shattered outline effects.

BALMAIN

Special note: Be careful to maintain an even tension when you take down each section of hair and place it onto the self-adhering strip. You can only position the weft once, as when it has adhered to the hair, you won't be able to remove and reposition it again!

A successful extension service must position the wefts as close to the roots as possible, any slack areas will cause the effect to either fail prematurely or to become unmanageable for the client at home.

Caution: If you use heated styling equipment to finish the effect, make sure that you don't apply any excessive heat to the hair extensions. They will distort, get matted and unmanageable or melt!

Hair by Theresa Bullock, Photography by Ozzie Rizzo

Final shaping and styling

The reason why clients have extensions is because they want their hair to appear longer and/or thicker; but sometimes, the effect created by the extensions is then out of balance with the remainder of their own hair and needs further work.

So after applying the extensions and finish to the hair you should show the client the effect to see if it compares with what they expected.

In nine cases out of ten the client will be thrilled at the quick results of added length and the job is done. However, there will be the odd occasion where the added length seems disproportionate with the rest of the client's hair, or they have stray

Activity

Revision questions

Each hairdressing service has its own particular aspects that need care and thought. The questions below will help you to focus upon the things that you need to know about attaching hair

1 Why do you need to do a consultation beforehand?

2 What sorts of things would be contra-indications to this service?

3 Why does tension and positioning make a big difference to the attachment techniques?

4 Why do you need to do a skin test for attaching self adhesive extensions?

5 What has traction alopecia got to do with hair extensions?

6 What sorts of advice should you give the client?

7 What things can you do with natural hair that you can't with artificial/ synthetic hair?

ends that need tidying up. In either event, you need to do some freehand cutting or trimming to finish the effect.

(See Unit GH12 Cut hair using basic techniques, for more information.)

GH15.4 Remove pieces of hair

Clip-on extensions

Clip-on hair extensions can, with care, be removed by the client themselves. So you need to show them how they are attached and how the clips snap into position. Explain to them how they should be removed carefully and how this will prevent any lasting damage to their hair.

Self-adhesive extensions

The amount of time that hair extensions last is difficult to estimate. The durability of the effect is always directly proportionate to the handling and care that the client provides herself. So with this in mind a client can be told that they can expect them to last up to a certain point; then after this they must be removed so that they don't become too difficult to manage or cause any longer-lasting damage to the hair.

Unlike clip-on extensions, the self-adhesive type need to be removed professionally, with a revisit to the salon.

You need to make this clear to the client right from the start. At the point where the hair with the attached extension has grown more than 1 cm away from the root area (which is approximately four weeks) the hair will start to become harder to manage. It will be more difficult to shampoo as rubbing will work the edges of the extension away from the hair. Brushing/combing will be more problematic as the hair will keep snagging and tangling on the bristles or teeth. At the point when this starts to happen, the extensions must be removed; even if a new set are to be applied.

Self-adhesive extensions use special chemical sprays or solutions to dissolve the bond attaching them to the hair. When this is applied/sprayed on to the self-cling tape it quickly reduces the adhesion and therefore releases the weft from the hair. The removed weft can then be inspected to see if it is worth keeping or whether it should be thrown away.

BALMAIN

complete extension
hair Make-Up

EKU statement

GH15.30) The average rate of hair growth

GH15.53) Removal requirements for attached hair

EKU statement

GH15.45) How to correctly detangle hair from point to root using specialised combs and brushes

GH15.46) The importance of following manufacturer's instructions when shampooing and conditioning the hair

GH15.47) Products for home use that will benefit the client and those to avoid and why

Activity
Create a style portfolio

The effects that are created by the addition of hair extensions aren't necessarily obvious to the untrained eye. Therefore you would be better off using visual aids that show hair with extensions rather than not.

Your clients would like to see effects that can be created for them and the most obvious way that you can do this is by developing a portfolio of the work and effects that your salon can do and provide as a service.

Start by collecting as many pictures that show this type of work. You can then, over time, add to this by taking pictures of work that you have completed in the salon.

The self-cling strips can be removed from the weft in the same way that the extension is removed from the hair and, depending on its quality, the weft can be washed, re-conditioned and retained for future use, or discarded. If the weft is to be reused, new, double-sided self-adhesive tapes will need to be applied after the wefts have been dried.

Step-by-step: Removing self-adhering extensions from dry hair

Step 1 Pour a small amount of the removal solution onto a cottonwool pad. Wipe the top side of the tape near the root area then lift the tape weft and wipe the underside of the weft.

Step 2 Allow the removal solution to penetrate for 30 seconds to one minute.

Step 3 Hold the end of the extension hair contained in the tape and gently pull it away from the hair and scalp. The weft comes away easily from the natural hair in a matter of seconds.

Finally The hair and scalp should be shampooed and conditioned thoroughly and carefully to remove any dead skin cells or product build-up. It can then be dried in preparation for other salon services.

Hair by Theresa Bullock, Photography by Ozzie Rizzo

GH15.5 Provide aftercare advice

EKU *statement*

GH15.54) How to give effective advice and recommendations to clients

The durability and the quality of your client's new hair extensions are dependent upon the information and advice that you provide to the client. If clients aren't given the right or sufficient information on how they can handle their hair afterwards then the effect won't be very successful or won't last very long.

Typical problems with artificial/synthetic hair extensions

Problem:	Advice to give:
Hair extensions tend to tangle or get knotted easily	Suggest suitable products and tools that will help to make grooming and brushing easier.
	Explain that the longer lengths should always be combed from points to roots. Long hair and particularly synthetic hair needs to be disentangled by working and freeing-up from the ends

Problem:	Advice to give:
	back through the lengths towards the bonded area of the weft with a wide tooth comb rather than a brush.
Hair lengths tend to get matted when they are shampooed	Suggest conditioning products that are designed to work on synthetic/artificial hair. Sometimes the conditioners for acrylic hair are best applied before the hair is wetted; this reduces the locking and matting result caused by the action of rubbing during shampooing. Suggest that the hair is shampooed in a different way along the lengths by a smoothing action, rather than rubbing at the scalp.
Longer lengths get matted or knotted during sleep/overnight	People who are more restless during sleep may find that the rubbing action of the hair on the pillow makes the extensions lock together overnight. Suggest tying the hair in ponytail with a soft fabric ribbon; this reduces the movement and the effects caused by chaffing on the pillow. Alternatively, if the hair is very long, you can advise wrapping the hair in a silken scarf. This holds the lengths together and stops any chance of knotting.
Hair gets in the way at work or in sport	Clients who are used to shorter hair will not be familiar with the problems associated with long hair. Explain the benefits of wearing hair up as opposed to down during work/sport as this may have a more professional or beneficial effect.
Limited styling options after extensions have been applied	When artificial extensions have been applied to the hair, the options available to the client for future styling/finishing in other ways are limited. Synthetic hair does not respond well to hot styling, the hair can't be moulded or shaped in the same ways that you would style natural hair. You must make the client aware of this from the outset. Any excess heat applied to the hair will cause it to distort, mat together or melt. When this occurs, the only course of action is to cut the damaged lengths off, or to remove them altogether! This can be avoided as long as you point out the problems before they leave the salon.

Home-aftercare checklist

✔	Talk through the style as you work; that way the client sees how you handle different aspects of the look.
✔	Show and recommend the products/equipment that you use so that the client gets the right things to enable them to achieve the same effects.
✔	Explain how routine styling with blow-dryers, heated tongs or straighteners can have detrimental effects on hair extensions.
✔	Demonstrate the techniques that you use so they can achieve that salon hair look too.
✔	If you use clip-on extensions give the client the advice on how to take the extensions out safely without causing damage to the hair.
✔	Tell the client how long the extensions are likely to last.

(For more information about the advice to give clients about aftercare see Unit G7 Advise and consult with clients.)

EKU *statement*

GH15.48) How to protect the hair when sleeping and why

GH15.49) How lifestyle can affect the client's choice of style (eg active sports, career requirements)

GH15.50) How the use of artificial hair can affect styling possibilities

GH15.51) How to maintain their agreed style

EKU *statement*

GH15.52) How long the hair extensions can be expected to last

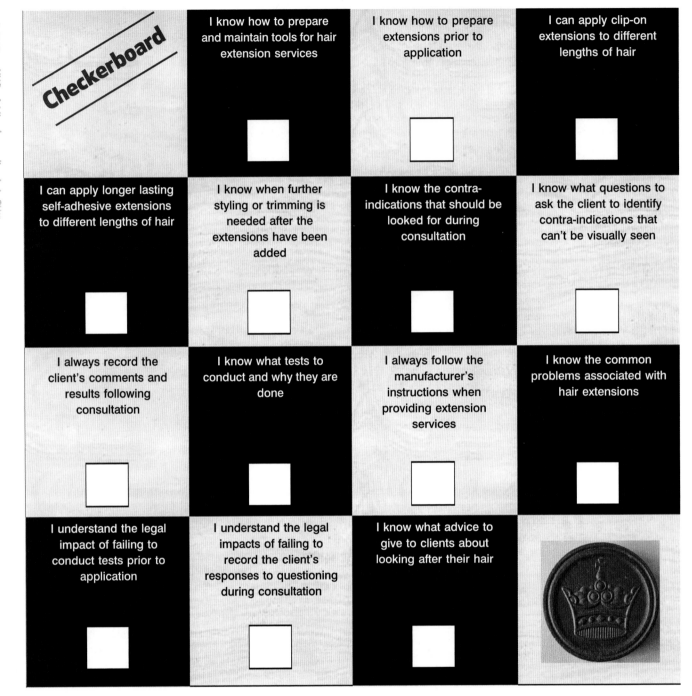

Checkerboard

I know how to prepare and maintain tools for hair extension services

I know how to prepare extensions prior to application

I can apply clip-on extensions to different lengths of hair

I can apply longer lasting self-adhesive extensions to different lengths of hair

I know when further styling or trimming is needed after the extensions have been added

I know the contra-indications that should be looked for during consultation

I know what questions to ask the client to identify contra-indications that can't be visually seen

I always record the client's comments and results following consultation

I know what tests to conduct and why they are done

I always follow the manufacturer's instructions when providing extension services

I know the common problems associated with hair extensions

I understand the legal impact of failing to conduct tests prior to application

I understand the legal impacts of failing to record the client's responses to questioning during consultation

I know what advice to give to clients about looking after their hair

Assessment of knowledge and understanding

Project

For this project you will need to gather information from different sources.

Collect photos, digital images or magazine cuttings for different hair extension types. Include different looks for both longer and shorter hair for the following occassions:

A weddings

B parties

C general going out.

In your portfolio describe:

● how the styles were achieved

● why each is suitable for its purpose

● the type of extension that was used to create each effect.

Revision questions

A selection of different types of questions to check your knowledge about extensions

Q1	Hair extensions can either be natural hair or _____ made fibres.	Fill in the blank
Q2	Synthetic/artificial hair can be styled with tongs and straightening irons.	True or false
Q3	What sorts of attachment are used for temporary hair extensions?	Multi selection

Hot bonding ☐ 1
Cold bonding ☐ 2
Clips ☐ 3
Self-adhesive strips ☐ 4
Glue ☐ 5
Cement ☐ 6

Q4	Hot bonded extensions are permanent.	True or false
Q5	Which type of extension is suitable for a single event or 24 hours?	Multi choice

Clip-on extension ○ a
Glued-on extension ○ b
Plaited extension ○ c
Self-adhesive extension ○ d

Q6	Clip-on extensions are a quick way of making hair appear fuller/longer than it is.	True or false
Q7	To what positions are hair extensions normally affixed so that they can blend with the client's own hair?	Multi selection

On the ends of the hair ☐ 1
Near the roots of the hair ☐ 2
At the crown of the head ☐ 3
Over the top of the head ☐ 4
In areas lower than the temples ☐ 5
In areas lower than the ears ☐ 6

Q8	Hair extensions are pre-bonded _____ of either natural or artificial hair.	Fill in the blank

Q9   Which item of equipment would smooth and flatten frizzy, unruly hair before attaching hair extensions?   Multi choice

Curling tongs   ○ a

Ceramic straighteners   ○ b

Crimping irons   ○ c

Blow-dryer   ○ d

Q10   Hair extensions can not be worn up after they have been attached to the hair.   True or false

Preparing for assessment checklist

Remember to:

✔	prepare clients correctly for the services you are going to carry out
✔	put on the protective wear available for attaching hair
✔	listen to the client's requirements and discuss suitable styling options
✔	adhere to the safety factors when working on clients' hair
✔	keep the work areas clean, hygienic and free from hazards
✔	promote the range of services, products and treatments within the salon
✔	clean and sterilise the tools and equipment before they are used
✔	work carefully and methodically through the processes of attaching hair
✔	place, position and tension the hair correctly when attaching extensions
✔	communicate what you are doing to the client as well as your fellow staff members.

Chapter**twelve**
Cutting

More Information
See units:

G7 Advise and consult with clients

G20 Make sure your own actions reduce risks to health and safety

G8 Develop and maintain your effectiveness at work

G17 Give clients a positive impression of yourself

Cutting: quick overview

Unit title

GH12 Cut hair using basic techniques

This is a **mandatory** unit for hairdressing at Level 2, it is made up of three main outcomes

Main outcomes

GH12.1 Maintain effective and safe methods of working when cutting hair

GH12.2 Cut hair to achieve a variety of looks

GH12.3 Provide aftercare advice

What do I need to do for GH12.1?

- Make sure that the client is adequately covered and protected
- Make sure that your working position is comfortable and safe
- Keep the work area clean and tidy and that waste materials are disposed of properly
- Work without causing risks to you or your client's health and safety
- Work efficiently and effectively

What do I need to do for GH12.2?

- Choose suitable visual aids to help with style selection for your client
- Prepare your client's hair before cutting
- Seek confirmation of the desired look before starting
- Cut your client's hair using a variety of creative cutting techniques
- Check that the final effect is accurate, that it compliments the client's features and their personal image and that the client is satisfied with the results

What do I need to do for GH12.3?

- Give accurate constructive advice on how the client can maintain the look

Information covered in this chapter

- The tools and equipment used during cutting, their maintenance and the preparations that you should make before cutting
- The factors that influence hair cutting
- Basic cutting techniques
- The aftercare advice that you should give

What aspects do I need to cover for GH12.1, GH12.2 and GH12.3?

- A variety of cutting tools and equipment
- A range of factors that influence or limit the choice of styling
- Different types of cutting techniques that are used to create creative effects

What aspects do I need to know for GH12.1, GH12.2 and GH12.3?

- Your salon's requirements for preparation, timings and standards of service
- How to work safely, effectively and hygienically when cutting hair
- Factors about hair that affect styling choice, suitability and durability
- The ways of methodically cutting wet or dry hair to achieve the desired effects
- How to correct commonly occurring problems that can occur during cutting
- The aftercare advice and recommendations that you should give to clients

Introduction

Cutting is the most important aspect of hairdressing, even if it is not considered number one by hairdressers and professionals within the craft: ask any member of the public. The difference between watching someone cut and being able to cut doesn't seem much in one sentence, but they are often years apart.

When you watch a senior stylist cut hair they make it seem so simple. They seem to work at different points around the head taking bits off in a random way. Then after 30 minutes or so they put down their scissors and comb and start to style the client's hair.

When you know how to cut hair the paragraph above will sound so alien. All of those little changes in the way that the stylist holds the hair, the position that they stand and the techniques that they use will all fall into place.

This chapter aims to start you on that learning journey.

Basic building blocks for cutting

As you became more familiar with the basic cutting techniques you will find that you can achieve a lot of the everyday styles that clients want by combining the skills of freehand, club and scissor over comb work together, to create all sorts of layered and one-length effects.

Cutting at Level 2 is a constant process of building on the basics and practising a range of techniques, gaining more experience and building on your confidence.

This chapter aims to tackle all of the disciplines that you need to cover under the following topics:

- preparation and maintenance
- client consultation
- identifying the influencing factors that affect style choice
- controlling hair cutting
- cutting techniques
- providing clients with recommendations and advice.

GH12.1 — Maintain effective and safe methods of working when cutting hair

Preparation and maintenance

Preparing the client

Your salon has its own policy and codes of practice for preparing clients and you must observe these. Some things are general common sense and courtesy, whereas others are client or salon specific. But at the very least your salon will have a procedure for gowning and protecting the client from spillages or hair clippings, methods for preparing tools and equipment and the expectations for personal standards in relation to technical ability and hygiene.

You may be an experienced operator but don't forget the basics.

Above all you do need to remember the client's personal comfort and safety throughout the salon visit i.e. cover the client with a clean, laundered gown and place a cutting collar around the shoulders.

Make sure that the gown is on properly and fastened around the neck. It should cover and protect their clothes and come up high enough to cover collars and necklines. Don't make the fastening too tight, but it should be close enough at least to protect the client's clothes and stop hair clippings from going down their neck which is both uncomfortable whilst they are in the salon and irritating if they are returning to work or doing things for the rest of the day.

Make sure that the hair is clean

You can't cut hair well if it is loaded with hairspray or it has product build-up. If the client uses a lot of finishing products on their hair you will need to make sure that this has been thoroughly washed out before you start. The quality of the finish that you can achieve upon the hair is directly related to the freedom needed to complete the job without the hair locking together with grease or gum. The hair should comb easily and freely during

EKU *statement*

GH12.1) Your salon's requirements for preparation

GH12.4) The range of protective materials that should be available for clients

GH12.5) Why it is important to protect clients from hair clippings

GH12.7) The safety considerations which must be taken into account when cutting hair

DENMAN

Cutting collar

EKU *statement*

GH12.19) Why it is important to check the hair before and after shampooing prior to cutting

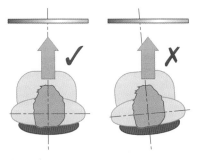

Chair/client angle to mirror

Remember

 Always dry the client's hair well to remove the excess water before cutting, blow-drying or finger-drying.

EKU *statement*

GH12.14) The importance of personal hygiene

sectioning so that you achieve the correct holding angles and cutting angles without tangles or binding.

Check the client's hair after washing too. If the hair hasn't been rinsed thoroughly and still has lather or conditioner in it, you won't be able to see the natural fall of the hair and this could cause you to miss significant factors.

Adjust the working position and height

Client positioning has a lot to do with your safety too. If a client is slouched in the chair, they are a danger not only to themselves but to you too as they will put unnecessary pressure on the spine and you will not be able to stand up properly, causing fatigue or risk of injury from poor posture.

Client comfort should extend to the point where it makes the salon visit a welcome and pleasurable experience. They shouldn't clutter the floor around the styling chair with bags, magazines and shopping. Anything that can safely be stored away should be: it is not only a distraction, it's a safety hazard too.

Salon chairs are designed with comfort and safety in mind; your client should be seated with their back flat against the back of the chair, their legs uncrossed and the chair at a height at which it is comfortable for you to work. You need to be able to get to all parts of the head, so the chair's height should be adjusted to suit the particular height of the client. Don't be afraid of asking the client to sit up: it is in their best interest too!

Position in relation to mirror   The positioning of the client in front of the mirror is very important. Any angle of the head other than perpendicular to the mirror and the angle of the head to the seated position will affect the line and balance of the haircut.

Many salon workstations have built-in foot rests and there are good reasons for this. The foot rest

1 is there to improve the comfort for the seated client at any cutting height

2 helps balance the client and encourages them to sit squarely in front of the mirror

3 tries to discourage the client from sitting cross-legged

4 promotes better posture by making the client sit back properly with their back flat against the back of the chair.

All of the above factors are critical for you and the client in ensuring their comfort throughout, and that you are not hindered in doing your task. For example, if your client sits with crossed legs, it will alter the horizontal plane of their shoulders and this will make your job of trying to get even and level baselines more difficult.

Rough dry the hair so that you work only with damp hair throughout the cut.

Dry off the client's hair so that they are not sitting with saturated hair, it is uncomfortable for them as wet hair soon feels cold even if it doesn't drip onto the gown and their clothes. During cutting, having the hair pre-dried allows the natural tendencies, movements and growth directions of the hair to be seen. This is extremely important for cutting, as the wave movement and hair growth patterns are all being considered as the style develops.

Your personal hygiene

Personal hygiene can't be stressed enough; it is vitally important for anyone working in personal services.

For more information on this topic see Unit G20 Make sure your actions reduce risks to health and safety.

I-STOCK/©ALVAREZ

Science

Hair science: did you know

We all carry large numbers of micro-organisms inside us, on our skin and in our hair. These organisms, such as bacteria, fungi and viruses, are too small to be seen with the naked eye. Bacteria and fungi can be seen through a microscope, but viruses are too small even for that.

Many micro-organisms are quite harmless, but some can cause disease. Those that are harmful to people are called pathogens. Flu and cold sores for example, are caused by a virus, thrush and athletes foot by a fungus and bronchitis often by bacteria. Conditions like these, which can be transmitted from one person to another, are said to be *infectious*.

The body is naturally resistant to infection; it can fight most pathogens using its inbuilt immunity system, so it is possible to be infected with pathogenic organisms without contracting the disease. When you have a disease, the symptoms are the visible signs that something is wrong. They are the results of the infection and of the reactions of the body to that infection. Symptoms help you to recognise the disease.

Infectious diseases should always be treated by a doctor. Non-infectious conditions and defects can be treated with products available from the chemist.

Preparing the tools and equipment

Get your own scissors, clippers, combs and sectioning clips ready beforehand; that doesn't mean as the client arrives in the chair from the basin! You must be prepared; your tools and equipment must be hygienically clean, sterilised and safe to use. You would have needed to have removed your combs from the Barbicide™ or steriliser prior to use. These would be rinsed and dried and put near to your workstation. All cutting tools would need to be checked and maintained on a daily basis.

Plastic and rubber cutting accessories

Never use dirty or damaged tools. Germs can breed in the crevices and corners and can cross-infect other clients.

Clean or wipe all tools before disinfecting or sterilising.

Cutting collars should be washed and dried before use.

Other metal cutting tools

Some disinfectants can corrode metal and blunt edges. Check the manufacturer's instructions before using them.

EKU statement

GH12.7) The safety considerations which must be taken into account when cutting hair

EKU statement

GH12.3) Your salon's and legal requirements for disposal of waste materials

If corrosion or rusting occurs the equipment is rendered unsafe. Always make sure that this doesn't happen.

Take special care when cleaning and lubricating scissors.

All electrical repairs should be carried out by professional people. Do not attempt to undertake them yourself.

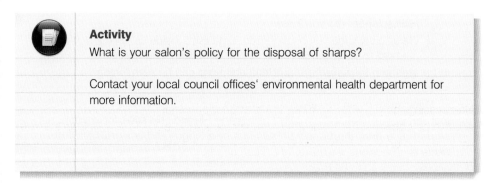

Activity

What is your salon's policy for the disposal of sharps?

Contact your local council offices' environmental health department for more information.

Remember

Disposal of sharp items
Used razor blades and similar items should be placed into a safe container ('sharps' box'). When the container is full it can be disposed of correctly. This type of salon waste should be kept away from general salon waste as special disposal arrangements may be provided by your local authority.

EKU *statement*

GH12.8) Why it is important to avoid cross-infection and infestation
GH12.11) Methods cleaning, disinfecting and or sterilisation used in salons

Preventing infection

A warm, humid salon can offer a perfect home for disease-carrying bacteria. If they can find food in the form of dust and dirt, they may reproduce rapidly. Good ventilation, however, provides a circulating air current that will help to prevent their growth. This is why it is important to keep the salon clean, dry and well aired at all times. This includes clothing, work areas, tools and all equipment. Every salon uses some form of sterilising device as a means of providing hygienically safe work implements.

Sterilisation means the complete eradication of living organisms. Different devices use different sterilisation methods, which may be based on the use of heat, radiation or chemicals.

Ultraviolet radiation

Ultraviolet radiation cabinets may be utilised to store previously sterilised/disinfected tools and equipment.

Chemical sterilisation/disinfectants

Chemical sterilisers should be handled only with suitable personal protective equipment, as many of the solutions used are hazardous to health and should not come into contact with the skin. The most effective form of salon disinfectant is achieved by the total immersion of the contaminated implements into a jar of fluid such as Barbicide™.

Autoclave

The autoclave provides a very efficient way of sterilising using heat. It is particularly good for metal tools although the high temperatures are not suitable for plastics such as brushes and combs. Items placed in the autoclave take around 20 mins to sterilise (check with manufacturer's instructions for variations).

COURTESY OF ELLISONS

An autoclave

Your working position and posture

The client's position and height from the floor have a direct effect on your posture too. You must be able to work in a position where you do not have to bend 'doubled up' to do your work. Cutting involves a lot of arm and hand movements and you need to be able to get your hands and fingers into positions where you can cut the hair unencumbered, without bad posture.

1 You should adjust the seated client's chair height to a position where you can work upright without having to over-reach on the top sections of their head.

2 You should clear trolleys or equipment out of the way so that you get good all-round access (300°) around the client.

Hairdressing, as you already know, involves a lot of standing and because of this you need to be comfortable in your work. You should always adopt a comfortable but safe work position and sometimes comfortable and safe are not necessarily the same thing.

(For more information see Unit GH10 pages 176–177).

Cutting access

Working efficiently, safely and effectively

Working efficiently and maximising your time are essential so making the most of the resources available should occur naturally. Always treat the salon's materials in the same way that you would look after your own equipment; always try to minimise waste, being careful of much product you use.

Salon cleanliness is of paramount importance–the work area should be clean and free from clutter or waste items. Any used materials should be disposed of and not left out on the side; failure to do so (a) is unprofessional and (b) presents a health hazard to others. (See the section on preventing infection in Unit G20 Make sure your actions reduce the risk to health and safety, pages 10–15.)

You need to work in an orderly environment; you need to have the materials that you need at hand and the equipment that you want to use in position and ready for action. This is a good exercise in self-organisation and shows others that you are a true professional.

Keep an eye on the clock; you must remember that you need to be working to time and that means providing the service in a commercially acceptable time.

Activity
Every salon has their own way of doing things. Write down in your portfolio under the following headings what your salon's code of practice in respect to:

● meeting and greeting clients

● gowning

● maintaining tools and equipment

● hygiene and preventing the spread of infection or infestation.

● expected timings and duration for a one-length hair cut, cutting hair with uniform layers, a short graduation, a long hair graduation.

EKU *statement*

GH12.6) How the position of your client and yourself can affect the desired outcome and reduce fatigue and the risk of injury

EKU *statement*

GH12.9) Why it is important to keep your work area clean and tidy

GH12.12) Methods of working safely and hygienically and which minimise the risk of cross-infection and infestation

GH12.10) Why it is important to position your cutting tools for ease of use

EKU *statement*

GH12.2) Your salon's expected service times for the looks in the range.

Remember

 Look out for ways and things that can make your client's visit more comfortable and pleasurable. This is the first step in providing a better customer service.

© HABIA

Postural faults

Consultation

Effective communication with the client, as in any service, is an essential part of cutting hair. Consultation is not just a process that takes place before a service; it is a continual process of reconfirming *what* is taking place *whilst* it is taking place. So, during your discussions, you must determine what the client wants and weigh this against the limiting factors that will influence what you need to do.

You need to understand your client fully and be able to negotiate and seek agreement with her throughout the service.

Be sure to listen to your client's requests. Many mistakes can be avoided if you achieve a clear understanding of what the client is asking for.

The haircutting style that you choose with your client should take into account each of the following points about the client's:

- face and head shape
- physical features and body shape, size and proportion
- hair quality, abundance, growth and distribution
- age, lifestyle and suitability
- purpose
- ability or time to recreate the effect themselves.

(You may have already completed Unit G7 in Chapter 5 which covers consulting with the client in chapter 5. Read the chapter again to refresh your knowledge and find out which parts are important to cutting.)

Head and face shapes

The proportions, balance and distribution of the hairstyle will be a frame for the head and face. Therefore you need to examine the head and face carefully. If you look at the outline of your client's face, you will see that it's round, oval, square, heart shaped, oblong or triangular. Only an oval face suits all hairstyles, so all the others listed present some form of styling limitations; in other words they become an influencing factor in the choices for styling.

EKU *statement*

GH12.20) The importance of consulting with clients throughout the cutting process

EKU *statement*

GH12.18) How the factors in the range can affect the way the hair is cut

General styling limitations

Physical feature	How best to work with it
Square and oblong facial shapes	are accentuated by hair that is smoothed, scraped back or sleek at the sides and top. The lines and angles are made less conspicuous by fullness and softer movement.
Round faces	are made more conspicuous if the side and front perimeter (the longest outline hair) lengths are short or finish near to the widest part of the face. This is made worse if width is added at these positions too. Generally this facial shape is complimented by length beyond the chin and/or height on the top.
Square angular features, jaw, forehead etc.	are improved with softer perimeter shapes, avoid solid, linear effects around the face. Shattered edges and texturising will help to mask these features.
Flatter heads at the back	are improved by graduation, creating contour and shape that is missing from having a flatter occipital bone.

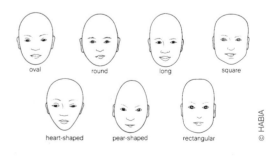

oval   round   long   square

heart-shaped   pear-shaped   rectangular

© HABIA

Hair growth patterns

Working with the natural fall of the hair

Hair doesn't just grow out of the scalp and downwards; it would be very easy to deal with if it did. Unfortunately, people's hair grows in all sorts of ways and you need to consider this and the impacts that it will have on your haircut.

Some hair growth patterns provide useful aspects to work with and can enhance what you are trying to do. Here are some helpful ones:

- A client with a low front hairline will naturally have hair that falls as a fringe. Don't ignore this as a fringe is a good choice for this client: it hides their narrow forehead.
- Some nape hair growth tends to grow inwards towards the centre of the neck and not straight down. Now this is not really noticeable on long hair, but if it is cut short and tightly graduated on to the neck, you can make a feature of this as the finished effect will always look really neat and tidy even if after washing, it doesn't always get blow-dried.
- Natural partings should always be noticed. If a client with longer hair tends to have a definite split in hair directions around the parting at the front, then you can safely suggest shorter styles as options too. The hair around the face, even if it is cut shorter, will always lie well as it won't fall across the face when it is finished. (Needles to say if you ignore a strong natural parting and try to create a new one somewhere else, it just won't work.)

Other growth patterns to look out for

EKU *statement*

GH12.15) The factors that must be taken into consideration prior to and during cutting (e.g. hair density, hair growth patterns, etc.) and how these affect the service

GH12.16) The factors which should be considered when cutting wet and dry hair

GH12.27) The importance of working with the natural fall of the hair when considering the weight distribution within a haircut

Double crown	The client with a double crown will benefit from leaving sufficient length in the hair to over-fall the whole area. If it is cut too short, the hair will stick up and will not lie flat.	
Nape whorl	A nape whorl can occur at either or both sides of the nape. It can make the hair difficult to cut into a straight neckline or tight 'head-hugging' graduations. Often the hair naturally forms a V-shape. Tapered neckline shapes may be more suitable, but sometimes the hair is best left long so that the weight of the hair over-falls the nape whorl directions.	
Cowlick	A cowlick appears at the hairline at the front of the head. It makes cutting a straight fringe difficult, particularly on fine hair, because the hair often forms a natural parting. The strong movement can often be improved by moving the parting over so that the weight over-falls the growth pattern. Sometimes a fringe can be achieved by leaving the layers longer so that they weigh down the hair.	
Widow's peak	The widow's peak growth pattern appears at the centre of the front hairline. The hair grows upward and forward, forming a strong peak. It is often better to cut the hair into styles that are dressed back from the face, as any 'light fringes' will be likely to separate and stick up.	

© HABIA

EKU *statement*

GH12.17) The average rate of hair growth

Reason for hairstyle

The reason or purpose for the hairstyle is a big factor in deciding what is suitable or otherwise.

A style suitable for a special occasion will differ from one that is selected for work. The requirements for competition or show work are quite different from those for general daily wear. But versatility needs to be considered for everyone: people want styles that they can dress up or down. Modern hairdressing has parallels with modern lives: both are about flexibility and choice. People like options, so build this into your plans. The majority of clients need hairstyles that are easy-to-manage and that can be dressed up with styling products or accessories for social events. Versatility is definitely the key: while people like simple, easy-to-manage effects, they also like the opportunity to look different now and again.

Some jobs have special conditions about hair lengths and styles; for example, people working in the armed services or police have to wear their hair above the collar while at work. Men have easily accommodated this by using clippers for very short styles. Women have either had to have short layered styles or hair that is long enough to wear up and out of the way.

How quality, quantity and distribution of hair affect styling

Good hair condition is essential for great hairstyling. It doesn't matter how much work has gone into the thought and design of a hairstyle, if the hair is in poor condition to start with, it still will be after. Some aspects cannot be altered by cutting alone; for instance, if the hair is dry, dull and porous when the client enters the salon, it still will be when she leaves.

Regular salon clients in the UK – the ones you tend to see more often than the others – tend to have something in common. Difficult hair. It can be difficult for a number of reasons; it can be fine or unmanageable, lank and lacking volume or just not responsive to styling without force. Thin, sparsely distributed hair is always a problem: if there isn't enough hair to get coverage over the scalp, then there is not a lot you can do about it. One thing that you should remember though is not to put too much texturising into it; this will only make the problem more noticeable. Fine hair presents many problems too. Very fine hair is affected by dampness and quickly loses its shape. This type of hair always benefits from moisture repelling styling products so get your client used to using them.

Dry, frizzy hair can also be a problem, as the more heat styling it receives, the more moisture is lost and the less it responds to staying in shape – in other words, the harder it is to style. The problem just keeps going on like a merry-go-around. Dry, unruly thick hair needs to be tamed and most clients with this problem would like their hair to look smoother and shinier. Again this is a conditioning issue and you need to attack the problem before tackling the style. Sometimes this type of hair benefits from finishing products so put them on as you finish and define the hairstyle.

Very tight curly hair can be difficult to cut too. Is it possible to smooth or straighten out the hair first so that you can see more clearly what you have to work with?

Cutting wavy hair presents some problems but not if it is looked at carefully before it's wet. Avoid cutting across the crests of the waves; you can't change the natural movement in the hair so try to work with it.

Straight hair, particularly if it is fine textured, can be difficult to cut. Cutting marks or lines can easily form if the cutting sections and angles are not right. Make sure that you only take small sections of hair and remember to crosscheck after, at 90° to the angle in which you first cut, to avoid this happening to you.

Hair tends to grow at a steady regular rate of about 1.25 cm per month, so you need to consider this as a factor for how long a hairstyle will last. For example, a one-length classic bob may look really good if it is cut so that it creates a continuous line just above the shoulders. But how long will it last like that? When it gets to the point of touching the shoulders, the clean sharp line to which it was originally cut to will now be broken up by falling in front and behind the shoulder line. Always consider the impact that a small amount cut off will make and more importantly how long a style will last.

Remember

When you choose a suitable hairstyle always allow for the natural fall of the hair.

Working with the natural fall such as partings, growth patterns etc. will make the style easier for the client to handle and the style last longer.

Activity
Hair growth patterns

Hair growth patterns do have an impact on the way that hair can be styled. For each of the listed growth patterns below, write down in what ways this will influence your cutting options.

Hair growth pattern	Effect on styling
Widow's peak	
Nape whorl	
Double crown	
Cowlick	

Style suitability

Style suitability refers to the effect of the hair shape on the face, and on the features of the head and body. A hairstyle is, quite simply, suitable when it 'looks right'. But this is a difficult or certainly a subjective thing to quantify.

Aesthetically and artistically speaking, the client's 'hair will look right' when the hairstyle does one of two things. It either harmonises (i.e. fits the shape of the face and head) and is therefore a backdrop to an overall image, or contrasts (i.e. accentuates features of the face and head) creating a prominent frame for the overall image.

Age

As much as you would like to demonstrate your creative ability on everyone who walks through the salon door, bear in mind that some styles are inappropriate for certain clients. Beyond the physical aspects of style design, age does create some barriers to suitability.

Younger children (7- to 11-year-olds) are better suited to simpler hairstyles that don't require too much maintenance. More often than not, and certainly from a hair health and hygiene point of view, they are better off with shorter hairstyles. The next age banding (12- to 16-year-olds) want to have fashionable looks and many want colours too!

Unfortunately, these are still minors and the paying parent and educational establishments must have the last say.

Young men and women can get away with anything, but fashion will always dictate, and, more often than not, even if there are reasons for not doing a particular style, they will insist on it. This group can enjoy more extreme and dramatic effects and what's more they can get away with it. There are more styles applicable to this age group (16- to 25-year-olds) than to any other. This is because of social cultures and the diversity of music and TV; these people are influenced by the music they buy, the celebrities they follow on TV and the people they mix with.

Professional men and women tend to go for watered-down versions of young fashion. Thinking this in another way: in the clothing fashion world the designs that are seen on catwalks in Paris, London and New York are always the catalysts and precursors for what the high street shops will sell. Dozens of the haute couture fashion houses demonstrate their season's offerings at the pre-season shows. But not all designs are picked up by the buyers of commercial high street fashion chains; they usually go for the lesser extremes. People want to appear to be trendy and in touch, but not look ridiculous. ·

Older clients require greater consideration. Often the signs of ageing in the skin show quite clearly and therefore they must influence the way in which you select only appropriate and suitable effects.

EKU *statement*

GH12.13) The correct use and maintenance of cutting tools

Activity
Facial shapes

For consultation purposes, as hairdressers, we tend to group clients into categories that follow a range of basic facial shapes.
From the list below, what styling options or limitations does each one provide?
From the list below, what styling options or limitations does each one provide?

Facial shape	Styling options/limitations
Round	
Oval	
Square	
Oblong	
Heart	
Triangular	

Diversion

See Unit G7 Advise and consult with clients for more information on factors that influence styling choices.

Cutting tools

Scissors

Scissors are and will always be the most important piece of hairdressing equipment that you will ever own. Your future income, popularity and success will rely upon this relatively inexpensive item. If you look after them you will be surprised how long a single pair will last. Scissors can be used on either wet or dry hair and vary greatly in their design, size and price. There isn't any single way of choosing the correct pair for you; however, there are a number of aspects that you should consider. Scissors should never be too heavy or too long to control; heavy scissors become cumbersome in regular use and if they are too long you may not be able to manipulate them properly for precision, angular work. Long blades are really good for cutting solid baselines on longer hair, but a real nuisance for precise work around hairlines and behind ears!

To judge a pair of scissors' balance and length, put your fingers in the handles as if you were about to use them. When the scissors are held correctly the pivotal point should just extend beyond the first finger. This allows the blades to open easily and means that the thumb is in an ideal position to work them.

The more expensive scissors will often have one single blade that has small serrations throughout the length. This is really beneficial as this lower blade has cutting grips that stop the hair from being pushed away by the closing blades. Sharpening of this type of scissor blade is not recommended though as this factory finish will be removed immediately, leaving the scissor with a flat surface.

Cutting comb

Get into the habit of only using good-quality cutting combs. You will find that by spending only a little more you will get so much more out of them.

The design of a cutting comb for hairdressing is different to that of barbering. The hairdressing cutting comb is parallel throughout its length whereas the barbering comb is tapered. There are two sorts of cutting comb. The first and by far the most popular have two sets of teeth, one end to the middle is fine and close together the other end is wider and further apart. This provides more control with finer sections on fine hair and wider sections on coarser hair. The second type of cutting comb has uniform teeth throughout the length of the comb.

The length of cutting combs varies greatly. Again, what's best for you depends on the size of your hands and what you can manage and manipulate quite easily. The normal length of a cutting comb is around 15 cm but long ones are now very popular and provide a better guide when cutting freehand baselines.

The quality of combs and the materials they are made from varies greatly. The best-quality combs are made from plastics that have the following properties:

- They are very strong but flexible; the teeth do not chip or break in regular use.
- They remain straight in regular use and do not end up looking like a banana after a couple of weeks!
- They are constructed by injection moulding and do not have sharp or poorly formed edges (as opposed to combs that are made from pressings and have flawed seams and tend to scratch the client's ears and scalp).
- They are resistant to chemicals making them ideal for cleaning, sterilisation and colouring (as they will not stain).
- They have anti-static finishes that help to control finer hair when dry cutting, reducing the hair's tendency to become fly-away.

Remember

Take care with your scissors; they are precision instruments that will be easily damaged if they are dropped.

IT&LY

Large cutting comb

DENMAN

Barbering comb

DENMAN

Thinning scissors

Thinning scissors can be used on dry or wet hair and can have either one or both blades with serrated teeth. These cutting surfaces will remove bulk or density from the hair depending on the way in which they are used. This has two useful applications for cutting:

1 the tips or last ¼ of finely serrated/castellated scissors provide a quick way for texturising the perimeter edges of hairstyles;

2 the whole blades can be used for removing weight (tapering or thinning) from sections of hair but closer to the head.

Tools	Method of cleaning/ sterilisation
Neck brush	Wash in hot soapy water and place in ultraviolet cabinet for 10 mins
Sectioning clips	Wash in hot soapy water and immerse in Barbicide™ jar for 30 mins
Cutting comb	Wash in hot soapy water and immerse in Barbicide™ jar for 30 mins
Scissors	Brush away hair fragments from pivot area and blades with a colouring brush. Carefully wipe the blades with sterile wipes and then place them in an open position in the ultra-violet cabinet for 15 mins each side.
Thinning scissors	Brush away hair fragments from pivot area and blades with a colouring brush. Carefully wipe the blades with sterile wipes and then place them in an open position in the ultra-violet cabinet for 15 mins each side.

Neck brush
DENMAN

Sectioning clips
IT&LY

Cutting comb
DENMAN

Scissors
IT&LY

Thinning scissors
IT&LY

Thinning scissors with both blades serrated will remove hair more quickly than those with serrations on just one side, and this is more noticeable on scissors that have broader castellations or 'notches' in them as opposed to fine teeth.

Neck brushes, water sprays and sectioning clips

Neck brushes are used to remove loose hair clippings from around the neck and face. Get used to passing the neck brush to your client when you are cutting dry hair as the small fragments are irritating when they fall onto the face. Neck brushes usually have soft synthetic bristles and these are easily washed and dried before they are sterilised in a UV cabinet.

Water sprays are used for damping down dry or dried hair to assist you in controlling the haircut. Stale water is unhygienic, so make sure that the water is emptied out and refilled on a daily basis.

Sectioning clips are usually made from plastic or thin alloys. They are used to divide the hair and keep bulk out of the way whilst you work on other areas. They are sterilised by immersing them into Barbicide™ solution for the manufacturer's recommended length of time.

Activity
Wet and dry

There are advantages and disadvantages for cutting both wet and dry hair. Write down your reasons in the table below.

Cutting wet hair

Advantages   Disadvantages

Cutting dry hair
Advantages

Activity
(With the electric clippers removed from the power supply or rechargeable clippers 'rundown'.) Knowing how to remove, replace and maintain the clipper blades is an essential part of hairdressing. Get your supervisor to show you how the lower blade-retaining screws are undone and removed. This will give you access to both cutting blades and the area below the armature (the vibrating arm that works them) for cleaning purposes.

When you have dismantled the blades get used to checking for signs of corrosion. If a rusted area exists it will look like blackened areas around the blade edges. If blades have been allowed to get to this stage they should be replaced by new ones as their ability to cut cleanly without friction has been greatly reduced.

With the blades stripped down, you can now use clipper oil to lubricate the two blades, wiping any excess away. Now you can replace the blades (the right way up) and partially re-tighten the retaining screws. Finally, readjust the alignment of the blades and tighten the screws. Check the alignment once more: the lower cutting blade should extend around 3 mm further than the upper cutting blade with the clippers adjusted fully forwards to the shortest cutting length.

Hand them back to your supervisor so that your maintenance can be checked.

Remember

Maintain your scissors
Carefully wipe over the blades at the end of the working day to remove any fragments of hair and then apply a little clipper oil to the pivot point to prevent any corrosion around the fastening screw. This will prolong their life and stop them from binding or getting stiffer to use.

Cutting checklist

✔	Prepare your tools and equipment making sure that everything that you need is close at hand.
✔	Make sure that the client is protected.
✔	Always gain agreement before attempting anything new or different.
✔	Make sure you consider the reasons and the purpose for the style.
✔	Assess the style limitations, hair problems or physical features.
✔	Avoid technical jargon or style names. If jargon is used, by you or the client, always clarify in simple terms what it means to avoid confusion.
✔	Don't just do the style if you think that it's wrong. If there are reasons why you think it will be unsuitable, you will be doing the client a big favour in the longer term if you tackle the issue straight away.
✔	Always give the client some advice on how to handle the style themselves.
✔	Give the client an idea of how long it will take to do.

GH12.2 Cut hair to achieve a variety of looks

Cutting and styling hair

Accurate sectioning

With everything else done, the only thing that you need to consider is how you go about tackling all that hair. Very short hair doesn't really pose any problem but sectioning isn't just for those with very long hair; any hair not being worked on needs to be sectioned up and out of the way.

EKU statement

GH12.21) The importance of applying the correct degree of tension to the hair when cutting

GH12.22) How and why to use club, freehand and scissors-over-comb cutting techniques

GH12.23) The reasons for establishing and following guidelines

In order for you to be able to manage sizeable amounts of hair at any one time, you must organise and plan the haircut. The planning bit becomes automatic; it's the few moments that you spend thinking:

- How do I go about this?
- Where do I start?
- What is the finish going to be like?

So, if the planning is automatic it's the organisation bit that you have to address. Quite simply, being organised is about working in a methodical way. It is the way in which you routinely start at one point; divide all the rest of the hair out of the way, finish that bit, and then take down the next part to work on, and so on. Each part or section that you work on should be small enough for you to cope with, without losing your way and continuing on blindly! It seems a strange term to use, but 'blindly' is exactly the right word. If the sections are too deep or too wide you will not be able to see the cutting guide that you need to work to. Accurate sectioning guarantees that every cut mesh is addressed to the same length every time.

Cut hair with natural fall

Cutting with the natural fall of the hair is extremely important. Looking for the directions of growth within the hair is an essential part of consultation as it is within the execution of the haircut. If you work with the natural fall i.e. partings, nape hair growth, double crowns etc. you will be compensating for these anomalies and be able to produce an easier to manage result. Ignore these factors and you will be aftercare advice is about giving the client the correct advice on looking after their both you and the client a hard job in styling it.

As previously covered in the section on preparation, always try to wash the hair, even if you are only providing a haircut. This way when you dry the hair off, you will be able to see the natural fall far easier and be able to work with it.

EKU *statement*

GH12.27) The importance of working with the natural fall of the hair when considering the weight distribution within a haircut

Remember

Cutting baselines/perimeter outlines

A baseline is a cut section of hair, which is used as a cutting guide for following sections of hair. There may be one or more baselines cut: for example, a graduated nape baseline may be cut; another may be cut into the middle of the hair at the back of the head. Other baselines may be cut at the sides and the front of the head. The baselines will determine the perimeter of the hairstyle, or part of the style, and may take different shapes according to the effects required:

Symmetrical: The baseline for evenly balanced hair shapes in which the hair is equally divided on both sides of the head. Examples are hairstyles with central partings or with the hair swept backwards or forwards.

Asymmetrical: The baseline to be used where the hair is unevenly balanced, for example where there is a side parting and a larger volume of hair on one side of the head, or where the hair is swept off the face at one side with fullness of volume on the other.

Concave: The baseline may be cut curving inwards or downwards. The nape baseline, for example, may curve downwards.

Convex: The baseline may be cut curving upwards and outwards – the nape baseline, for instance, may be cut curving upwards.

Straight: The baseline may be cut straight across, for example where you wish to produce a hard, square effect.

Controlling the shape

There are three aspects of cutting that you must get right on every haircut:

1 *The holding angle* – the angle at which the hair is held out from the head.
2 *The cutting angle* – the angle at which the scissors, razor etc. cuts the hair.
3 *The holding tension* – the even pressure applied to sections of hair when it is held ready for cutting.

That doesn't seem much to guarantee success, but it does take a lot of practice and concentration. Even if you start well in the haircut you cannot afford to lose it in the closing stages.

Cutting lines or perimeter lines are the outline shape created when layered hair is held directly out with tension (perpendicular) from the head. The curves and the

EKU *statement*

GH12.24) How to create and follow a guideline for one-length, uniform layer, short graduation and long graduation looks

angle in relation to the head, determines the shape of the cut style. The main ones are:

- the contour of the shape from top to bottom
- the contour of the shape around the head, side to side.

Cutting guidelines are prepared sections of hair that control the uniform quality of the haircut. When the cutting guide is taken and first cut, it is to this length and shape that all the other following sections relate. In preparing this cutting guide you need to take all the client's physical features and attributes into consideration, i.e. eyes, eyebrows, nose, bone structure, head shape, neck length, hairlines etc.

Creating guidelines

The guideline is the initial cutting line that is created as a sort of template for all the subsequent sections that are taken.

As a general rule the simpler or more basic the hairstyle the fewer the guidelines there will be. On the other hand, the more complex the hairstyle, the more guidelines will be involved.

So at Level 2 the styles that need to be done involve fewer guidelines:

- uniform layered haircut has one
- a basic graduation has two
- and one-length hair cuts have one

A uniform layered haircut has layers of equal length all around the head, so the first cutting guideline dictates the overall length for the rest of the haircut.

For easier control of a haircut, they are always started at the back; this way the bulk of the hair is tackled and checked before moving onto the sides and top. So after dividing the hair vertically and evenly down the back, take a horizontal section at both sides about 2 cm above the hairline and secure with sectioning clips out of the way. Cut this baseline to the length that you need to and after checking, take down the next section 2 cm above and secure the remainder.

(a) uniform layers

(b) graduation

At the point beneath the vertical division in the hair, take and hold a vertical section as shown in figure (a) without twisting and with an even tension. Cut this perpendicularly (at a vertical angle) to the head. (The client's head should be horizontal and not chin down or head back.)

With the guideline cut, you take the next section; parallel to the guideline; with the same even tension, so that you can see the lengths of the previously cut guideline through the held mesh. Cut this to the same length as the guideline. Continue this throughout each section until the complete horizontal area has been cut. Then take down another 2 cm on either side and repeat the process, slowly working up the back to the crown.

With the back done, you take a horizontal section above the ears; through to the front, cut your perimeter baseline and follow the guideline through from behind the ear working towards the front hairline. Repeat up to the top and cut the other side in the same way.

Finish the haircut over the top working forwards from the known guidelines at the top. Finally, trim the front hairline perimeter shape to complete the hairline profile shape and cross-check to see that the sides, back and top are all in balance.

The graduated haircut uses a similar guideline process to that of uniform layering; the only difference is that the hair is held out at an angle from the head as opposed to perpendicular. The steeper the angle is held away from the head, the lower the bulk line will be and the greater the weight distribution for the overlying lengths. Conversely, the shallower the angle of the cut, the higher the bulk line will be and the less weight distribution for the overlying lengths.

(For more information on cutting guidelines on uniform layers or graduation see the step by steps later in this Chapter.)

Cross-checking the cut

Possibly at different points during the cut, but certainly after the cut you will need to recheck what you have already done. This is done by taking and holding sections at an angle which is at right angles (90°) to the original cut sections. (In other words if you originally cut the hair in vertical meshes, your cross-check will be done with horizontal meshes.)

Cross-checking provides a final technique for checking the continuity and accuracy of the hair cut. Where you find an imbalance in weight, or extra length that still needs to be removed, it provides you with the opportunity to remove it in order to create the perfect finish.

Dealing with cutting problems

A lack of attention during the cut or a missed detail or aspect during the consultation can lead to cutting mistakes. The variety of mistakes is too varied to cover, but normally result in an imbalance in weight proportions or a difference in perimeter lengths.

If, on finishing a symmetrical cut, you feel that one side seems to be slightly longer than the other; you need to stop before taking anything off the apparently longer side. If it is obviously longer and the client has commented too, you need to put your comb and scissors down and recheck through the fingers.

Standing behind the client you take a small piece of hair from the same position on the head at either side with your forefingers and thumbs. Then slowly slide your fingers down either side until you get to the ends. Looking at the length through the mirror, see if the

EKU *statement*

GH12.25) How the angle at which the hair is held will affect the weight distribution, balance and degree of graduation of the cut

EKU *statement*

GH12.28) The importance of cross-checking the cut
GH12.29) How to cross-check and balance the cut

HAIR: SHARON PEAKE @ ETHOS, MANCHESTER
PHOTOGRAPHY. JOHN RAWSON @ TRP

ends terminate at the same lengths either side; if they do, the cut is fine. Often a cut can seem wrong and the more you look at it the worse it seems. By putting the scissors and comb down you break the fixation and blind panic and have a chance to review it again calmly, with your hands empty. (Most hairdressers make the fatal mistake of immediately taking some off the apparently longer side; only to find that the other side then seems wrong and then as they continue, each side gets shorter and shorter!) If, however, there is a difference in both lengths then you now have the chance to redress the balance.

Clients are particularly attached to their fringes (pardon the pun); if a fringe is taken too short the client generally feels very conspicuous. So how can you replace hair that is already too short? Well you can't replace the hair but you can lessen the effect by reducing a solid fringe line by slightly point cutting to 'break up' the density and reveal a little skin of the forehead through.

What really bothers people is the stark contrast created between the solid line created by the fringe against the skin; this focuses even more attention on the area. Therefore the solution is to reduce this contrast by softening this demarcation line between the two areas. (This technique of reducing obvious mistakes can be used throughout the perimeter of hairstyles as it works in most cases.)

Finally, another popular cutting fault is caused by an imbalance of weight in layering on one side to the other. Again if you get to a cross-check situation and find that the layer pattern on one side seems different to the other side; stop.

You need to find out if it is due to:

- one side being longer than the other, or
- a greater reduction in weight by texturising on one side rather than the other.

If it is length then you can easily re-cut the longer side to match. But if it is due to weight reduction, you will see a 'collapse' in the overall style shape on the side that has had the greater amount of texturising. You can then remedy the fault by further texturising the hair from the thicker side.

Cutting and styling techniques

Club cutting

This is the method of cutting hair bluntly straight across. It systematically cuts all the hair, at an angle parallel to the first and middle finger, to the same length. It is the most popular technique and often forms the basis or first part of a haircut, before other techniques are used.

Club cutting is used in both a uniform layered cut and one-length cut. As the most popular and easily controlled form of cutting, it is the one technique that optimises the amount of hair at the points and is therefore used for maintaining or creating bulk and volume.

The majority of clients visiting salons within the UK have finer to normal hair textures so this technique is ideal for them as most people with finer hair types like to make their hair fuller or more bodied.

As previously covered in this chapter, cutting with the correct tension is an essential part of achieving an accurate finished result. In club cutting the hair is held out away from the head and the fingers form a guiding line, beyond which the cut is made. This basic principle is replicated throughout the cut providing a progressive and systematic approach to creating the effect.

Cutting faults will occur:

- if you don't maintain the correct tension throughout the cut
- if you twist the cutting meshes whilst you are holding and cutting them
- if you over-direct the hair, allowing parts of the cut meshes to be longer than needs be.

Incorrect holding/cutting techniques for club cutting

Holding with an even tension

Cutting with the scissor blades parallel to the fingers

A completed 'club cut' section

Freehand cutting

Freehand cutting is mainly used on straighter hair for creating the baseline perimeter shape. The technique is used on straighter hair because curlier hair needs more control, through holding and tensioning.

As the name suggests, freehand cutting relies upon one hand holding and combing the hair into position, and the other controlling the scissors to make the cut. More often than not, when cutting longer, one-length hair, the comb is used to create the guide for making the cut.

This technique is more widely used in cutting fringes though. Adults with fringes are particularly cautious about what the exact finished length should be. Therefore it is easier to comb the length into position and create a profile shape that both suits the client and follows or covers the eyebrows. This would be guesswork if the hair were held between the fingers and cut because the width of your fingers would obscure the exact length and position you are trying to cut.

Therefore, the freehand cut is made with the scissors very close to the skin or body, as this gives you a clearer idea of what needs to be cut off to achieve the exact length required by the client. Obviously, you need to be particularly careful in cutting your profiles as it would be easy to snip an eyebrow or an ear! One thing that you can do to minimise any risk to the client is to use your comb behind the hair you want to cut; as this has a couple of benefits.

- The comb can be held in parallel to the angle of the scissor blades giving you a useful back-up guideline.
- The comb keeps eyebrows, ears and lined or 'sagging', skin back away from the cutting edges/points of the scissors.

PAUL FALLTRICK FOR MATRIX

Freehand cutting using the comb
to hold the hair

PAUL FALLTRICK FOR MATRIX

Re-checking the accuracy of the line

PAUL FALLTRICK FOR MATRIX

A completed 'freehand cut'
section

Scissor over comb

This technique has been traditionally a barbering technique. In recent years there has been a move in hairdressing generally towards easier-to-manage hairstyles, so therefore this technique is widely used in hairdressing for cutting short styles on both men and women.

Activity
Planning your work

Any service that you provide to the client needs to be thought about before you start. This planning is essential for achieving a successful result, so in this activity, complete the table below to create a checklist of things that you should consider before carrying out the service.

Checklist for cutting

1

2

3

4

5

6

Scissor over comb cutting is ideal for producing:

A tapered layering shapes with close-cut, 'fade-out' perimeters (faded or graduated perimeters have no set baselines; they rely upon the hairline profile and are graduated out from that into the rest of the hairstyle).

B Uniform layered shapes with layers of equal lengths.

The technique is used with either wet or dry hair and uses the comb as a guide to hold the hair and maintain an even lift or tension away from the head, whilst you cut.

Scissor over comb is ideal for very short hair that can not be held between your fingers, it is best started at the lower nape area providing that the hair isn't too long. The hair is lifted away from the head and the comb mirrors the contour of the back of the head so that the upper edge is tilted away and not towards the back of the head. If the angle of the comb leans towards the head your finished cut length will gradually get shorter as you work upwards.

The image below shows the correct sectioning position.

Graduation   **Reverse Gradution**

Correct angle for scissor over comb

Thinning

Thinning is a technique which can be done with scissors or a razor and can be used for reducing or tapering bulk from thicker hair without reducing the overall length. It is also used as a way of texturising the edges of hairstyles to remove solid lines from profile shapes to create more; softer, faded or 'shattered' effects.

When thinning is done to remove bulk and weight in short or long layered hair: the hair sections should be held in vertical meshes and the thinners should be introduced to the hair at an angle so that the longest parts of the thinned hair are nearer to the base-lines or perimeter. This helps the hair to remain smoother without 'bunching' when it is dried. (When longer thinned hair over-lies shorter thinned hair an unflattering result occurs; producing width with fluffy, unruly edges.)

Remember

 One-length cuts, layering and graduation
A one-length cut is achieved by combing vertically down and cutting straight across.

A graduation or graduated cut is achieved by creating a layered shape that is longer on the upper sections and shorter underneath.

A reverse graduation is achieved by creating a layered shape that is shorter on the upper sections and longer underneath.

Remember

 Cutting combs used for scissor over comb need to be very flexible. You may benefit from buying a tapered barbering comb as this makes cutting easier and quicker.

Remember

The most important factor in cutting hair
Very few people can do two things at the same time! You will have to learn very quickly that you need to hold a conversation with the client without losing your way and concentration on the haircut. This is the biggest single cause of poor quality hairdressing! (If you cannot do this yet, tell your client that you need the time to focus on the task ahead. Believe it or not, they won't mind.)

PAUL FALLTRICK FOR MATRIX

Point cutting with thinning scissors.

PAUL FALLTRICK FOR MATRIX

Removing the bulk from the ends.

PAUL FALLTRICK FOR MATRIX

Maintaining the same cutting angle through-out the technique.

PAUL FALLTRICK FOR MATRIX

Finally removing any definition to the pre-viously club cut lengths.

PAUL FALLTRICK FOR MATRIX

Razor tapering.

PAUL FALLTRICK FOR MATRIX

Removing weight from the ends.

PAUL FALLTRICK FOR MATRIX

The tapered effect.

Activity

Write down the meanings of the following cutting terms:

1 Graduation
2 Reverse graduation
3 Scissor over comb
4 Club cutting
5 Clipper over comb
6 Freehand cutting
7 Clubbing

Remember

Always ask how much the client wants cut off.

A trim is a trim, in other words a **reshape** or reshaping cut, whereas a different or new cut is a **restyle** or restyling cut (if the client is not used to these words explain the difference).

An inch to one person may be a centimetre to another. Don't be ambiguous, find out exactly how much needs to be cut off!

Checklist – Before the cut

✔	Prepare the client and your working area.
✔	Communicate with your client and discuss the requirements.
✔	Use visual aids to help interpret the client's wishes or to show ideas and themes.
✔	Examine the hair – its type, length, quality, quantity and condition. Look for factors that influence the choice of style and cutting methods.
✔	Explain if there are any limitations that will affect the result.
✔	After your analysis, agree or negotiate with the client the suitable courses of action to take.
✔	Try to show the hair length to be removed.
✔	Discuss the time that will be taken and the price that you will charge.
✔	Proceed only when all checks have been made and the client has agreed to your proposals.
✔	Ensure that you choose the correct tools and techniques for achieving the variety of effects.

Checklist – During the cut

✔ | After shampooing and towel drying, dry off the hair so that any previously masked tendencies can clearly be seen.

✔ | Try to keep the hair damp but not saturated so that any newly added technical features can easily be seen.

✔ | Take care with your precision or accuracy by checking each angle at which the hair is taken and held from the head.

✔ | Create your baselines and guideline cuts first, so that there is a continuity within the section patterning.

✔ | When preparing baselines and guide sections, make sure that you attend to the features of your client's face and head. Use these as guides for accurate directions in the cut lines.

✔ | Remember always that the first cuts you make often determine the finished shape of the style.

Checklist – After the cut

✔ | Cross-check each of the sections of the side, nape, top and front for accuracy and finish.

✔ | Check the density, texture and features of the haircut.

✔ | Position, place and mould the hair where necessary to see the shape clearly.

✔ | When all the loose hair clippings have been removed and the client is prepared and comfortable, continue to blow-dry, set and finish the style.

Remember

 Far more customers are dissatisfied as a result of the stylist not listening and taking too much off than because of poor or inaccurate haircuts.

EKU statement

GH12.24) How to create and follow a guideline for one-length, uniform layer, short graduation and long graduation looks

GH12.25) How the angle at which the hair is held will affect the weight distribution, balance and degree of graduation of the cut

GH12.26) How to create the looks in the range

Step-by-step: One-length haircut

One-lenght hair cut before.

Step 1 Take off the bulk of the ends ready to cut the perimeter length.

Step 2 Comb hair evenly into place.

Step 3 Cutting the perimeter length.

Step 4 Extending through to the sides.

Step 5 Cross-check to maintain an even layer.

Step 6 Cutting the sections to the same length.

Step 7 Finishing the side profile.

Step 8 Final effect.

Step-by-step: Uniform layers

Uniform layer before.

Step 1 Cutting the perimeter length.

Step 2 Hair is held perpendicular to the head.

Step 3 The cutting angle is parallel to the holding angle.

Step 4 Cutting the profile perimeter length.

Step 5 Creating a new cutting guideline by blending in from the back layering.

Step 6 Layering through the top.

Step 7 Blow-drying the hair.

Step 8 Final effect.

Step-by-step: Graduated bob

Before.

Step 1 Shampoo, condition and detangle the hair, put the parting in and comb roughly into place.

Step 2 Section and secure the hair at the lower back of the head. Start the cutting guideline centrally at the nape.

Step 3 Create a new perimeter shape.

Step 4 With both sides symmertical; start your graduation by creating a guideline held out vertically from the head.

Step 5 With the lower meshes cut to the same guideline length; move up to the next section at the back.

Step 6 Gently, over-extend each section back towards the centrally cut guideline.

Step 7 With the back done; take a horizontal section through the sides and continue the perimeter shape so that it connects to the previously cut back outline shape.

Step 8 Gently over-extend the layering backwards to maintain density and weight at the sides.

Step 9 After completing the opposite side; continue to cut the profile graduation.

Step 10 Blow dry into shape to create the final effect.

Step-by-step: Graduation

Graduation before.

Step 1 Separate out the sections.

Step 2 Cutting the perimeter length.

Step 3 Cross-check to maintain an even layer.

Step 4 Hair is held with an even tension.

Step 5 Hair is held at an angle, away from the head.

Step 6 The cutting guidelines are followed throughout the cut.

Step 7 Check the side profile.

Step 8 Final effect.

Step-by-step: Reverse graduation

Before.

Steps 1–2 Cutting the perimeter length.

Steps 3–4 The next section over-falls the previously cut lengths.

Step 5 The reverse graduation showing the angle of the cut and the holding angle.

Step 6 Continue by following the guidelines.

Step 7 Extending through to the sides.

Step 8 Create the graduation around the sides.

Steps 9–10 Joining pre-cut guidelines into the sides.

Steps 11–12 Check accurancy of layering by holding up and cross-checking.

Step 13 Finishing of the profile shape.

Final effect.

Fringes

SHARON COX @ SANRIZZ

SCOTT SMURTHWAITE @ CREAM

SHARON COX @ SANRIZZ

VICKY TURNER @ GOLDSWORTHY'S

GH12.3 Provide aftercare advice

EKU statement

GH12.17) The average rate of hair growth

GH12.31) The recommended time interval between cuts

GH12.32) How to give effective advice and recommendations to clients; see also Unit G18 Promote additional services to clients

GH12.30) The importance of having regular cuts

Good service is supported through good advice and recommendation. The work that you do in the salon needs to be cared for at home by the client too. What would be the point of creating something if the client doesn't know how to achieve and maintain the same effects at home?

Style durability

Hair grows at a steady rate of around 1.25 cm per month so at the six to eight week point the hair will be considerably longer than when it was first cut. If the hair is thick and coarse the first thing that the client will notice is an increase in the width of the hairstyle on both sides. Similarly, if a client has a shoulder-length cut, then it will now be beyond the shoulders and separating in front and behind. In other words whatever the client selected for a style at the beginning, it will now have taken on a different look.

Make a point of outlining the benefits of having a regular cut; give your client an idea of how long the style will last and, ideally, because you know how long that will be, get them to rebook their style reshape before they leave the salon. People who don't make appointments before they leave the salon often tend to drift beyond the normal interval times. Then, when they do realise that their hair needs doing, they find that they can't get an appointment at a time that suits them. So by the time you get to work on it again the hair really needs a sort out.

Home- and aftercare checklist

✔	Talk through the style as you work; that way the client sees how you handle different aspects of the look.
✔	Show and recommend the products/equipment that you use so that the client gets the right things to enable them to get the same effects.
✔	Tell the client how long the style can be expected to last and when they need to return for reshaping.
✔	Demonstrate the techniques that you use so they can achieve that salon hair look too.

KEN PICTON @ KEN PICTON

Talk through the style as you work

Make a point of talking through your styling techniques as you go as:

A it eliminates long periods of silence whilst you are working and, more importantly,

B it is really useful to the client as they get useful advice on how to recreate a similar effect at home.

Show and recommend the products/equipment that you use

As you talk about the ways in which you have styled the hair, make a point of talking through the products that you have used as well.

This way they will be able to see a direct link between the effects that you are achieving on their hair, with the added benefits of buying those particular products that will help them to recreate a similar effect.

KEN PICTON @ KEN PICTON

Explain how routine styling tools can have detrimental effects

Only hair in good condition is easy to maintain. You know how difficult it is to make dry, damaged hair look good. With these known facts, you would be doing an injustice to your clients if you didn't warn them of the pitfalls of repeatedly using hot styling equipment, so make a point in asking them if they use them at home too. If they say that they use straighteners or tongs on a daily basis then tell them about the benefits of using heat protection sprays.

Demonstrate the techniques that you use

Clients want to be able to recreate the effects that you achieve in the salon and this is your chance to show them how to do it. Clients haven't had the benefit of your training; they don't know the little tricks and techniques that make it seem so simple. Show them how to do things; correct combing, blow-drying or positioning of brushes. We have all seen the effects when these are not done properly, so make a point of giving them a few tips on how they can achieve a similar result themselves and how long they can expect it to last.

PAUL HAWES @ REVIEW

Activity

Home-care advice

Good home-aftercare advice is about giving the client the correct advice on looking after their hair.

This will include advice on:

- products
- tools and equipment
- future salon services.

1 What advice should you give regarding products?

2 What advice do you need to provide regarding tools and equipment?

3 What advice could you provide regarding future salon services/ treatments?

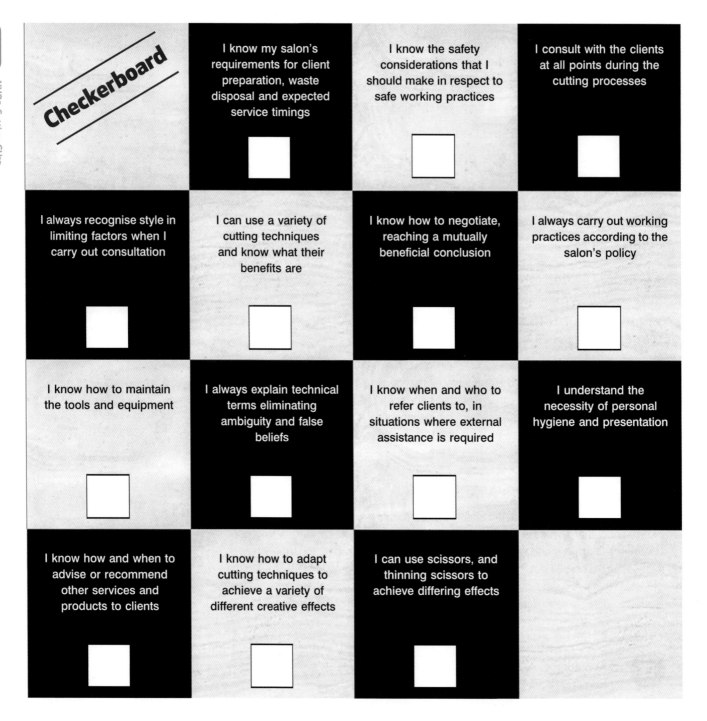

Checkerboard

I know my salon's requirements for client preparation, waste disposal and expected service timings ☐	I know the safety considerations that I should make in respect to safe working practices ☐	I consult with the clients at all points during the cutting processes ☐
I always recognise style in limiting factors when I carry out consultation ☐	I can use a variety of cutting techniques and know what their benefits are ☐	I know how to negotiate, reaching a mutually beneficial conclusion ☐	I always carry out working practices according to the salon's policy ☐
I know how to maintain the tools and equipment ☐	I always explain technical terms eliminating ambiguity and false beliefs ☐	I know when and who to refer clients to, in situations where external assistance is required ☐	I understand the necessity of personal hygiene and presentation ☐
I know how and when to advise or recommend other services and products to clients ☐	I know how to adapt cutting techniques to achieve a variety of different creative effects ☐	I can use scissors, and thinning scissors to achieve differing effects ☐	

Assessment of knowledge and understanding

Project

For this project you will need to gather information from a variety of sources.

Close observation of your senior colleagues whilst they work is an invaluable means of learning. At first, cutting hair can be slow and difficult, but with practice this soon changes.

To gather together information on cutting and styling you will need to visit hairdressing demonstrations, exhibitions and competitions. Using photography and video recording is ideal. Practising first cuts, or experimenting with the various techniques, can be carried out on practice blocks, slip-ons and models.

You need to record as much as you can, including the following:

1   Carefully list the movements and techniques that you see and outline the effects produced. Try to capture the positions of the sections taken, the angles of cut, the direction of cutting lines etc.

2   Outline the plan of the cut and list the important factors to consider.

3   How do the different growth patterns affect your cutting? Describe these and try to illustrate them in your notes.

4   Try to describe the different cutting procedures and refer particularly to the different parts of the head – the fringe, sides, nape, top and back. Explain how these parts are blended or fit together.

Investigate other sources of haircutting information: magazines, DVDs, TV. The information you collect could include these items:

●   how to choose suitable cutting tools

●   the effects produced by the different tools

●   how metal cutting tools are maintained and cleaned

●   how to select the right tool for the effect required

●   the difference between wet and dry cutting, and the tools used for each

●   how tools should be used safely.

Revision questions

A selection of different types of questions to check your cutting knowledge.

Q1   Accuracy is achieved by _____ and cutting the hair at the correct angle.   Fill in the blank

Q2   Scissors should be sterilised in Barbicide^{TM}.   True or false

Q3   Select from the following list those that are *not* texturising techniques: Multi selection

Club cutting	☐	1
Graduation	☐	2
Slice cutting	☐	3
Layering	☐	4
Point cutting	☐	5
Chipping	☐	6

Q4   Symmetrical shapes produce equally balanced hairstyles.   True or false

Q5   Which of the following is not a cutting term?   Multi choice

Cross-checking	○	a
Thinning	○	b
Free hand	○	c
Free style	○	d

Q6   Precision cutting is dependent upon cutting angles and even tension.   True or false

Q7   Which of the following hair growth patterns will effect the natural fall and way that a fringe lies after it is cut?   Multi selection

Nape whorl	☐	1
Double crown	☐	2
Widow's peak	☐	3
Low hairline	☐	4
Cow's lick	☐	5
High hairline	☐	6

Q8 A _____ is the perimeter shape produced by cutting.   Fill in the blank

Q9 Which of the following cuts would easily describe a disconnection?   Multi choice

Graduation in a long hairstyle   ○ a

Reverse graduation in a long hairstyle   ○ b

A fringe in a shoulder-length bob style   ○ c

Texturising in a short cropped style   ○ d

Q10 Clubbing is a technique of cutting that maximises the hair density.   True or false

Preparing for assessment checklist

Remember to:

✔	prepare clients correctly for the services you are going to carry out
✔	put on the protective wear available for styling and dressing hair
✔	listen to the client's requirements and discuss suitable courses of action
✔	adhere to the safety factors when working on clients' hair
✔	keep the work areas clean, hygienic and free from hazards
✔	promote the range of services, products and treatments within the salon
✔	clean and sterilise the tools and equipment before it is used
✔	work carefully and methodically through the processes of cutting hair whether wet or dry
✔	place, position and direct the hair appropriately to achieve the desired effect
✔	communicate what you are doing with the client as well as your fellow staff members

Chapter**thirteen**
Cutting men's hair

GB3

GB3.1

GB3.2

GB3.3

More information
Diversion See Unit G7 Advise and consult with clients

Unit G20 Make sure your own actions reduce risks to health and safety

Unit G8 Develop and maintain your effectiveness at work

Unit G17 Give clients a positive impression of yourself

See the appendices for Electricity at Work Regulations EKU GB3.4 your responsibilities under the Electricity at Work Regulations

Cutting men's hair: quick overview

Unit title

GB3 Cut hair using basic barbering techniques

This is a **mandatory** unit for Barbering at Level 2, it is made up of three main outcomes

Main outcomes

GB3.1 Maintain effective and safe methods of working when cutting hair

GB3.2 Cut hair to achieve a variety of looks

GB3.3 Provide aftercare advice

What do I need to do for GB3.1?

- Make sure that the client is adequately covered and protected
- Make sure that your working position is comfortable and safe
- Keep the work area clean and tidy and that waste materials are disposed of properly
- Work without causing risks to you or your client's health and safety
- Work efficiently and effectively

What do I need to do for GB3.2?

- Choose suitable visual aids to help with style selection for your client
- Prepare your client's hair before cutting
- Seek confirmation of the desired look before starting
- Cut your client's hair using a variety of creative cutting techniques
- Check that the final effect is accurate, that it compliments the client's features, their personal image and that the client is satisfied with the results

Keywords

Club cutting

A technique of cutting hair by holding it between the first and middle finger and cutting it straight accross

Fading

A cutting term that refers to the smooth blending of two different hair lengths within a haircut or, alternatively, as a tapering technique where very short hair is faded out to the perimeter skin, for example at the nape area where clippered hair lengths are blended down to a length of grade 1.

Freehand

A method of cutting without holding between the fingers, or below or above a comb

Scissor over comb

A technique of cutting hair with scissors, using the back of the comb as a guide, especially when the hair is at a length that cannot be held between the fingers

Clipper over comb

A technique of cutting hair with electric clippers, using the back of the comb as a guide, especially on very short hair and hairline profiles
(continued)

What do I need to do for GB3.3?

- Give the client accurate, constructive advice on how they can maintain the look themselves

What aspects do I need to cover for GB3.1, GB3.2 and GB3.3?

- A variety of cutting tools and equipment
- A range of factors that influence or limit the choice of styling
- Different types of cutting techniques that are used to create creative effects

What aspects do I need to know for GB3.1, GB3.2 and GB3.3?

- Your salon's requirements for preparation, timings and standards of service
- Any salon or local limitations relating to the use of fixed blade razors
- How to work safely, effectively and hygienically when cutting hair
- Factors about hair that affect styling choice, suitability and durability
- The ways of methodically cutting wet or dry hair to achieve the desired effects
- How to correct commonly occurring problems that can occur during cutting
- The aftercare advice and recommendations that you should give to clients

Introduction

Men and women share the same hair types, hair textures, hair tendencies and colours, so what are the differences? Traditionally the differences were more to do with length. But now, even those differences are less defined. With women having really short hair and men wearing theirs longer, the barber of today has to cover far more hairstyles for men and therefore needs to have greater skills to cover an ever expanding range of choices.

Barbering at Level 2 is only the starting point for learning more about cutting. This following on and into Level 3 gives men's barbers a better understanding of what's needed in a continually *growing* market.

Basic barbering

Basic barbering involves the traditional aspects of club cutting, scissor over comb and clipper work, with a range of techniques that cross over to ladies' hairdressing. This chapter takes you through the aspects of contemporary barbering under the following topics:

- preparation and maintenance
- client consultation
- identifying the influencing factors that affect style choice
- cutting techniques and accuracy
- good customer care.

Remember

 Cutting men's hair (as with many other services) uses many of the principles of cutting women's hair. Review other chapters in this book for more information.

LEONADO RIZZO @ SANRIZZ

 Diversion Some of the EKUs you need for this unit may be found in other units. To save you from unnecessary duplication we have cross-referenced each unit to other areas. You may have already studied that unit in which case a revision of the information will help you apply that knowledge to this unit. If you have not studied that information before then it will help you when you do study that unit.

Where you see this sign it will guide you to the unit in which you will find the information you need.

Remember

 A finished hairstyle always looks better if it is cut wet. Try to get your clients to booking for a wet cut at the very least.

- It will be easier for you to create new effects.
- They will be able to see a better, more professional result.
- You will generate a better professional service with your clients.
- You will break the habits of men expecting a quick, cheap haircut.
- It is more hygienic for everyone concerned.

GB3.1 Maintain effective and safe methods of working when cutting hair

The preparatory outcome for this unit is very similar to other technical services although there are variations that relate to:

- specific differences for doing male and female clients
- the individual salon policy where you work
- the differences in the tools and equipment used.

As client protection is the first aspect that you must consider, a quick reference for cutting dry or wet is listed below along with the essential knowledge components.

Protecting the client

EKU *statement*

GB3.1) Your salon's requirements for client preparation

Gowning for the client can either take place before or after the consultation, it really depends upon the salon's policy. In either event, client protection must always take place before a dry cut is started or, if the service is a wet cut, then before the client is shampooed.

For dry cutting   Use a clean fresh cutting gown and put it on your client while he is sitting at the styling location. Make sure that the back is fastened and that any open, free edges are closed together, keeping any loose clippings away from the client's clothes. Place a cutting collar around his neck to ensure that any bumps or lumps in his clothing don't present any false, physical baselines for the haircut and that the collar edges fit snugly against the neck, so that there are no irritating hair fragments that will leave the client itching until he gets home.

For wet cutting   Do the same as above but, when your client is at the basin, place a clean fresh towel around his shoulders before positioning him back carefully and comfortably. Make sure that the basin supports the client's neck properly and that the flanged edges of the basin nestle comfortably on to the client's shoulders which are protected from any spills or seepage by a clean fresh towel. (See Unit GH8 on page 149 for more information.)

Like all other practical services in hairdressing, it is essential that you work safely when cutting hair. In doing this you must take the time to prepare and protect the client adequately.

This means that you have:

- pre-selected all the equipment that you are going to use; gowns, towels, combs, scissors, razor and clippers etc.
- checked that they are ready for use e.g. new blades for the razor, freshly laundered towels and gowns, washed cutting collars, cleaned and sterilised combs, brushes, clipper blades and scissors
- have them all at hand at the work station and ready for use
- ensured that the client is comfortable and in a position where you can work safely.

More information can be found elsewhere, here is a quick reference guide to other parts in this book covering the essential information.

Topic	Related information	Knowledge reference	See page
Client preparation and protection	Unit GH12 Cut hair using basic techniques	EKU statement GB3.5) The range of protective equipment that should be available for clients GB3.6) Why it is important to protect clients from hair cuttings	273
Working position and height	Unit GH12 Cut hair using basic techniques	EKU statement GB3.7) How the position of your client and yourself can affect the desired outcome and reduce fatigue and the risk of injury	274–277
Preparing tools and equipment	Unit GH12 Cut hair using basic techniques	EKU statement GB3.8) The safety considerations which must be taken into account when cutting hair GB3.11) Why it is important to position your cutting tools for ease of use	275
Working efficiently, safely and effectively	Unit GH12 Cut hair using basic techniques	EKU statement GB3.2) Your salon's expected times for cutting hair to shape GB3.10) Why it is important to keep your work area clean and tidy GB3.13) Methods of working safely and hygienically and which minimise the risk of cross-infection and cross-infestation	277
Personal hygiene	Unit GH12 Cut hair using basic techniques	EKU statement GB3.15) The importance of personal hygiene	274–275

Remember

Disposal of sharp items
Used razor blades and similar items should be placed into a safe container (sharps box). When the container is full it can be disposed of. This type of salon waste should be kept away from general salon waste as special disposal arrangements may be provided by your local authority.

EKU *statement*

GB3.3) Your salon's and legal requirements for disposal of sharps and waste materials

EKU *statement*

GB3.9) Why it is important to check for infestation and avoid cross-infection

GB3.12) Methods of cleaning, disinfecting and or sterilisation used in salons

Activity
Every salon has their own way of doing things. Write down in your portfolio under the following headings what your salon's code of practice is in respect to:

- meeting and greeting clients
- gowning
- maintaining tools and equipment
- disposal of sharps
- hygiene and preventing the spread of infection or infestation
- expected standards of service.

Disposal of waste and sharps

Much of the waste produced in a salon or barbers is harmless, and as long as it has been placed in a strong polythene bin liner and tied at the top, it can be disposed of as general commercial rubbish. However, some items should be cleared away promptly or handled and disposed of with care.

Salons also use a lot of chemicals and many of these such as shampoos, conditioners and styling products, are not necessarily potential hazards. In fact much of the other chemical waste created by salons ends up being rinsed down the sinks too and unless this form of disposal has local by-laws ruling against it; then these chemicals shouldn't present a disposal hazard either.

But sharp items such as disposable razor blades do need to be handled with extreme care. Used sharps must be disposed of carefully to prevent any injury or cross-infection. They should be put in the sharps box and sealed properly before refuse collection.

(See notes below for special conditions for disposal of sharps with certain authorities.)

Prevent infection

Infection and disease occurs by two obvious methods within the salon/barber shop environment. It is:

- either brought in by a 'carrier' visiting the salon who then cross-infects other people within the salon
- or the result of poor hygiene and cleanliness within the salon.

Activity
What is your salon's policy for the use of razors and the disposal of sharp items?

Most of the preparatory aspects covered in this chapter aim to keep the standards of hygiene within your working environment very high.

But there would be little point in maintaining the healthy environment unless you checked your clients for signs of infections or infestations during your consultation, as warm, humid salon conditions can offer a perfect home for disease-carrying bacteria. If they can find food in the form of dust and dirt, they may reproduce rapidly.

Good ventilation, however, provides a circulating air current that will help to prevent their growth. This is why it is important to keep the salon clean, dry and well aired at all times. This includes clothing, work areas, tools and all equipment. Sterilisation provides the most effective way of providing hygienically safe work implements in salons. Sterilisation means the complete eradication of living organisms.

Different types of equipment use different sterilisation methods, which may be based on the use of heat, radiation or chemicals.

Ultraviolet radiation

UV cabinets may be utilised to store previously sterilised disinfected tools and equipment.

Chemical sterilisation/disinfectant

Chemical sterilisers should be handled only with suitable personal protective equipment, as many of the solutions used are hazardous to health and should not come into contact with the skin. The most effective form of salon disinfection is achieved by the total immersion of the contaminated implements into a jar of fluid such as Barbicide™.

Ultraviolet radiation for sterilisation

IMAGE COURTESY OF SORISA

Autoclaves

The autoclave provides a very efficient way of sterilising using heat. It is particularly good for metal tools although the high temperatures are not suitable for plastics; such as brushes and combs. Items placed in the autoclave take around 20 mins to sterilise. (Check with manufacturer instructions for variations.)

Further information on working position and safety can be found on pages 274 and 277 in Unit GH12.

Barbicide™ solution

IMAGE COURTESY OF ELLISONS

Activity
Wet and dry

There are advantages and disadvantages for cutting both wet and dry hair. Write down your reasons in the table below.

Cutting wet hair

Advantages	Disadvantages

Cutting dry hair

Advantages	Disadvantages

Preparation checklist

✔	Make sure that the styling section and chair is clean, safe and ready to receive clients.
✔	Make sure that the seat is lowered, providing easier access for the clients whether they be young, old or with physical conditions.
✔	Make sure that the client is well protected with a clean fresh gown and a close-fitting cutting collar.
✔	Make sure that you have your tools prepared and close at hand.
✔	Find out what the client wants. Men can often be more difficult during consultation as they are often reluctant to use a technical term that they are not sure about or even express themselves clearly to people they don't know (see the section on consultation below).
✔	Style books/files provide lots of male looks to help the diagnostic process.
✔	Make sure you comb or brush the hair thoroughly before you start to remove tangles; see if all product can be removed and check for growth patterns.
✔	Assess the styling limitations – hair and skin problems or physical features.
✔	Avoid technical jargon or style names; if you do use them, always clarify in simple terms what you mean to avoid confusion; this will help to educate your clients for the future.
✔	Don't just do the style if you think that it's wrong. If there are reasons why you think it will be unsuitable, you will be doing the client a big favour in the longer term if you tackle the issue straight away.
✔	Always give them some advice on how to maintain their hairstyle; men often need products to help them achieve similar effects themselves. Make sure you show them how they can use and apply any new product at home to maintain their own hair/skin condition or styling effect.
✔	Give them an idea of how long it will last and remember to re-book their next appointment before they leave. Alternatively, if they prefer just to pop in on the off-chance, tell them when they should expect to revisit.

LEE MORAN @ SANRIZZ

Client consultation

Finding out what the client wants

Finding out what the client wants is fundamental to achieving a satisfactory result. Factors such as practicality, suitability and the client's ability to cope with his hair are aspects that you should never overlook.

The final effects will be influenced by other considerations too:

- the amount of hair
- the distribution of the hair over the scalp
- the texture of the hair
- the condition of the hair and scalp
- the tendency of the hair, i.e. the amount of wave or curl.

Unless you do take all these factors into consideration, you could have an unhappy, disgruntled client on your hands.

For more information on consultation see Unit G7 Advise and consult with clients (page 96).

DAMIEN CARNEY FOR JOICO

Brush or comb the hair before you start

You must try to get as much information about the client's hair before you start; even if they are only having a dry cut. Part of this may seem obvious; it's the questions that you ask the client regarding what they want. But that's not the only way you find out what's needed. You need to brush or comb the hair in different directions to see if the hair and scalp has:

- *Growth patterns* – that limit or influence the way that the hair can be cut such as double crowns, widow's peak, nape whorls, cowlick etc.
- *Product on it* – if products like wax, gel or grooming cream are on the hair you won't be able to cut the hair properly. It will stick together and stop you from being able to cut it correctly, you must wash the hair before you start the cut.
- *Any infections or infestations* – if there are any signs of a suspected condition you need to know what it is, so you know whether it is possible to proceed. If you do find something that you are not sure about seek assistance (see Unit G7 Advise and consult with clients, page 128).

Check the client's requirements

The main aims of hairdressing and barbering are about delivering a continuing, repeated service that satisfies our clients. We can only satisfy the clients if we find out what they want and act upon those instructions. We demonstrate this by getting confirmation of the things we are doing throughout the service. This does a number of things:

- it ensures that we only do things that the clients want
- it makes them more confident about what we are doing
- it removes any ambiguity or confusion
- it gives us more confidence in what we are doing for the client
- it involves the client and helps to develop a professional relationship.

EKU statement

GB3.22) The importance of correctly combing out the hair prior to cutting

GB3.18) Why hair products should be removed from the hair prior to cutting

GB3.17) The factors which should be considered when cutting wet hair and dry hair

GB3.25) The importance of consulting with clients throughout the cutting process

Remember

As many men have shorter hair, their nape hair growth patterns will have far more impact on what hairstyle you choose.

Remember

Personal hygiene is especially important to hairdressers. You work in close proximity to the client so make sure that you eliminate body odour, bad breath or dirty hands and nails by taking the appropriate action.

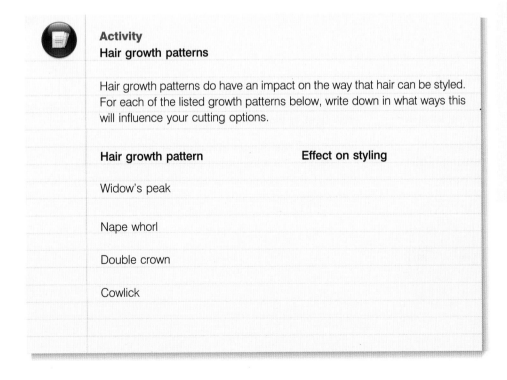

Activity
Hair growth patterns

Hair growth patterns do have an impact on the way that hair can be styled. For each of the listed growth patterns below, write down in what ways this will influence your cutting options.

Hair growth pattern	Effect on styling
Widow's peak	
Nape whorl	
Double crown	
Cowlick	

EKU *statement*

GB3.16) The factors that must be taken into consideration prior to and during cutting (e.g. hair and scalp disorders, presence of male pattern baldness, etc.)

GB3.20) The known causes of male pattern baldness

EKU *statement*

GB3.21) The typical patterns of male pattern baldness

Influencing factors affecting style choice

Male pattern baldness

Your consultation will cover a wide variety of factors that influence what happens next and male pattern baldness or the early signs of it should be high upon your list of things to look for.

Male pattern baldness (MPB) is a balding or thinning condition the cause of which, regardless of claims, is still eluding the scientists. MPB may be due to high levels of the male hormone testosterone within the body. Many treatments have been developed with little or no long-term remedial effects. Hair transplants have been a possible option in the past, but this type of treatment is expensive and needs a lot of upkeep.

Depending at what stage the MPB is, you need to find out how your client feels about it. If the hair loss is relatively slow, there is no need to rush immediately for the clippers and a grade 2. There could be some considerable time before the condition requires a focused attention and, therefore, you need to provide advice and reassurance with a range of styling alternatives.

If however, the MPB is in a progressed state then it is obviously going to impact on what styles are achievable. For example, if there is a significant general thinning or hair loss on top (MPB type 1) then your styling options are far more limited than if MPB is only apparent in the recession area around the forehead (MPB type 2).

If your client has lost their hair and wears a toupee, you must account for this in your styling. Obviously, there has to be some blending between the natural, remaining hair and the added hair. Be careful not to leave the hair either too long or too short around the blend area. If there is any imbalance in lengths between the two, it is definitely going to show.

If, however, the client wears a full hairpiece then they might just prefer to keep whatever remaining hair very short beneath it. This makes fitting and positioning of the hairpiece easier and will be more comfortable to wear over long periods of time.

© HABIA

Male pattern baldness

Facial shapes

Remember

 Many men elect to go very short when they are faced with thinning or bald areas on the scalp. If you can, provide them with alternatives; let them see the benefits of styling their hair in different ways if at all possible.

Facial shapes	How best to work with it
Square and oblong facial Shapes HABIA	Square and oblong are typically masculine and provide a perfect base for traditional classic well groomed looks on shorter hair. These facial shapes have less impact on longer men's hairstyles.

Facial shapes	How best to work with it
Round faces	If shorter, more classic styles are required, the round face is improved by the introduction of angular or linear perimeters. On the other hand, if the hair is to be worn longer the roundness of the face will be reduced, as more will be covered.
Square angular features, jaw, forehead etc.	Again these are traditionally accepted as a feature of masculinity. They do not really pose any limitations for classic type work. They also work well with longer hair too. Squarer more angular features are softened with beards and moustaches.
Flatter heads at the back	They are improved by contoured graduation, which creates shaping and tapering that is missing from having a flatter occipital bone. Sometimes the head is both flat and wide and this can make the problem harder to deal with. Wider, flatter heads are made less noticeable by longer hair, if this is not possible then explain what the effect will look like if taken very short.

EKU *statement*

GB3.24) How the factors in the range can affect the way the hair is cut

Examination of hair and scalp

While you are looking at the client's hair and scalp, be particularly aware of the texture of the hair. If it is coarse and tightly curled, you will need stronger combs to stretch the hair out from the head before cutting, and firmer movements will need to be applied. The density of the hair is important too: if it is thick, then styles with varied hair lengths are possible.

On the other hand, sparse hair, particularly if it is fine, requires a great deal of attention and expertise. If finely textured hair has to cover sparse area of the head, it will have to be longer than hair of coarser texture. The amount, type and growth patterns of hair are all-important too. Younger men may have distinctly higher forehead hairlines than women of similar age. Thinning crowns and decreasing density of hair marks many male patterns.

Hair grows at a rate of about 1.25 cm each month and this is more noticeable with shorter layered styles. Regular trimming is essential to keep them tidy.

Hair growth patterns

For more information on hair growth patterns see Unit G7 page 121

Although men can wear longer hair as well as short, a whole range of modern contemporary styling effects has developed since the basic and traditional short back

EKU *statement*

GB3.19) The average rate of hair growth

EKU *statement*

GB3.16) The factors that must be taken into consideration prior to cutting (e.g. hair density, hair growth patterns, hair and scalp disorders, etc.)

GB3.17) The factors which should be considered when cutting wet hair and dry hair

GB3.24) How the factors in the range can affect the way the hair is cut and sides. The application of hair products will often 'dress up' an otherwise professional or classic looking hair turning it into something with a more distinctive 'fashion look' for social and special occasions.

Now and again a men's named style becomes fashionable. Some of these names, such as 'Tony Curtis' a 'DA' a 'crew cut', the 'mullet', the wedge or a mohawk, have passed at some time or another into the general vocabulary. Always make sure that you know what

Look out for:	Why is it a concern?
Hair density	Scalps with densely populated hair can always be reduced, thinned or controlled in some way, whereas thinner hair or male pattern baldness create a range of limitations that you will need to both express and contend with.
Hair tendency	Curly hair has more styling limitations than straighter hair. Wavy hair is always easier to direct or position than straight hair. Point these factors out before you start.
Hair texture	Fine hair is always difficult to handle, whereas coarser hair when straight will often appear spiky or blunt. Conversely, coarse, wavy hair can often appear dry regardless of natural condition. Each hair texture type creates a different problem.

Activity

Knowing how to remove, replace and maintain the clipper blades is an essential part of hairdressing. With the electric clippers removed from the power supply or rechargeable clippers 'rundown', get your supervisor to show you how the lower blade-retaining screws are undone and removed. This will give you access to both cutting blades and the area below the armature (the vibrating arm that works them) for cleaning purposes.

When you have dismantled the blades get used to checking for signs of corrosion. If a rusted area exists it will look like blackened areas around the blade edges. If blades have been allowed to get to this stage they should be replaced by new ones as their ability to cut cleanly without friction has been greatly reduced.

With the blades stripped down, you can now use clipper oil to lubricate the two blades, wiping any excess away. Now you can replace the blades (the right way up) and partially re-tighten the retaining screws. Finally, readjust the alignment of the blades and tighten the screws. Check the alignment once more: the lower stationary cutting blade should extend around 3 mm further than the upper cutting blade with the clippers adjusted fully forwards to the shortest cutting length. Hand them back to your supervisor so that your maintenance can be checked.

your client means if he uses a name to describe a style; remember, it may be completely different from your idea of that style.

Cutting tools and equipment

Clippers

Clippers are and have been an essential item of equipment for men's styling. They have been invaluable for the popularity of short hairstyles but are equally important for the shaping and trimming of necklines and facial hair shapes.

The electric clippers cut hair by oscillation: the side-to-side movement of an upper metal blade passing over a lower rigid or fixed one. On each pass of the upper blade, the hair caught between the teeth of the lower blade is cut and falls away.

Regular cleaning and lubrication will prolong the blades' useful life and keep the cutting edges sharp. Without this care the constant friction of one blade passing over another will affect their ability to work properly: electric clippers generate quite a lot of heat and, if they have not been maintained, their ability to cut cleanly and efficiently deteriorates over time. New blades are relatively expensive, as they can often cost half the price of a new pair of clippers. If the clipper blades are unable to cut keenly you will not be able to trim, shape and style neck or facial hair shapes accurately.

You should always take care not to drop them, as this can easily cause damage to the cutting teeth or even break them! Any missing areas of teeth along the blades will be extremely dangerous and could easily cut the client if they were used. So when they are not in use, hang them up out of the way or replace them back in the charger unit.

Clipper blades should always be checked for alignment before each time they are used. The fixed lower blade is adjustable and this allows for small adjustments to be made backwards, forwards or even side to side.

Loosening the small retaining screws underneath allows the blades to be adjusted. This also provides access to the upper blade, for removal, cleaning out the fragments of hair and essential oiling/lubrication.

When the blades are replaced the retaining screws must be retightened properly. If this is not done, the vibration will dislodge the alignment and this could easily take a chunk out of your client's hair, or worse, even cut him!

Well-maintained clippers will cut either wet or dry hair with equal ease, although many stylists prefer to cut the hair first, and then wash the hair after to remove any small fragments and make any final checks.

Remember

 Always take care when using any sharp items of equipment. Your safety and the safety of the client are in your hands; take care not to be distracted while you are working.

 Diversion Good care and regular maintenance of your tools are an essential part of hairdressing and barbering. For more information on looking after these items see Chapter 10.

See also Unit GH12 Cut hair using basic techniques, pages 283–285, which covers

- scissors
- thinning scissors
- combs, neck brushes and sectioning clips.

EKU *statement*

GB3.23) Which tools can be used on either wet or dry hair or both

GB3.14) The correct use and maintenance of cutting tools

KINDLY SUPPLIED BY WAHL (UK) LTD

KINDLY SUPPLIED BY WAHL (UK) LTD

KINDLY SUPPLIED BY WAHL (UK) LTD

IT&LY

Clipper blade

Standard clipper grades/attachments

Clipper attachment size	Length of cut hair
No. for attachment	Very close to skin, almost as close as shaving
Grade 1 = 3 mm ($\frac{1}{8}$ inch)	Very short, on darker hair it will only leave a stubbly shadowing effect
Grade 2 = 6 mm ($\frac{1}{4}$ inch)	Close cut, will see some skin on finer hair types but short enough for the hair to appear straight even if it is naturally curly
Grade 3 = 9 mm ($\frac{3}{8}$ inch)	Popular length grade for short groomed effects. Typically cuts to that of short scissor-over-comb lengths
Grade 4 = 13 mm ($\frac{1}{2}$ inch)	Popular length which has a similar effect to longer scissor-over-comb type effects
Grades 6–8 = 16 mm–25 mm ($\frac{1}{2}$–1 inch)	Popular longer length used for beard shaping

Note: There are no set standard sizes for clipper attachment combs/grades; you will need to adapt the hair length required by your client in light of the make and model clippers that you have/or your salon provides.

Razors

The open or 'cut-throat' style razor used in shaving is made out of a single steel blade which is hinged and closed into a protective handle. The modern counterpart for this has disposable blades which can be removed and discarded after use. (Blades are discarded after each client to avoid cross-infection. They should be disposed of safely into the salon's sharps box.)

The razor used for hair styling is called a *shaper*; it too has disposable blades which are fitted into a hinged sheath that provides a handy, safe styling tool. Razor cutting is *always* carried out on wet hair and with sharp blades. This is because of the way in which razors are used; and the angle at which they cut through the hair, razoring should never be done on dry hair as this will be painful for the client, and pull and tear the hair, possibly causing it to split, even if the blades are new.

Type of razor	Description
Open (cut-throat) razor	This razor has a fixed/rigid blade that folds into its handle for safety. The blade is kept keen by regular stropping and honing and must be sterilised on each use between clients.
Safety razor	This razor simulates the shape and feel of the open razor with disposable blades which make it more hygienic as blades can be replaced for each client.
Shaper	This is a popular razor with disposable blades that is used for cutting and styling hair, but not for shaving. It therefore has uses for both women's and men's hairstyling.

The hairstyle that you choose for your client is influenced by a number of different factors. We have listed the main considerations in the table below. What impacts do these features have upon your decisions?

Aspect to consider	Effect/impacts on styling
Head and facial shape	
Body physical features	
Reason and purpose for the style	
Quality, quantity and distribution of the hair	
Hair positioning, type, growth and tendency	
Style suitability	
Age and ability	
Lifestyle	

Cutting techniques

Cutting tools	Techniques that can be achieved	Explanation of technique
Scissors (straight or flat parallel blades) IT&LY	Club cutting (blunt cutting)	The most basic and most popular way cutting sections of hair straight across, parallel to the index and middle finger. The blunt, straight sections of cut hair that it produces are ideal for precise lines. The different angles that the hair can be held will produce either; square, graduating and reverse graduating layer patterns.
	Freehand cutting	Cutting without holding with the fingers is known as freehand cutting. It is a technique that allows for cutting with natural fall and without tension. Its main uses are at the perimeter edges around ears, fringes and trimming awkward growth patterns.

EKU *statement*

GB3.27) How and when to use club, freehand, scissors over comb, clipper over comb, thinning and fading techniques and the effects achieved

Cutting tools	Techniques that can be achieved	Explanation of technique
Thinning scissors	Thinning/ texturising	Thinning scissors will remove uniform bulk from any point between the root area and ends. However, they have more creative uses when they are used to 'feather' the perimeter edges of hairstyles (which is often more difficult with straight bladed scissors).
Electric clippers	Clippering with grade attachments	Clipper grades (the attachments that provide uniform cutting lengths) are made in a range of sizes for different purposes, and are numbered accordingly they will provide closely cut uniform layering or if differing grades are used; they can provide graduation on hair that is too short to hold between the fingers.
	Fading	A way of blending short hair at the nape or edges of a hairstyle down or 'out' to the skin. It is achieved by using the clippers with the blade 'backed off' creating a very short, tapered effect with a smooth blended effect without any lines.
	Clipper over comb and scissor over comb	Both techniques are a popular way of layering or fading very short hair into styles that can't be held between the fingers. The hair is held and supported by a comb and the free edges protruding through are removed.

IT&LY

WAHL

GB3.2   Cut hair to achieve a variety of looks

Cutting rules

EKU *statement*

GB3.32) The importance of working with the natural fall of the hair when considering the weight distribution within a hair cut

There isn't any mystery about cutting, it's like most other things: if you follow the procedural steps and do each thing at the right time and you will get the right results. These rules maintain a consistent approach to the way that you tackle any hairstyle and the consistency bit ensures that you achieve the correct quality levels during the execution of the work.

These rules are set out below:

Cut hair with natural fall

Being aware of and cutting with natural fall is extremely important. Looking for the directions of growth within the hair is an essential part of consultation as it is within the execution of the haircut. If you work with the natural fall in terms of partings, nape hair growth, double crowns etc., you will be compensating for these anomalies and be able to produce an easier to manage result. Ignore these factors and you will be giving both you and the client a hard job in styling it.

As previously covered in preparation, always try to shampoo the hair, even if you are only doing a dry hair cut. This way when you dry the hair off, you will be able to see the natural fall far easier and be able to work with it.

Accurate sectioning

Having made the previous considerations of safety, care and the hair design aspects, you are almost ready to start cutting. The only other thing that you need to consider is how you tackle all that hair, when parts of it can easily get in the way whilst you work. Very short hair doesn't really pose any problem but sectioning isn't just for those with very long hair.

In order for you to be able to manage sizeable amounts of hair at any one time, you must organise and plan the haircut. The planning bit becomes automatic; it's the few moments that you spend thinking:

- How do I go about this?
- Where do I start?
- What is the finish going to be like?

So, if the planning is automatic it's the organisation bit that you have to address. Quite simply, being organised is about working in a methodical way. It is the way in which you routinely start at one point, divide and secure all the rest of the hair out of the way, finish that bit, and then take down the next part to work on, and so on.

Each part or section that you work on should be small enough for you to cope with, without losing your way and continuing on blindly! It seems a strange term to use, but 'blindly' is exactly the right word. If the sections are too deep or too wide you will not be able to see the cutting guideline that you need to work to. Accurate sectioning guarantees that every cut is addressed to the same length every time.

Controlling the shape

There are three aspects of cutting that you must get right on every haircut:

- *The holding angle* – the angle at which the hair is held out from the head
- *The cutting angle* – the angle at which the scissors, razor etc. cuts the hair
- *The holding tension* – the even pressure applied to sections of hair when it is held ready for cutting.

That doesn't seem much to guarantee success, but it does take a lot of practice and concentration. Even if you start well in the haircut you cannot afford to 'lose it' in the closing stages.

Cutting lines, or perimeter lines are the outline shape created when layered hair is held directly out with tension i.e. perpendicular and without twisting or sagging, from the

EKU *statement*

GB3.26) The importance of applying the correct degree of tension to the hair when cutting

GB3.37) How the angle at which the cutting tools and the head are positioned will affect the weight distribution, balance and degree of graduation of the cut

EKU *statement*

GB3.28) The reasons for establishing and following guidelines

EKU *statement*

GB3.30) The importance of cross-checking the cut

GB3.31) How to cross-check and balance the cut

EKU *statement*

GB3.29) How to create and follow a guideline for uniform layer, graduation, with a fringe, without a fringe, with a parting, without a parting, around the ear outline and fade

head. The curves and the angle in relation to the head, determines the shape of the cut style. The main ones are:

- the contour of the shape from top to bottom
- the contour of the shape around the head, side to side.

When cutting the lines and angles, comb the hair and hold the sections with an even tension. The tension ensures that accuracy is maintained throughout the cut and the position in which you hold and cut the hair determines the position the cut sections take when combed back on the head. The angles and lines of cutting depend on the different lengths required by the style. The first cutting line – the outer perimeter line – may be related to the nape (when starting at the back). The second cutting line – the inner perimeter line – depends on the different lengths required throughout the style.

cross checking

correct tension

Creating guidelines

The guideline is the initial cutting line that is created as a sort of template for all the subsequent sections that are taken.

As a general rule the simpler or more basic the hairstyle the fewer the guidelines there will be. Conversely, the more complex the hairstyle the more guidelines will be involved.

So at Level 2 the styles that need to be done involve fewer guidelines:

- a uniform layered haircut has one
- a basic graduation has two.

A uniform layered haircut has layers of equal length all around the head, so the first cutting guideline dictates the overall length for the rest of the haircut.

For easier control, haircuts are always started at the back; this way the bulk of the hair is tackled and checked before moving onto the sides and top. So after dividing the hair vertically and evenly down the back, take a horizontal section at both sides about 2 cm above the hairline and secure with sectioning clips out of the way. Cut this baseline to the length that you need to and after checking, take down the next section 2 cm above and secure the remainder.

Cutting guidelines

uniform layers

graduation

At the point beneath the vertical division in the hair; take and hold a vertical section as shown in figure (a) without twisting and with an even tension. Cut this perpendicularly (at a vertical angle) to the head. (The client's head should be horizontal and not chin down, or head back.)

With the guideline cut, you take the next section, parallel to the guideline, with the same even tension, so that you can see the lengths of the previously cut guideline through the held mesh. Cut this to the same length as the guideline. Continue this throughout each section until the complete horizontal area has been cut. Then take down another 2 cm on either side and repeat the process, slowly working up the back to the crown.

With the back done, you take a horizontal section above the ears through to the front, cut your perimeter baseline and follow the guideline through from behind the ear working towards the front hairline. Repeat up to the top and cut the other side in the same way.

Finish the haircut over the top working forwards from the known guidelines at the top. Finally, trim the front hairline perimeter shape to complete the hairline profile shape and cross-check to see that the sides, back and top are all in balance.

The graduated haircut uses a similar guideline process to that of uniform layering; the only difference is that the hair is held out at an angle from the head as opposed to perpendicular. The steeper the angle is held away from the head, the lower the bulk-line will be and the greater the weight distribution for the overlying lengths. Conversely, the shallower the angle of the cut; the higher the bulk line will be and the less weight distribution for the overlying lengths.

(For more information on cutting guidelines on uniform layers or graduation see the step by steps later in this chapter).

Cross-checking the cut

Possibly at different points during the cut, but certainly after the cut you will need to recheck what you have already done. This is done by taking and holding sections at an angle which is at right angles (90°) to the original cut sections. (In other words, if you originally cut the hair in vertical meshes, your cross-check will be done with horizontal meshes.)

Cross-checking provides a final technique for checking the continuity and accuracy of the hair cut. Where you find an imbalance in weight, or extra length that still needs to be removed, it provides you with the opportunity to create the perfect finish.

Outline shapes

Many short, layered cuts are graduated at the sides and into the nape sometimes by clipper-over-comb or, when left slightly longer, by scissor-over-comb techniques. On shorter hairstyles the neck- and hairlines become the main focal perimeters of the hairstyle and, in emphasising these, you will need to give them careful attention as it is very easy to infringe into the hairline and remove hair that is needed for the outline shape.

Where possible always use the natural hairlines as the limit for the hairstyle. This produces a smoother effect on the eye and produces styles that look balanced and right. If you ignore the natural hairlines and cut above them, you will find that the hair below will grow back very quickly and produce a stubbly effect within a few days. Or, if on done on dark hair, it will produce a 'shadowed' effect within 24 hours.

EKU statement

GB3.33) How the angle at which the hair is held will affect the weight distribution, balance and degree of graduation of the cut

EKU statement

GB3.34) How to create the neckline and outline shapes in a range

EKU statement

GB3.35) The importance of cutting to the natural hairline in barbering

Remember
Hair growth patterns The movement and direction of hair is particularly problematic on shorter hair styles. Make sure that you take this into consideration during your consultation with your client.

Remember
In order to create clean lines around the ears on shorter hairstyles, you will need to hold the tops of the ears down so you can see what you are doing and ensure that you are working safely.

However, natural necklines often lack consistency; the growth is often uneven, intermittent or sparse. Therefore the outline shapes for these men wearing shorter hair need to be defined. The more natural the nape line, the softer and less severe will be the look.

Activity
Planning your work
Any service that you provide to the client needs to be thought about before you start. This planning is essential for achieving a successful result, so in this activity, complete the table below to create a checklist of things that you should consider before carrying out the service.

Checklist for cutting

1

2

3

4

5

6

Round neckline

Tapered/faded neckline

Square neckline

The shaping of front hair into a fringe can produce a variety of facial frames and the focal point it creates changes the overall effect dramatically. In many men the front hairline recedes and this is often a sign of male pattern baldness. This influences the choice and positioning of perimeter fringe shapes. Always give this some thought before cutting the hair.

In men, the side hairlines, sideburns or sideboards bridge the hairstyle and beard shape. These need to fit, and care must be taken in shaping them. Lining the hair above the ears and along the sides of the nape is usually carried out with the scissor points or carefully angled inverted clippers.

Common cutting problems

Necklines

All of the classic perimeter neckline shapes above can easily be ruined if a lack of care and attention occurs. The detail of the outline of very short hair can easily be spoiled by careless layering or clippering. Every millimetre counts. You need to make sure that your outlining with the clippers is even and smooth throughout. If you do make a mistake and find that you have encroached on the outline shape you would be better off re-cutting the outline slightly shorter to eliminate the fault.

Blending from clipper lengths to scissor length

Another common problem on short hair is found at the blend area between different clippered grades, or between the clippered and hand-held cut lengths. If a careful blending hasn't been made cutting marks will show at the point where the two areas combine.

There are two ways of tackling this problem:

1 If the hair is still too long on the hand-cut/held side, you can re-fade the two zones together by scissor over comb methods. Be careful not to undercut the longer lengths as this will mean that you will have to re-cut all the clippered area.

2 If the lengths of hair between the two areas are slightly uneven it will definitely show unless you correct it. In any area where clippers fade out to club cut lengths you can resurface the hair by using thinning scissors over comb just on the very tips of the hair. A light blending of thinned hair produces an optical illusion that cheats the eye by softening the two hard cut edges and the final effect appears correct.

Ears

Nature does not guarantee symmetry, and this is particularly true with faces. One side of the face is not exactly the same as the other and this applies to ears too. One may be larger than the other; they may be irregular in shape or at different heights; you need to make sure that you have considered this before you start. Unevenness on long hair doesn't matter, but when it's on short hair the imperfections will be made clear.

You need to find out how your client feels about his facial features. Sometimes these natural imperfections are not a concern, they are merely a characteristic of the client's personality. Don't forget to check on whether your client wears glasses or a hearing aid; take all of these factors into your assessment.

Finally you and your client will be able to agree exactly what look is required, and you will then have a basis on which to decide how the work is to be carried out.

Hair type

If your client's hair is very curly, do remember that it will coil back after stretching and cutting. Similarly, wavy hair, when cut too close to the wave crest, can be awkward to style as it tends to spring out from the head. Very fine straight hair will easily show cutting marks or can disclose unwanted lines from clippering if you take too large sections. Make sure that the sections you take are accurately divided and sectioned.

Remember

 Always check the clipper blade alignment before using them for each client.

Remember

 In order to create clean lines around the ears on shorter hairstyles, you will need to hold the tops of the ears down so you can see what you are doing and ensure that you are working safely.

Remember

 Removing cutting marks
The thinning-over-comb technique can be used as a corrective method on most clipper-cut or scissor-cut lengths to 'join' areas of differing grades/lengths or to remove cutting marks on fine, medium and coarse hair textures.

Remember

Men's short hairstyles often benefit from washing again after cutting. This removes all the shorter clippings and makes them more comfortable.

Tapering and thinning encourage the hair to curl at the ends, while club cutting increases density and reduces that tendency.

Feathering and texturising can produce extra lift and bounce.

If your client has a build-up of wax, gel or moulding crème on their hair you must insist that the hair is washed to get it out or off the hair before you attempt the hair cut.

Final points to remember

1   If the hair is dirty, then for hygienic reasons it must be washed before you cut it. Wet hair is a necessity for blow-drying and finishing, but not necessarily a convenient arrangement for a quick trim before work or during lunch.

2   Clean, dry hair should not be cut with a razor because of the discomfort to your client caused by the tearing and dragging action of the razor on the hair.

3   Accurate sectioning and graduation produces fine layering. This is partly determined by how much hair there is to cut. Longer lengths can be sectioned with the comb and taken between the fingers, while short lengths are best tackled either by clipper-over-comb or scissor-over-comb techniques. A section (that cannot be held between the fingers) is lifted with the comb and a guideline is created by cutting straight across. Subsequent lifting with the comb to the guideline length produces the next section to be cut.

4   Clippers must be used to tidy the necklines on short styles, graduating from the natural line out from the head. How far up the head and how short the cut needs to be is determined by the style and shape agreed with your client. If longer lengths are required higher in the back hair, then the clippers need to graduate away from the head sharply.

5   Cross-checking is an essential part of cutting. It's your way of including a quality control. As you progress through the cut, you obviously need to change your stance, holding position and holding angle. These factors can lead you to go wrong. Typically problems might be that the back section doesn't integrate with the sides properly or the top doesn't blend with the sides, or the fringe doesn't fit with the top. Whatever the potential problem the easiest way to compensate for this is to cross-check to make sure that the cut works well in different planes.

Step-by-step – Graduation

Step 1 Before

Step 2 Put on clean gown or cutting square and place a cutting collar around the shoulders

Step 3 For graduation, the angle of the clippers should always be held and used in parallel with the contour of the lower back of the head

Step 4 Affix the *longest* selected clipper grade to the clippers and start at the lower hairline

Step 5 Work up the back in one continued movement to the occipital bone and fade the clippering out

Step 6 Continue around the head and in to the sides

Step 7 Remember to adjust the cutting angle of the clippers so that it picks up all of the hair that needs to be cut

Step 8 As you work around the hairline by the ears, remember to hold the ears away from the clippers

Step 9 With most of the graduation done cross-cut over the ares to check that all of the hair has been cut

Step 10 Change your clipper grades to a *shorter* cut. Now start at the lower areas and fade out the cut to form the graduation

Step 11 Continue this into the back and sides until the lower area is finished

Step 12 Now using scissor over comb, blend the edge of the clippered area into the scissor cut area. Remember the angle of the comb should *mirror* the angle of the graduation

Step 13 Keep the cutting angle parallel with the barbering comb

Step 14 Now start the top area at the crown by club cutting

Step 15 Work forwards over the towards the front

Step 16 Break up the weight of the fringe area by point cutting into the hair

Step 17 With most of the hair cut finished, you can tidy up the outlines by using the clippers in an inverted position. (Remember to check the blade alignment before you do this otherwise you could easily cut the client's skin)

Step 18 Continue the outlines around the hairlines

Step 19 Finish the shaping and fading

Step 20 Final effect

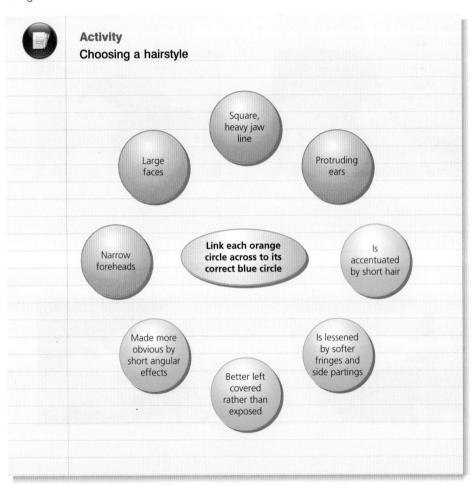

Activity
Choosing a hairstyle

Square, heavy jaw line

Large faces

Protruding ears

Narrow foreheads

Link each orange circle across to its correct blue circle

Is accentuated by short hair

Made more obvious by short angular effects

Better left covered rather than exposed

Is lessened by softer fringes and side partings

Step-by-step – Uniform layering

Step 1 Put on clean gown or cutting square and place a cutting collar around the shoulders

Step 2 Section off the hair at the back so you can cut the lower perimeter length first

Step 3 With the base line cut, you can tidy the neck hair now or leave it to the end

Step 4 Start your guide line at the centre of the back with a vertically held mesh. Now cut all the other sections around the lower nape to the same length

Step 5 Continue up the back by taking a centrally held section directly above your first guide line

Step 6 Cut the other sections around the back to the same length

Step 7 Adjust your holding position to suit your stance and comfort

Step 8 Cut the outline shape by safely cutting away from the ears

Step 9 Cross–check your layering to maintain the accuracy

Step 10 Carefully outline the shape to create the profile

Step 11 Continue into the top by taking your guideline over the crown

Step 12 Work towards the front by club cutting

Step 13 Blend in the top to the previously cut sides

Step 14 Finish off the front by point cutting the fringe to reduce unwanted weight

Step 15 Final effect

Step-by-step – Men's square layering

Step 1 Shampoo, condition and detangle the hair, put the parting in and comb roughly into place

Step 2 Section and secure the hair at the lower back of the head. Start the cutting guideline centrally at the nape

Step 3 Cut the outline perimeter shape

Step 4 Start the square layering by taking a vertical section, centrally at the back; then cut a vertical guide line

Step 5 Continue the layering around the head

Step 6 Work up through the sections at the back of the head

Step 7 Now take a horizonatal section throught the sides to continue the perimeter shape

Step 8 Continue the layering to match both sides

Step 9 Finally check the accuracy and balance of the cut

GB3.3   Provide aftercare advice

EKU statement

GB3.38) The recommended time interval between cuts

Product knowledge

More information on products can be found elsewhere in this book; please see the styling products table in Unit GB5 Dry and finish men's hair (pages 206–207). This provides a useful reference and range of products that would be suitable for recommending to men to help them manage their hair between visits.

In Unit GH12 we looked at aftercare that you should give the clients. We should follow that procedure for male clients in the barber shop, read page 300 and remind yourself of the procedure.

Home- and aftercare checklist

✔	Talk through the style as you work; that way the client sees how you handle different aspects of the look.
✔	Show and recommend the products/equipment that you use so that the client gets the right things to enable them to get the same effects.
✔	Tell the client how long they can expect the style to last and when they need to return for reshaping.
✔	Demonstrate the techniques that you use so they can achieve that salon hair look too.

For further information on how to give advice to clients see Units G7 Advise and consult with clients and G18 Promote additional products and services to clients.

EKU *statement*

GB3.39) How lifestyle can influence the client's choice of style (e.g. active sports, career and job requirements)

GB3.40) Products for home use that will benefit the client and those to avoid and why

GB3.41) Styling suitable for home use between cuts

GB3.42) How to give effective advice and recommendations to clients

 Diversion

Checkerboard

Checkerboard	I know my salon's requirements for client preparation, waste disposal and expected service timings ☐	I know the safety considerations that I should make in respect to safe working practices ☐	I consult with the clients at all points during the cutting processes ☐
I always recognise style in limiting factors when I carry out consultation ☐	I can use a variety of cutting techniques and know what their benefits are ☐	I always try to work with the natural fall of the hair ☐	I always carry out working practices according to the salon's policy ☐
I know how to maintain the cutting tools and equipment ☐	I always explain technical terms eliminating misunderstandings ☐	I know when and who to refer clients to, in situations where external assistance is required ☐	I understand the necessity of personal hygiene and presentation ☐
I know what advice to give and what things I should recommend to clients ☐	I know how to adapt cutting techniques to achieve a variety of different creative effects ☐	I can use a variety of cutting tools: scissors, thinning scissors, razors and clippers to achieve differing effects ☐	

Assessment of knowledge and understanding

Project

For this project you will need to select two of your clients:

Client 1 should have short clippered hair.

Client 2 should have longer uniform layers.

For each of these clients:

1 Describe what your client's hair was like before you started.

2 Explain how you decided upon the style that was done.

3 Describe what methods, techniques and tools were used to complete the look.

4 Take a photograph (perhaps with your mobile) of the finished effect.

Revision questions

A selection of different types of questions to check your cutting knowledge

Q1 Accuracy is achieved by _____ and cutting the hair at the correct angle. Fill in the blank

Q2 Scissors should be sterilised in Barbicide™. True or false

Q3 Select from the following list those that are *not* texturising techniques: Multi selection

Club cutting	☐	1
Graduation	☐	2
Slice cutting	☐	3
Layering	☐	4
Point cutting	☐	5
Chipping	☐	6

Q4 Symmetrical shapes produce equally balanced hairstyles. True or false

Q5 Which of the following is not a cutting term? Multi choice

Cross-checking	○	a
Thinning	○	b
Free hand	○	c
Free style	○	d

Q6 Accurate clipper cutting is dependent upon the angle at which they are held in relation to the head. True or false

Q7 Which of the following hair growth patterns will affect the natural fall and way that a fringe lies after it is cut? Multi selection

Nape whorl	☐	1
Double crown	☐	2
Widow's peak	☐	3
Low hairline	☐	4
Cow's lick	☐	5
High hairline	☐	6

Q8 A _____ is the perimeter shape produced by cutting. Fill in the blank

Q9 Which of the following cuts would easily describe a disconnection? Multi choice

Graduation in a long hairstyle	○	a
Reverse graduation in a long hairstyle	○	b
A fringe in a shoulder-length bob style	○	c
Texturising in a short cropped style	○	d

Q10 Clubbing is a technique of cutting that maximises the hair density. True or false

Preparing for assessment checklist

Remember to:

✔	prepare clients correctly for the services you are going to carry out
✔	put on the protective wear available for styling and dressing hair
✔	listen to the client's requirements and discuss suitable courses of action
✔	adhere to the safety factors when working on clients' hair
✔	keep the work areas clean, hygienic and free from hazards
✔	promote the range of services, products and treatments with the salon
✔	clean and sterilise the tools and equipment before it is used
✔	work carefully and methodically through the processes of cutting hair whether wet or dry
✔	place, position and direct the hair appropriately to achieve the desired effect
✔	communicate what you are doing with the client as well as your fellow staff members

Chapter**fourteen**
Trimming beards and moustaches

GB4

GB4.1

GB4.2

GB4.3

More Information
See Units: G7 Advise and consult with clients GB3 Cut hair using basic barbering techniques G20 Make sure your own actions reduce risks to health and safety G17 Give clients a positive impression of yourself

See the appendices for Electricity at Work Regulations
EKU GB4.4) Your responsibilities under the Electricity at Work Regulations

Trimming facial hair: quick overview

Unit title

GB4 Cut facial hair to shape using basic techniques

This is a **mandatory** unit for Barbering at Level 2, it is made up of three main outcomes

Main outcomes

GB4.1 Maintain effective and safe methods of working when cutting facial hair

GB4.2 Cut beards and moustaches to maintain their shape

GB4.3 Provide aftercare advice

What do I need to do for GB4.1?

- Make sure that the client is adequately covered and protected
- Make sure that your working position is comfortable and safe
- Keep the work area clean and tidy and that waste materials are disposed of properly
- Identify factors that influence the service prior to starting
- Work without causing risks to you or your client's health and safety
- Work efficiently and effectively

What do I need to do for GB4.2?

- Prepare your client's facial hair before cutting
- Seek confirmation of the desired look before starting
- Cut your client's facial hair using basic cutting techniques
- Check that the final effect is accurate, that it has an even effect and that the client is satisfied with the results

Keywords

Freehand

A method of cutting without holding between the fingers, or below or above a comb

Scissor over comb

A technique of cutting hair with scissors, using the back of the comb as a guide, especially when the hair is at a length that cannot be held between the fingers

Clipper over comb

A technique of cutting hair with electric clippers, using the back of the comb as a guide, especially on very short hair and hairline profiles

Information covered in this chapter

- The tools and equipment used during cutting

- The preparations that you should make prior to cutting facial hair

- The factors that influence facial hair cutting decisions

- Cutting/trimming facial hair techniques

- The aftercare advice that you should give clients

EKU *statement*

GB4.9) The safety considerations which must be taken into account when cutting facial hair

What do I need to do for GB4.3?

- Give the client accurate, constructive advice on how they can maintain the look themselves

What aspects do I need to cover for GB4.1, GB4.2 and GB4.3?

- A variety of cutting tools and equipment
- A range of factors that influence or limit the choice of styling
- Different types of cutting techniques that are used to create the effects

What aspects do I need to know for GB4.1, GB4.2 and GB4.3?

- Your salon's requirements for preparation, timings and standards of service
- How to work safely, effectively and hygienically when cutting facial hair
- Factors about the client that affect styling choice, suitability and durability
- The ways of methodically cutting facial hair to achieve the desired effects
- The aftercare advice and recommendations that you should give to clients

Introduction

This unit looks at the basic skills of trimming and shaping men's beards and moustaches. The techniques involved are quite different to those used in other hair services although you will find that the same equipment keeps cropping up but it is now used in different ways.

These rudimental practices have always been a feature of men's barbering and this chapter explores the different aspects that you should consider before tackling the skills of this essential barbering service.

Facial hair trimming

If you have already covered the men's cutting unit GB3 you will already be familiar with the techniques of freehand, scissor-over-comb and clipper-over-comb techniques. These techniques and the other things that you will need to cover are set out within this chapter under the following topics:

- preparation and maintenance
- client consultation
- identifying the influencing factors that affect style choice
- cutting techniques and accuracy
- good customer care.

Preparing the client

Your duty and responsibilities towards health and safety are reinforced throughout all hair related services and each service has specific procedures that you should follow. This outcome addresses all of the health and safety issues that you need to consider when styling facial hair.

Gowning the client

Always use freshly clean, laundered protective equipment:

- Fasten a gown at the back, or secure the cutting square with a clip ensuring that the covering is close fitting around the neck and protects the client from any clippings or spillages.
- Place a towel around the front of the client so that the free edges are fastened at the back.
- Tuck a strip of neck wool (or neck tissue) in to the top edge of the towel to stop hair fragments from falling inside the client's clothes.

After consultation and just prior to starting, cover the client's eyes with a cotton wool pad to prevent snippings and clippings from entering their eyes.

Positioning the client

Facial hair cutting requires the client to tilt their head back so that you can work at an angle that enables you to work safely and carefully. The barbering chair is designed for this with its inbuilt head rest and reclining ability. (If you need to recline the chair do it before the client is seated.)

If you need to make any adjustments to working height or angle you can do this now.

Your working position and posture

Barbering, as you already know, involves a lot of standing and because of this you need to be comfortable in your work. You should always adopt a comfortable but safe work position and sometimes comfortable and safe are not necessarily the same thing.

Cutting involves a lot of arm and hand movements and you need to be able to get close enough so that your hands and fingers are in a position where you can cut the hair unencumbered, without bad posture.

1 You should adjust the seated client's chair height to a position where you can work upright without having to over-reach on the top sections of their head.

2 You should clear trolleys or equipment out of the way so that you get good all-round access (300°) around the client.

3 Your equipment should be close enough at hand for you to reach it safely without putting you or the client at risk; the items should be clean, sterile and ready for use.

EKU *statement*

GB4.1) Your salon's requirements for client preparation

GB4.5) The range of protective clothing that should be available for clients

EKU *statement*

GB4.7) How the position of you and your client can affect the desired outcome and reduce fatigue and the risk of injury

GB4.8) The importance of using the correct type of barber's chair

I-STOCK/© GEORGE CAIRNS

EKU *statement*

GB4.14) The importance of personal hygiene

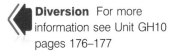 **Diversion** For more information see Unit GH10 pages 176–177

EKU *statement*

GB4.2) Your salon's expected service times for cutting facial hair to shape

GB4.11) Why it is important to keep your work area clean and tidy

GB4.13) Methods of working safely and hygienically and which minimise the risk of cross-infection and cross-infestation

Your personal hygiene

Personal hygiene can't be stressed enough; it is vitally important for anyone working in personal services. Your personal hygiene, or lack of it, will be immediately noticeable to everyone you come into contact with. You may have overslept, but if you haven't showered it will be very uncomfortable for you, your colleagues and the clients as BO is unpleasant in any situation. Other strong smells are offensive too; the smells of nicotine or smoking are very off-putting to the client, particularly if they are a non-smoker.

Remember

Bad breath is offensive to clients too. Bad breath (halitosis) is the result of leaving particles to decay within the spaces between the teeth. You need to brush your teeth after every meal. Bad breath can also result from digestive troubles, stomach upsets, smoking and eating strong foods such as onions, garlic and some cheeses.

Working efficiently, safely and effectively

Working efficiently and maximising your time is essential so making the most of the resources available should occur naturally. Always treat the salon's materials in the same way that you would look after your own equipment; always try to minimise waste, being careful for how much product you use.

Make full use of your time: don't leave things to the last minute as this will encroach into the appointment time: Prepare your tools and equipment so that they are cleaned and sterilised.

EKU *statement*

GB4.10) Why it is important to check for infestation and avoid cross-infection

GB4.12) Methods of cleaning, disinfecting and/or sterilisation used in salons

You need to work in an orderly environment; you must have the materials that you need at hand and the equipment that you want to use in position and ready for action. This is a good exercise in self-organisation and shows others that you are a true professional.

Keep an eye on the clock; you must remember that you need to be working to time and that means providing the styling service in a commercially acceptable time. Don't forget your client is expecting to go home at some point too.

Prevent infection

Infection and disease occurs by two obvious methods within the salon/barber shop environment. It is:

- either brought in by a 'carrier' visiting the salon who then cross-infects other people within the salon
- or the result of poor hygiene and cleanliness within the salon.

Most of the preparatory aspects covered in this chapter aim to keep the standards of hygiene within your working environment very high.

But there would be little point in maintaining the healthy environment unless you checked your clients for signs of infections or infestations during your consultation, as a warm, humid salon can offer a perfect home for disease-carrying bacteria. If they can find food in the form of dust and dirt, they may reproduce rapidly.

Good ventilation, however, provides a circulating air current that will help to prevent their growth. This is why it is important to keep the salon clean, dry and well aired at all times. This includes clothing, work areas, tools and all equipment. Sterilisation provides the most effective way of providing hygienically safe work implements in salons. Sterilisation means the complete eradication of living organisms.

Different types of equipment use different sterilisation methods, which may be based on the use of heat, radiation or chemicals.

EKU *statement*

GB4.3) Your salon's and legal requirements for disposal of waste materials

Activity
Disposal of sharps

What is your salon's policy for the disposal of sharps?
Contact your local council offices' environmental health department for more information.

Disposal of waste and sharps

Remember

Disposal of sharp items
Used razor blades and similar items should be placed into a safe container ('sharps box'). When the container is full it can be discarded. This type of salon waste should be kept away from general salon waste as special disposal arrangements may be provided by your local authority.

Diversion For more information on this topic see Unit G20 page 12

Prepare the client's facial hair

Many men with longer beards never comb them out because they don't want to lose the shape they naturally take on, or they simply don't see the benefits of doing so. Obviously this is a mistake, as regular grooming keeps them free from debris and reduces the chance of infections or ingrowing hair. You should always make a point of giving the clients advice on this or at least tell them how they can manage their own facial hair between visits.

Moustaches and beards get matted as they get longer because the bristles tend to get curlier and lock together. So these tangles have to be removed so that the longer hair is revealed; this allows you to style *all* of the hair and not just part of it.

Cleansing is important too; a beard with debris or grease cannot be styled until it has been cleaned. If you are shampooing the hair as part of another service, then the beard can be done at the same time; or alternatively, you can ask the client to wash their face and beard in the front wash basin, or cleanse with facial wipes.

EKU *statement*

GB4.23) The importance of consulting with clients throughout the cutting process
GB4.35) How to give effective advice and recommendations to clients

Diversion (For more information on effective communication see Unit G7 and G17.)

LEONARDO RIZZO @ SANRIZZ

EKU *statement*

GB4.20) How the factors in the range can affect the way the facial hair is cut and shaped

GB4.19) The factors that must be taken into consideration prior to cutting (e.g., hair density, head and face shape, facial piercing, adverse skin conditions, etc.)

Consultation

Check the client's requirements

The main aims of hairdressing and barbering are about delivering a continuing, repeated service that satisfies our clients. We can only satisfy the clients if we find out what they want and act upon those instructions. We demonstrate this by getting confirmation of the things we are doing throughout the service. This does a number of things:

- It ensures that we only do things that the clients want.
- It makes them more confident about what we are doing.
- It removes any misunderstanding or confusion.
- It gives us more confidence in what we are doing for the client.
- It involves the client and helps to develop a professional relationship.

You need to understand your client fully and be able to negotiate and seek agreement with him throughout the service.

Identify factors that influence the service

Be sure to listen to your client's requests. Many mistakes can be avoided if you achieve a clear understanding of what the client is asking for.

The facial style that you choose with your client should take into account each of the following points about the client's:

- face and head shape/size
- facial physical features (including any scars or blemishes that need disguising)
- hair quality, abundance, growth and distribution
- age, lifestyle and suitability.

(For more information see Unit G7 Advise and consult with clients – Using visual aids in consultation, page 101.)

Facial features

Facial features	How best to work with it
Square and oblong facial shapes	Square and oblong are typically masculine and provide a perfect base for traditional classic well groomed looks. The angular features of the face can be augmented with closer, shorter beards or moustaches and would probably benefit from fewer curves and more angular, linear effects.
Round faces	The effect of a round face can be lessened or increased: it depends what the client wants. If the plan is to reduce the effects, then choose beard designs that lengthen the jawline and incorporate lines and angles rather than curves. If the round features suit the personality and image of the client then work with it by cutting uniform length shapes.
Square angular features, jaw, forehead etc.	Again these are traditionally accepted as a feature of masculinity. These can be handled in a similar way to that of the squarer features above. Squarer, more angular features can also be easily softened with beards and moustaches.

Facial features	How best to work with it
Small faces	Smaller faces should be balanced with facial hair designs that don't overpower the overall effect. Keep your designs close cut and uniform in length.
Wider heads	These wide features will be increased with full, long beards. Create beard designs that are closer cut at the sides and extend to more length at the chin.
Scars, marks and blemishes	If the client has any scars or blemishes this may be the reason for growing a beard or moustache in the first place. You need to ask if there are any features that the client wants to disguise. *Always make a point of looking for these during your consultation.*
Facial piercing	Facial piercings around the mouth and ears do need to be considered during your consultation as well. It is unlikely that the client will want to remove them/it so you have to be very careful in combing, detangling and cutting anywhere near to the area(s) of the piercing(s).

You need to find out how your client feels about his facial features. Sometimes these natural imperfections are not a concern, they are merely a characteristic of the client's personality. Don't forget to check on whether your client wears glasses or a hearing aid; take all of these factors into account.

Finally you and your client will be able to agree exactly what look is required, and you will then have a basis on which to decide how the work is to be carried out.

Aspects to consider

Some men have a heavy, daily growth of facial hair and they find that they need to shave every day. This heavy growth can be obvious for a range of reasons.

1 The growth appears heavy because of the contrast against the skin due to natural colour.
2 The hair seems to grow particularly fast.
3 The density of hair distributed on the face is particularly thick.
4 Combinations of these factors put together.

So, bearing these aspects in mind – initially, the males that are most likely to choose to grow beards and/or moustaches will have ticked two or more of the above. But they are not the only ones who choose to do this, as many others with a poorer growth or definition will grow facial hair for other reasons.

Mouth and width of upper lip to base of nose

The size and width of the mouth forms the basis for any moustache. The distance between the upper lip and the base of the nose creates a sort of canvas for the moustache. If the distance between the two areas is quite deep, it will provide more outline shape options for the wearer rather than if it were narrow.

Similarly, the width of the face at the cheeks will also determine the best, suited affect. Someone with a wide face, will be able to wear a fuller moustache, whereas someone with a narrow face could be *swamped* by this much hair.

Remember

Always make sure that the clippers are cleaned before they are used. Any hair caught between the blades will limit their ability to work, and is unhygienic for the client.

DAMIEN CARNEY FOR JOICO

Bone structure and facial contours

You should take particular care for clients who have a well-defined bone structure, i.e. cheekbones, jaws and facial contour. If they have a particularly linear aspect to their facial features then it would be wiser to retain that similar effect with the overall shapes and outlines. (That's unless they want to disguise themselves or have physical features they want to cover up.)

On the other hand, the man who has a rounder, fuller face can benefit from a shape that defines the face with a more structured effect. Remembering that these people can wear beards with fuller effects than those men with narrower facial features.

Width of chin and depth of jawline

EKU *statement*

GB4.16) How to safely use all the tools and equipment in the range

Facial hair growth forms a frame for the physical features of the face and it is the width of the chin and the depth down to the bottom of the jaw that become the focal point of any facial hair shaping. The outlines of the shapes created here are more noticeable than any others. Historically, beards were left relatively full; this meant that there was very little upkeep for the wearer, apart from keeping the beard from getting too bushy. Latterly, the fashion for wearing more chiselled effects has meant that not only thickness but an outline shape must be maintained.

Tools and equipment

Scissors

Diversion For more information on scissors see Unit GH12 page 283

Scissors are and will always be the most important piece of hairdressing equipment that you will ever own. If you look after them you will be surprised how long a single pair will last. Scissors can be used on either wet or dry hair and vary greatly in their design, size and price. There isn't any single way of choosing the correct pair for you; however, there are a number of aspects that you should consider.

Thinning scissors Thinning scissors can be used on facial hair but have a limited practical use. They have blades with serrated teeth. These cutting surfaces will remove bulk or density from hair but can leave a beard a little endy.

Cutting combs

Get into the habit of only using good-quality cutting combs. You will find that by spending only a little more you will get so much more out of them. The design of a cutting comb for hairdressing is quite different to that of barbering.

The hairdressing cutting comb is parallel and rigid throughout its length whereas the barbering comb is tapered and more flexible. For trimming and styling beards or moustaches you will probably find that the rigid, hairdressing comb is more useful. It will be easier to comb out tangled facial hair and it also provides a better cutting guide for scissor- and clipper-over-comb work.

There are also two sorts of cutting comb. The first and by far the most popular have two sets of differently spaced teeth: at one end they are finer and set closer together while the other half are wider and further apart. This provides more control with finer sections on fine hair and wider sections on the coarser more bristly hair. The second type of cutting comb has uniformly spaced teeth throughout the length of the comb.

The length of cutting combs varies greatly. Again, what's best for you depends on the size of your hands and what you can manage and manipulate quite easily. The normal length of a cutting comb is around 15 cm but long ones are now very popular and provide a better guide when cutting freehand baselines.

The quality of combs and the materials they are made from varies greatly. The best-quality combs are made from plastics that have the following properties:

- They are very strong but flexible; the teeth do not chip or break in regular use.
- They remain straight in regular use and do not end up looking like a banana after a couple of weeks!
- They are constructed by injection moulding and do not have sharp or poorly formed edges (as opposed to combs that are made from pressings and have flawed seams which tend to scratch the client's ears and scalp).
- They are resistant to chemicals making them ideal for cleaning, sterilisation and colouring (as they will not stain).

Activity
Disorders and diseases

This task will help you to revise your knowledge of hair and scalp disorders and conditions.

Fill in the table below. We have completed the first one for you.

Name	Description	Cause	Treatment
Dandruff	Small, itchy, dry scales of shedding epidermal skin	Overactive cell production	Dandruff scalp treatments and shampoo designed to control the problem
Alopecia areata			
Psoriasis			
Seborrhoea			
Male pattern baldness			
Fragilitis crinium			
Damaged cuticle			
Trichorrhexis nodosa			
Monilethrix			
Barber's rash			

EKU *statement*

GB4.17) How to level and test clippers

Diversion See Unit GB3 pages 14 and 15 for more information in this topic

BABYLISS PRO

Remember

 Always take care when using any sharp items of equipment. Your safety and the safety of the client are in your hands; take care not to be distracted while you are working.

EKU *statement*

GB4.18) The size of clipper blades and attachments available and the effects that these achieve

EKU *statement*

GB4.15) Methods of cleaning and maintaining all the tools and equipment in the range

Clippers

Clippers are and have been an essential item of equipment for men's styling. They have been invaluable for the popularity of short hairstyles but are equally important for the shaping and trimming of necklines and facial hair shapes.

Maintaining the tools

Tools	Method of cleaning/sterilising
Neck brush	Wash in hot soapy water and place in ultraviolet cabinet for 10 mins
Sectioning clips	Wash in hot soapy water and immerse in Barbicide™ jar for 30 mins
Cutting comb	Wash in hot soapy water and immerse in Barbicide™ jar for 30 mins
Scissors	Brush away hair fragments from pivot area and blades with a colouring brush. Carefully wipe the blades with sterile wipes and then place with open blades in the ultraviolet cabinet for 15 mins each side
Thinning scissors	Brush away hair fragments from pivot area and blades with a colouring brush. Carefully wipe the blades with sterile wipes and then place with open blades in the ultraviolet cabinet for 15 mins each side

DENMAN

WAHL

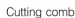

IT&LY

Remember

Maintain your scissors

 Carefully wipe over the blades at the end of the working day to remove any fragments of hair and then apply a little clipper oil to the pivot point to prevent any corrosion around the fastening screw. This will prolong their life and stop them from binding or getting stiffer to use.

<table>
<tr><td>GB4.2</td><td>Cut beards and moustaches to maintain their shape</td></tr>
</table>

Facial hair cutting techniques

Many of the techniques used to cut men's facial hair are common to barbering practices: see Unit GB3 and Unit GH12 for more information on:

- scissor cutting
- freehand cutting
- scissor over comb
- clipper over comb
- controlling the cut
- cross-checking the cut.

Every client is different; they all have differing needs, features and requirements. Therefore, they should always be handled with individual care and attention. Your consultation and analysis will need to reflect this and you will have to adapt to their requests. Normally, the process of trimming and shaping beards or moustaches will be the same in any event; that being:

- you remove the bulk from the interior of the feature first, then
- you tidy and shape the outline to finish the exterior effect.

Always work to and with the natural facial hairlines; it's OK to leave length longer than this but encroaching over this natural division will cause you and the client a lot of problems. If you take your outlines shorter then:

- the results will look strange, unnatural and out of balance
- the bristles will show and would need razoring to remove
- it will be difficult for the client to maintain the style, as he would need to change his shaving technique to keep the lines clean.

Work with the natural growth patterns too; you can't change the direction of the bristles as they grow out from the face. You have to accommodate them within the shaping and trimming. No two heads of hair are the same and this goes for the positioning and natural shapes of beards and moustaches on faces too.

Make allowances for any particular anomalies such as:

- strong directional movements, say to one side – this will limit the wearer to a particular length before it is very noticeable
- whorls or circulatory growth patterns – the effects of these are lessened by more length
- missing or thinning areas – again the effects of the affected areas are lessened by extra length or made more obvious if cut short.

Facial hair is bristle; it is stiffer than hair on the head and this is partly due to the frequency that it is cut in relation to hairstyles. This creates its own problems, as it is more difficult to cut by the scissor-over-comb method. This leads stylists and barbers to choose clipper over comb, as the mechanical advantage makes the job far easier. But as you need to use one hand to steady and position the comb, you can only use one to hold the relatively heavy clippers. This technique is more complex than using clippers held with two hands and clipper-grade attachments.

Activity
Service timings

Complete the table below to answer the following:

1 How much time is allocated for each of the following services in your place of work?

2 What are the correct tools to use for each?

Service	Timing	Tools/equipment
Dry cut		
Wet cut		
Beard trimming		
Cut and finish		

Clipper over comb

The clipper-over-comb technique should start by combing and lifting away the ends, then skimming over these to remove wispier bits first. The benefit of this will allow you to:

- see if any areas show less density in growth than others
- make sure that you don't reduce these areas resulting in skin showing through in a patchy effect.

Bristles are strong and when they are cut into smaller fragments they can fly all over you and the client. This can be dangerous as bristles can stick in any areas of unprotected skin! Or worse, they can enter into the eye. To prevent this happening to the client, it is safer to get him to close his eyes while you trim or, alternatively, place cotton wool pads over his eyes to protect them from the fragments.

When the interior of the facial hair shape has been cut, you can then concentrate on defining the shape by creating the outside perimeter line. Hair growth can often be uneven across the head, let alone the face. Even if the client is a regular visitor to the salon you will need to check for balance throughout the shaping, to make sure that the growth doesn't occur thicker and deeper on one side than the other.

Although comfort is always a major concern, for beard trimming it may be easier to start your outlining with the clippers, centrally up the neck, to the point below the chin to start the profile shape. By doing this, you can define the exact position where you stop and you will find that you can then work on either side of the client to create an even symmetrical finish. After this you can complete the shape behind or over the jaw, and finally from the cheek area down to the desired top profile of the beard.

On the other hand, most moustaches are trimmed at or above the upper lip using scissors, which are easier to handle and stops the vibration of the clippers tickling the client and causing him to pull back. The upper perimeter line can then be augmented by the clippers to give a clean, finished profile shape.

EKU *statement*

GB4.6) Why it is important to protect clients from hair clippings

HAIR BY JACKS OF LONDON, PHOTOGRAPHY BY JOHN RAWSON@TRP

Remember

Safety
Always take care when using sharp implements on the client's skin. Concentrate on the job in hand and ignore other distractions.
If you do cut the client:

1   Put on a pair of disposable non-latex gloves.
2   Use a medical sterilised wipe to clean the area and remove any hair or bristle.
3   Apply pressure to the cut to stem the flow of blood.
4   When the wound has stopped bleeding finish the service and give the client a clean, dry tissue for any minor seepage.

Removing unwanted hair outside the desired style line

Finishing and tidying is the last part of the service; you need to clean up any hair or stubble that lies outside the desired style line. After you have agreed with the client that the overall shape and design is OK, you take the electric clippers and turn them so that the fixed blade works away from the design line. You may find that you need to stretch the skin around the neck and face to get a cleaner, straighter, cut close to the skin. Then, working back from the design line, draw the clippers away over the neck/cheek or jaw to create a clean finish. Take a neck brush and carefully brush away any fragments. Then finally re-cut any areas still with signs of uncut bristle. A final brush and the cutting part is over.

Remember

Always make the skin taut when you are working with clippers around the outlines or removing hair outside of the desired design line. This provides a closer cut finish and acts as a safety feature for the client if he has 'rugged' or heavily lined features.

EKU *statement*

GB4.22) Basic beard and moustache shapes (e.g. moustaches that stay across the top lip, moustaches that curve around the side of the mouth, full beards that follow the contours of the face and that do not require the use of razors)

Examples of beard shapes

Step-by-step basic beard and moustache shaping

Step 1. Client in need of a maintenance based trim

Step 2. Remove excess hair using the clippers-over-comb technique Note the pads to protect the eyes from clippings

Step 3. Remove excess hair from the moustache using the clippers-over-comb technique

Step 4. Use the clippers carefully to produce a tidy edge above the top lip

Step 5. Be aware of critical influencing factors such as moles, scars, infected spots etc

Step 6. Mark out and create an edge using the clippers

Step 7. Remove unwanted hair up to the edge

Step 8. The finished result

Activity
Home-care advice

Good home- aftercare advice is about giving the client the correct advice on looking after their hair and skin at home.
This will include advice on:

- products
- tools and equipment
- future salon services.

1 What advice should you give regarding products?

2 What advice do you need to provide regarding tools and equipment?

3 What advice could you provide regarding future salon services/ treatments?

GB4.3 Provide aftercare advice

Much of the homecare advice relating to products, maintenance and handling is covered elsewhere. See Unit GH12 on pages 300–301 for more information on this topic.

No service is complete unless the client leaves in the knowledge that he can achieve the same result as that done in the salon. If he can't achieve a similar effect he is unlikely to return. You can make sure that he does and the real sign of client satisfaction is the rebooking of his next visit before he leaves the salon.

You can help to achieve this by making sure you tell him:

- how long the effect will last and when he needs to come back
- which products and equipment you have used and how they might benefit the client at home
- how to maintain the effect himself.

How long will it last?

Facial hair grows at an average 1.25 cm per month, so a shorter, closer styled beard or moustache will have grown out within a month, whereas longer facial designs will last longer. (Or, more to the point, the growth won't be quite as noticeable and therefore the

Diversion

client will tend to go longer in-between visits.) Remember, if the effect incorporates a moustache, then it will need trimming anyway, as it will over-fall the upper lip fairly quickly.

Whatever the length or effect created, you need to tell your client from the outset how long they can expect it to last, so that they don't have any unrealistic expectations.

Products and skin care

Explain to the client how they can manage the effect themselves. You need to provide advice on cleansing – what to use, in relation to their hair and skin types, how often to use it and what products wouldn't suit them and therefore should be avoided and your reasons why.

Skin care for men is now a very popular and growing business area. It is as important to men as it is for women; the only difference is the range of products that are available. Men who shave regularly will already know that blunt razors and shaving creams are a contributing factor for minor skin infections or blocking pores and follicles and starting inward-growing hairs. When this occurs, a spot forms on the surface of the skin and the bacteria will have started a small infection. This, like ingrowing hairs, is uncomfortable and itchy and can easily be avoided if you give the client the correct advice.

Exfoliation is beneficial to the client; it removes dead skin cells from the epidermis and stimulates blood circulation, which will generally improve the skin's condition. There are many different products now available for men and these can be bought as grains that are mixed with water and applied as a paste or, alternatively, a wide range of ready-to-use products with a variety of bases such as fruit acids or herbals with essential oils.

Home maintenance

Finally, no complete service can end without the professional advice on how a look or effect can be maintained between visits. You need to give your client the tips and advice on how he can keep the beard and moustache tidy. The hair will continue to grow between visits and the first thing that the client will be aware of is longer perimeter hair over-falling an upper lip or a beard that is getting rather bushy.

We don't expect the client to try and maintain the denser, inner parts of facial hair shapes, but he will want to tidy edges if they become an irritation or look wild!

A few suggestions on what tools he can use (such as trimmer edges on electric shavers, nail scissors for slight trimming) and some advice on how to use them will suffice; you can sort the rest of it out when they return.

LEONARDO RIZZO @ SANRIZZ

Checkerboard

I understand the reasons for and methods of sterilising barbering equipment

I know and understand the principles of positive communication

I know how to and why the client should be protected from loose hair clippings

I always recognise the critical influencing factors when I carry out consultation

I can utilise a range of barbering techniques and know when to use them in my work

I know how the angle at which hair is held and cut is critical to the finished effect

I always carry out working practices according to the salon's hygiene and safety policy

I know why I should keep the work area hygienic, safe and clean avoiding cross-infection and infestation

I always explain technical terms eliminating misunderstanding

I know how to achieve a variety of facial effects by using scissors and clippers

I understand the necessity of personal hygiene and presentation

I know how to work with the natural lie and fall of the hair and why I should cross-check the cut during and after the service

I know that my posture and the client's seated position is important for accuracy and health and safety aspects

I know the factors that affect the ways in which facial hair can be cut and shaped

I know and respect the client's rights: data protection, equal opportunities, anti-discrimination and consumer legislation

I know when and to whom to refer clients to, in situations where external assistance is required

Assessment of knowledge and understanding

Project

For this project you will need to collect historical examples of different beard and moustache shapes.

Use the Internet to find your examples, giving:

A a brief description for each of the styles and

B the following details for each look:
1 the source for the style/shape,
2 its historical time point in history and
3 either an image or sketch of the selected looks.

Revision questions

A selection of different types of questions to check your facial barbering knowledge.

Q1 Closer cutting is achieved by using the clippers without the _____ attached. Fill in the blank

Q2 Razors should be sterilised in Barbicide™. True or false

Q3 Select from the following those tools that need sterilising in a UV cabinet: Multi selection

Cutting collar	☐ 1
Cutting square	☐ 2
Scissors	☐ 3
Clippers	☐ 4
Thinning scissors	☐ 5
Clipper grades	☐ 6

Q4 Outline shapes for beards are best cut with clippers. True or false

Q5 Which of the following is not a cutting term? Multi choice

Cross-checking	○ a
Fading	○ b
Freehand	○ c
Free style	○ d

Q6 Close accurate cutting is dependent upon cutting angles and tensioning on the skin. True or false

Q7 Which of the following is not a facial hair term? Multi selection

Goatee	☐ 1
Side burns	☐ 2
Handlebar moustache	☐ 3
Mohawk	☐ 4
Full beard	☐ 5
Mullet	☐ 6

Q8 The pre-application of hot _____ will soften facial hair making it easier to cut. Fill in the blank

Q9 Which of the following should not be used for trimming facial hair? Multi choice

Clippers	○ a
Shaper	○ b
Scissors	○ c
Razor	○ d

Q10 Thinning is a technique of cutting that maximises the hair density. True or false

Preparing for assessment checklist

Remember to:

✔	prepare clients correctly for the services you are going to carry out
✔	put on the protective wear available for styling and dressing hair
✔	listen to the client's requirements and discuss suitable courses of action
✔	adhere to the safety factors when working on clients' facial hair
✔	keep the work areas clean, hygienic and free from hazards
✔	promote the range of services, products and treatments within the salon
✔	clean and sterilise the tools and equipment before it is used
✔	work carefully and methodically through the processes of cutting hair whether wet or dry
✔	place, position and direct the tools and facial hair appropriately to achieve the desired effect
✔	communicate what you are doing with the client as well as your fellow staff members.

TRACEY DEVINE @ ANGELS

Chapter**fifteen**
Basic hair patterns and designs

More information

See Unit G7 Advise and consult with clients

See the appendices for Electricity at Work Regulations

EKU *statement*

AH21.4) Your responsibilities under the Electricity at Work Regulations

AH21

AH21.1

AH21.2

AH21.3

AH21.4

Basic hair patterning: quick overview

Unit title

AH21 Create basic patterns in hair

This is an **optional** unit for Barbering at Level 2, it is made up of four main outcomes

Main outcomes

AH21.1 Maintain effective and safe methods of working when cutting patterns in hair

AH21.2 Plan and agree hair patterns in hair

AH21.3 Create patterns in hair

AH21.4 Provide aftercare advice

What do I need to do for AH21.1?

- Make sure that the client is adequately covered and protected
- Make sure that the client's skin is kept free of excess hair
- Make sure that your working position is comfortable and safe
- Keep the work area clean and tidy and that waste materials are disposed of properly
- Identify factors that influence the service prior to starting
- Work without causing risks to you or your client's health and safety
- Work efficiently and effectively

What do I need to do for AH21.2?

- Prepare and select suitable visual aids to help with pattern/design consultation
- Prepare your client's hair before cutting
- Seek confirmation of the desired look before starting

What do I need to do for AH21.3?

- Position your pattern/template in the correct position
- Cut your client's hair with accuracy and care

- Change or modify your work position according to the requirements of the design

- Check that the final effect is accurate, that it has an even effect and that the client is satisfied with the results

What do I need to do for AH21.4?

- Give the client accurate, constructive advice on how they can maintain the look themselves

What aspects do I need to cover for AH21.1, AH21.2, AH21.3 and AH21.4?

- A variety of cutting tools and equipment

- A range of factors that influence or limit the choice of styling

- Different types of cutting techniques that are used to create the effects

What do I need to know for AH21.1, AH21.2, AH21.3 and AH21.4?

- Your salon's requirements for preparation, timings and standards of service

- How to work safely, effectively and hygienically when cutting hair

- Factors about the client that affect styling choice, suitability and durability

- The ways of methodically cutting facial hair to achieve the desired effects

- How to correct commonly occurring problems that can occur during cutting

- The aftercare advice and recommendations that you should give to clients

Introduction

Hair design and scalp tattooing both have their origins in tribal and ethnic cultures. The ranges of effects achievable are only limited by the imagination and the subject matter for this work is international.

Hair design in the UK has only scratched the surface. It has been used, historically to differentiate between different ethnic groups. More recently it became a radical, anarchic statement of youth culture in the punk rock era and latterly in the USA it can differentiate between mobs and gangs. The main driver for its popularity is music and if the rap and hip hop genres continue in popularity, then there will be huge requirement for this type of work in the future.

Keywords

Freehand cutting
A method of cutting without holding between the fingers, or below or above a comb

Scissor over comb
A technique of cutting hair with scissors, using the back of the comb as a guide, especially when the hair is at a length that cannot be held between the fingers

Clipper over comb
A technique of cutting hair with electric clippers, using the back of the comb as a guide, especially on very short hair and hairline profiles

Fading
A cutting term that refers to the smooth blending of two different hair lengths within a haircut or alternatively to a tapering technique where very short hair is faded out to the perimeter skin, e.g. at the nape area where clippered hair lengths are blended down to a length of grade 1

Inverse clippering
A way of holding the clippers to produce outlines necklines and detail within a design

Tramliner
A specialist clipper with a tapered, narrow blade for detailing designs on hair

'T' liner
A type of clipper with a different blade type to standard clippers, enabling closer cut outlines around ears, necklines and facial hair shapes

Information covered in this chapter

- The tools and equipment used during cutting

- The preparations that you should make prior to cutting facial hair

- The factors that influence facial hair cutting decisions

- Cutting and styling hair techniques

- The aftercare advice that you should give clients

To prove its validity and to support it on a global scale, it is used within one of the eight test projects for the bi-annual WorldSkills competitions.

AH21.1 — Maintain effective and safe methods of working when cutting patterns in hair

 Diversion Some of the EKUs you need for this unit may be found in other units. To save you from unnecessary duplication we have cross-referenced each unit to other areas. You may have already studied that unit in which case a revision of the information will help you apply that knowledge to this unit. If you have not studied that information before then it will help you when you do study that unit.

Much of the preparations of materials, tools and clients needed for this service are similar to that elsewhere in this book. If you are not familiar with this aspect of the service then see Units GH12, GB3 and GB4 to cover this work.

For specific information on the following topics, review the pages specified.

'Tools and client preparation' – see Units GB4 Cut facial hair to shape using basic techniques pages 342–343 and Unit GB3 Cut hair using basic barbering techniques page 317.

Hygiene and sterilisation – see Units GB4 Design and create a range of facial shapes pages 345–348 and Unit GB3 Cut hair using basic barbering techniques pages 319–324.

EKU *statement*

AH21.8) The safety considerations which must be taken into account when cutting patterns in hair

EKU *statement*

AH21.3) Your salon's and legal requirements for disposal of sharps and waste materials

AH21.6) Why it is important to protect clients from hair cuttings

AH21.9) Why it is important to check for infestation and avoid cross-infection

AH21.11) Methods of sterilisation used in barber shops

AH21.12) Methods of working safely and hygienically and which minimise the risk of cross-infection and cross-infestation

AH21.15) The importance of personal hygiene

EKU *statement*

AH21.1) Your salon's requirements for client preparation

AH21.5) The range of protective equipment that should be available for clients

AH21.10) Why it is important to keep your work area clean and tidy

Cutting techniques – see Unit GH12 Cut hair using basic techniques pages 286–300 and Unit GB3 Cut hair using basic barbering techniques pages 319–330.

Working position, comfort and safety – see Unit GB4 Cut facial hair to shape using basic techniques page 337.

Working effectively and efficiently – see Unit GB4 Cut facial hair to shape using basic techniques page 338 (EKU AH21.2, EKU AH21.14). The preparations in this chapter focus upon the main differences that relate to barbering and barbering equipment as opposed to those relating to more general cutting activities.

EKU *statement*

AH21.7) How the position of you and your client can affect the desired outcome and reduce fatigue and the risk of injury

AH21.45) Why it is important to position your cutting tools for ease of use

Remember

 Disposal of sharp items
Used razor blades and similar items should be placed into a safe container ('sharps box'). When the container is full it can be disposed of. This type of salon waste should be kept away from general salon waste as special disposal arrangements may be provided by your local authority.

Cutting tools

For more information on scissors, types and maintenance of, see Unit GB4 Cut facial hair to shape using basic techniques pages 342–344.

EKU *statement*

AH21.8) The safety considerations which must be taken into account when cutting patterns in hair

EKU *statement*

AH21.13) The correct use and maintenance of cutting tools

> **Remember**
>
> **Maintain your scissors**
> Carefully wipe over the blades at the end of the working day to remove any fragments of hair and then apply a little clipper oil to the pivot point to prevent any corrosion around the fastening screw. This will prolong the scissors' life and stop them from binding or getting stiffer to use.

Clippers

Clippers are and have been an essential item of equipment for men's styling. They have been invaluable for the popularity of short hairstyles but are equally important for the shaping and trimming of necklines, facial hair shapes and design patterns in hair.

> **Remember**
>
> Always look for any contra-indications before you start any hair patterning. Look carefully for any suspected infestations or viral or bacterial infections.

> **Activity**
> **Hair design consultation**
>
> **A** List five main factors you should consider when carrying out a consultation for hair design/patterning wor/patterning work.
>
> 1 _____
> 2 _____
> 3 _____
> 4 _____
> 5 _____
>
> **B** Give a brief explanation for each of the points listed stating why you think these are important and how they will affect the techniques and methods you use.

Clipper type	Blade profile	Uses
Standard clipper		Standard width clippers are a general 'catch-all' piece of equipment. Available in mains or rechargeable power options; they will comfortably manage the cutting of large amounts of hair very quickly. They can be fitted with a variety of grade attachments and are essential to men's barbering.

Clipper type	Blade profile	Uses
T liner/outliner		'T' liners/outliners are a more specialised clipper that has a T-shaped blade. The fixed blade extends beyond the width of the clipper body enabling them to be used around the ears or facial hair shapes; providing a closer, (yet safe) cut finish than that of standard clippers.
Tramliner		A tramliner is a specialist narrow blade clipper, designed for intricate lining and detailing of hair. This type of clipper enables you to cut free-form designs without inverse etching techniques that you would need to use with the other types of clipper.
Mini clipper		Mini clippers are usually battery powered or have a rechargeable power supply. They have a narrower cutting width than standard clippers and are particularly useful for hair detailing or precision designs. They produce less vibration than standard clippers and are therefore more comfortable for the client when working across the scalp.

AH21.2   Plan and agree hair patterns in hair

Creating a portfolio of work and examples

EKU *statement*

AH21.17) Suitable sources of information and design ideas and how to access them

Design ideas or themes have to start somewhere and you can find sources in all sorts of things. Patterns and textures can occur in anything and you can start a comprehensive portfolio from very small beginnings. At a basic level you would do well to start with the patterns or textures that appear in nature. Everything from snowflakes to snail shells, or ripples on water to cloud formations, have been catalysts which have eventually become the basis of good design.

In hair dressings the basic shapes, patterns and designs have clear roots in tribal, ethnic and historical cultures. In the past (and still in the present day) hair dressings and adornment are associated with social grouping and within those groupings, the different levels of status by those wearing the different effects. You can look into the historical origins yourself as there is plenty of research material available on the Internet.

From a design point of view there are three distinct modes of fashions and knowing which one to use with a client will depend upon personal image, preference and motivation. You must get a clear indication of what is suitable for your client during your consultation.

Be warned, you need to create a range of designs, to suit all sorts of clients. This type of work is not a personal crusade; it is about providing a public service to those people who are willing to pay for your advice and expertise.

The three different mode lines are:

- classic or traditional
- current fashion
- futuristic or avant garde.

Classic or traditional work could be defined as timeless. That is to say that the effects are neither in nor out of fashion. Classic themes were created at a time when the basic design rules were first established. Classic work tends to be quite different from the other two groups of styles as it has the following distinct qualities:

- the effects tend to be quite simple in their design construction
- simple designs have greater impact because they are clearer; they have a less 'busy', 'uncluttered' appearance that creates better visual contrasts
- the effects are durable and last well.

Current fashion trends are changing all the time. These fashions are different to classic styling in that they are of the moment. They often start on the catwalks of fashion shows of London, Paris and New York, or on stages in arenas around the world, worn by music artists. Current fashion and the drivers that support it can easily be researched and found, as they appear on TV and fill printed media (and waste bins) everyday.

Future (avant garde) fashions try to push the boundaries of what is acceptable and what can be worn. The clients that warm to these emerging fashions are going to be confident at the very least, but more likely outrageously extrovert in their individual appearances. These people want exclusivity; they don't want to share their look with others; they are more than happy to carve out their own individual look.

Try to show breadth and depth in your portfolio of work; try to cover aspects that address all sorts of design modes, as this will indicate to others that you have the ability to adapt to/in any situation.

Working with designs

In looking for material to add to your portfolio, you are more likely to find aspects or elements of images that you want to use within larger designs or images. It is unlikely that you will find complete, finished compositions of work to show clients and without these finished effects, you can't expect a warm, enthusiastic response from clients.

Very few people have the artistic ability to be able to visualise a photograph of a finished look, let alone an element of a design or a pattern upon them. You need to find ways of:

- making the design or pattern larger
- incorporating the design into a finished effect.

Developing a portfolio of ideas

When you find a pattern or a design that you want to add to your portfolio, you need to keep the original image or source and create your artwork from it as the design that you will use as a visual aid with clients. This will become both the source for themes and ideas for the client as well a tool to prompt discussion about the work.

I-STOCK/© PESKYMONKEY

EKU *statement*

AH21.19) How to hold a discussion with a client and assist your client to reach an informed decision on a pattern

AH21.20) How to present information and recommendations on patterns clearly to clients

EKU *statement*

AH21.21) How to create simple repeated designs from lines and curves

Remember

Keep all the source material in your originating portfolio so that you can provide your assessor with a 'storyboard' of the elements that create your final designs.

You should have two physical components to the work:

1 The first is the original research or source item – this could be in the form of a photograph, magazine cuttings, Internet downloads or sketches. These original compositions could be on paper, textiles and packaging or on digital media. How you keep them for your portfolio is up to you, but you will need to show your themes to assessors as part of a 'storyboard' of ideas. (A storyboard is a creative narrative that is composed of ideas leading to a finished, physical result.)

2 The second is the composition of finished effects – for usefulness, it is more likely that you will want to use this within a working environment and therefore the research material is superfluous in a portfolio that you want to share with clients. The journey that you take in finding sources of design material and turning them into finished works is a personal, learning activity. It is unlikely that the design roughs will be of much interest to the client, other than the fact that they might be a topic for discussion – e.g. 'So where did you get the idea for this design?' 'Well actually; it was a photograph of an airbrushed design on the fuel tank of a Harley Davidson motorbike I saw on holiday.' The collections of finished works will probably be in an album: a visual aid that you can show and share with the client, compiled with individual pages and themes.

EKU statement

AH21.22) How to adapt patterns to suit different head shapes

This is only an idea and depends on the extent of presentation media you have in the shop. For example, a tattooist will cover their walls with themes and examples of their work. A swish, up-to-the-minute, computer-minded barbers' may use projected slide-shows or compositions burned to DVD and run as a visual presentation as part of the in-shop entertainment. The way that you put your ideas together, work and develop them and finally present them, is up to you.

Style aspects

Head and facial shape

EKU statement

AH21.23) The design possibilities and limitations when working with linear patterns on hair

AH21.40) How their hair texture affects their pattern design possibilities

The proportions, balance and distribution of weight in the design will be a frame for the head and face. Therefore you need to examine the head and face carefully, if you look at the outline of your client's face, you will see that it's round, oval, square, heart-shaped, oblong or triangular. Imagine what the head will look like with less hair; will it expose features that enhance the design plan, or will the factors work against your preliminary ideas?

Would the design benefit from more hair? Is the client's hair long enough to produce the 2D effect? These are the sorts of questions that you need to answer before embarking on some 'flashy' self-advertisement campaign.

Do the client's physical features present some form of styling limitations? These are issues that are critical to the achievement of a satisfactory result.

Hair design considerations

MK HAIR STUDIO & ACADEMY

The perimeters and design outlines formed by the hair in relation to the shape of the face is the first thing people will see. It is this effect that people make decisions upon and comments about, for example, 'That's a great effect', 'I think that really suits you'. The complete hair design is based upon suitability matched to personality or image aspects. How you 'fill in' the detail – the movement, direction, colour and patterning – is down to your interpretation and understanding of the client and what is suitable for them. Don't expect them to be the best at self-visualisation. If they produce ideas that seem off-beat or random, ask them if there is any particular reason why they would want to take that line.

Hair positioning, type, growth and tendency

Hair growth direction and distribution should be a major consideration for what is achievable within a hairstyle. You need to make allowances for strong movement, high or low hairlines, natural partings, hair whorls, cowlicks, widow's peaks and double crowns. Look for these before shampooing. The client cannot compensate for these themselves, so when the hair is in need of washing, they will be plain to see. After the hair is washed the degree and strength of the feature can be seen and then you can reconsider how you will tackle it.

Hair pattern suitability

Pattern suitability refers to the effect of the hair design in relation to the face and on the features of the head and body. From an aesthetic point of view, a hair design is suitable when it 'looks right'. But this is a difficult or certainly a subjective thing to quantify.

Aesthetically and artistically speaking, the client's 'hair will look right' when the design does one of two things:

- it harmonises i.e. fits and works with the shape of the face and head – and therefore provides an enhancement to an overall image; or
- it contrasts i.e. it accentuates features of the face and head – by creating a prominent, strong or stark overall image.

For example, when working with harmonising aspects, the features and lines of the face and its underlying bone structure are accentuated when the linear (straight) lines and patterns within the hair design are continuous with them.

Hair designs which contrast are not continuous and cross at right angles to the lines and features of the face.

Similarly, a softening effect is created when curves move away from the hairlines producing harmonising effects.

As a general rule linear, straight-lined effects and box-like shapes are visually harder and can appear more threatening or brutal than those designs incorporating curves, circles and ellipses.

Basic principles of design

Balance

Balance is the effect produced by the proportions and distribution of detail throughout the style. The opposite, i.e. imbalance, is lack of those proportions. Symmetry or symmetrical even balance occurs when the effects are distributed equally as in a mirrored image through a vertical or horizontal plane. Asymmetry or asymmetric effects occur when the overall shape does not have the same distribution on either side.

However, both symmetrical and asymmetrical shapes can be balanced. Here the aspect of perspective is brought into play where a visually larger component is counterbalanced by a smaller one further away.

Style line

Style lines are the directions in which the hair design is positioned or appears to flow. When a break occurs within this flow the eye is immediately drawn to it. A break can only happen for two reasons: either it's a style feature and accentuates what the observer is meant to see, or it's a mistake made by the inexperienced.

Partings and divisions

Partings or divisions in hair have a strong impact. Lines created upon the head will draw the attention of the eye and can be used to create flow and movement away from the face to the detail that lies beyond.

Movement

Movement refers to the variance of line direction within a hair design. The more variety in direction the more movement there will be. Sometimes this movement is because of natural tendency – to accommodate curls or waves – sometimes it is deliberately created by design shaping and placement.

Hard and soft effects

Hard and soft effects result from the balance or imbalance within a hair design or from the movement or lack of movement within it. Subtle lining will convey softer harmonising effects, whereas stronger lines produce contrasting effects, which work better in achieving more dramatic results.

The combinations of the above and the way in which these style variables are used will give you the basic rules for which you can create your own original effects. Creating completely new styles requires a great deal of thought and work, and your clients will want to benefit from your creative abilities.

Finalising the portfolio

With a collection of work done, your basic portfolio is complete. You now have designs covering a range of themes and along with this, you may want to give a small description or brief on how you found the sources for your artworks.

You may be very pleased with the results that you have achieved, but don't spoil things by not presenting the information properly. You need to compile your designs in a way that protects them from handling and keeps them all safely together. You also need to choose how you are going to present the collection to clients; would they be better bound in an album or would transparent pockets in a ring binder be better? The choice of presenter is up to you, but whatever medium you choose make sure that the portfolio shows:

- professionalism in the way in which it is compiled
- a variety in its themes,
- quality in its reproduction and
- that it portrays realistic options for the clients that *you* can do.

PHOTO COURTESY OF UK SKILLS

Donna Leach representing the UK in WorldSkills 2007 Team UK Medals Shizuoka, Japan

Consultation

With most of the planning and preparations done, your main concern is establishing with the client exactly what is going to happen and gaining from them the confirmation that what you have selected as a design is both appropriate and satisfactory. If there is any hesitation or uncertainty, you need to either provide more information about what you intend to do, or look again at the visuals from your portfolio to explore other options.

The other aspects for consideration in general consultation relating to adverse or influencing factors are covered elsewhere in this book. Review the chapters on Unit G7 Advise and consult with clients for more information pages 96–131.

EKU *statement*

AH21.16) The importance of keeping and maintaining client records

AH21.39) How lifestyle can influence the client's choice of style (e.g. active sports, career and job requirements)

Contra-indications to hair design work

The request for a hair design or close-cut patterning may be wanted by the client, but not every client will be able to have the service. Always look closely for signs to see if the service *can* be provided and *ask* the client if they have any reasons that they know of that would *not permit* the service to be conducted.

Do not provide this service when:

- there are signs of cuts or abrasions on the scalp
- there are signs of reddening from conditions like eczema or skin sensitivity or skin allergies
- there are any other adverse symptoms such as infections or infestations
- the skin surface is too uneven to produce a successful, finished result.

If you have any doubts about symptoms and contra-indications, always ask a senior member of staff for their assistance. You may be putting the salon at risk from legal action or claims for compensation if you don't follow this process properly. Make sure

EKU statement

AH21.18) The importance of consulting with clients throughout the cutting process

AH21.28) Methods of preparing the hair prior to cutting patterns

AH21.29) The range of haircuts which form a suitable foundation for cutting linear patterns into the hair

AH21.32) The importance of visually checking the cut

AH21.33) How to visually check the design, pattern and cut

AH21.35) The types of problems that can commonly arise when cutting patterns in hair and ways in which they can be resolved, if possible

that you keep a record of your consultation and the responses made by the client after the service, for future reference.

Activity

Create a portfolio

This section has explored the aspects of design and looked at the possible sources for gaining and developing a working portfolio that you could use and continue to build upon when you are working with clients in the barber shop.

Use the information covered within this chapter to create your own portfolio of work. How you choose to display this information depends upon your skill and artistic abilities. Whether you want to collect examples of work you find, sketches from ideas or pictures of your own work, it's all up to you.

Remember

If you have any doubts about symptoms and contra-indications; always ask a senior member of staff for their assistance. You may be putting the salon at risk from legal action or claims for compensation if you don't follow this process properly.

Pre-cutting

In order to work with manageable lengths of hair, you need to pre-cut the client's hair to a length that will enable you to transfer your designs to the head allowing for the longest parts of the detailing. Carefully, look at the length you are working with and make sure that you don't undercut the hair length that you need to complete the total effect.

Inaccurate detailing

Remember

Don't try to cover up mistakes; be honest and keep the client informed. In nine cases out of ten they won't mind a slight modification to the overall plan.

The most common cutting problem is that of inaccurate detailing. It happens when clippers take too much hair away from the area you want to work with.

1 Make sure that you remove all loose clippings as you go along. Any cut hair left on the scalp will lead you into believing that there is still more to work with; keep brushing away the area that you are working with so that you clearly see where you are.

2 If you do take too much hair away in a particular area, you need to stop and see how much impact it will make on the overall design. You can then choose between modifying your patterning to incorporate a different detailing or re-working the design plan to accommodate another theme or effect.

Create patterns in hair

Clippers

Intricate design requires accurate cutting and having the correct tools to do the job is everything. Normal everyday clippers are fine for removing large amounts of hair very quickly; but when it comes to working the detail of smaller textures and designs, the other varieties of smaller, narrower-bladed clippers are essential.

General purpose, mains-electric clippers have a cutting blade width of approximately 3 cm. This is OK for cutting straighter lines (i.e more linear patterns). But for anything more detailed, you need to use lighter and narrower, rechargeable clippers, that have blade widths down to less than 1 cm. These can be easily manipulated without having trailing leads in the way, so that you can create both curves and lines just as easily.

There are two ways of holding clippers for cutting purposes:

1 Fixed blade down – the normal way for removing hair and for using the different sized clipper grades.

2 Inverse, i.e. fixed blade up – this provides a lining tool for cutting outline perimeter shapes such as necklines, or as an etching tool for creating detail within a hairstyle.

EKU *statement*

AH21.30) How and when to use clipper over comb, scissors over comb, fading, negative and positive imaging and freehand techniques when creating designs in hair

EKU *statement*

AH21.31) Equipment handling techniques for achieving accurate patterns in hair

Clippers held for normal and inversed cutting techniques

©HABIA

©HABIA

Different types of clippers

BABYLISS PRO UK

Tramliner

WAHL

T-liner

WAHL

Trimmer

Remember

Clippers used in the inverse position are used for lining, neckline shapes and detailing so more care must be taken as the cutting edges are very close to the skin.

Remember

Machine clippers cut hair very quickly, so clear away any loose clippings so that you can see exactly where you are within the design.

If you do make a mistake within the design by cutting too much hair away, you will need to adapt your overall design to compensate for the missing hair, possibly by making a design feature of the area.

Remember

Always use the clippers carefully and safely at all times and make sure that you *always* level the clipper blades before using them upon the client.

EKU *statement*

AH21.38) The products suitable for home care and those to avoid and why

AH21.41) Grooming requirements

Cutting a 2D pattern

With the outlines and detail drawn on to the pre-cut hair, you can carefully start etching away the unwanted hair; using the correct size clippers in the inverse holding technique. As the clippers remove the hair and create the desired lines, make sure that you brush away the cut hair so that you can clearly see the patterning/lining that you are creating. Any cut hair left in position will mislead you into thinking that the area still needs work. Beware: this is the simplest way for mistakes to be made.

Activity
Health and Safety

With reference to this particular unit, AH21:

A What health and safety things do you need to be particularly aware of for this type of work?

B List your responsibilities under the Health and Safety at Work Act 1974.

Step 1 Client preparation for creating patterns in hair – ensure a thorough consultation is carried out first.

Step 2 Clipper cut hair length to client's requirements.

Step 3 Comb against the growth pattern to check evenness of clipper cut and observe for critical influencing factors such as warts, moles or scars etc.

Step 4 For delicate designs, use extended fingers to steady clippers – always be aware that the client may move!

Step 5 For delicate designs, use extended fingers to steady clippers – always be aware that the client may move!

Step 6 Check through mirror for accuracy of hairline width using your fingers as reference points.

Step 7 Begin the design keeping a sense of proportion. A good tip is to regularly step back to observe all the emerging pattern.

Step 8 Use the corners of the clippers to create curves – a powerful clipper is considered more advantageous than outliners at this stage.

Step 9 If required, hold head still with free hand.

Step 10 Clippers can be held at any angle.

Step 11 Shorten areas within the design to create a three dimensional effect.

Step 12 [As 11].

Step 13 Note how the faded area contrasts with the lines and curves – this is sometimes termed creating 'light and shade'.

Step 14 Outliners are very useful for enhancing edges.

Step 15 [As 14].

Step 16 [As 14].

Step 17 Trim off any loose hairs using the scissors free hand.

Step 18 Use a bristle brush to remove loose clippings and groom the hair.

ALL PHOTOS © HABIA

Step 19 Using finishing products of your choice, apply with a pad to produce a gloss finish.

Step 20 Result – a professionally designed pattern.

AH21.4   Provide aftercare advice

Design work and patterns created on close-cut hair need very little maintenance, the effects are long-lasting (in hair style terms) and easy to maintain. They will withstand frequent washing and normally need little more than a rub with a towel.

However, some design work involves colouring too and if different areas of hair have contrasting colour segments, you may need to provide your client with advice for which type of shampoos will work best by not causing the colours to fade or 'run' together. If the hair has had a permanent colour service then the effects should be less problematic.

Finally, tell your client how long the effects will last: as hair grows longer the impacts of lining lessen. This is particularly true where the lining and detail is created by showing the scalp. The contrasts created by showing skin as opposed to just hair are far more striking, so tell them how long the effect will last before they need to return.

For more information covering general aftercare advice and the following essential knowledge see Unit GH12 Cut hair using basic techniques (page 271) and Unit GB4 Design and create a range of facial shapes (page 335).

Diversion Some of the EKUs you need for this unit may be found in other units. To save you from unnecessary duplication we have cross-referenced each unit to other areas. You may have already studied that unit in which case a revision of the information will help you apply that knowledge to this unit. If you have not studied that information before then it will help you when you do study that unit.

Checkerboard

I understand the reasons for and methods of sterilising barbering equipment

☐

I know and understand the principles of effective communication

☐

I know how to and why the client should be protected from loose hair clippings

☐

I always recognise the critical influencing factors when I carry out consultation

☐

I can utilise a range of barbering techniques and know when to use them in my work

☐

I know how the angle at which equipment is held and the hair is cut is critical to the finished effect

☐

I always carry out working practices according to the salon's hygiene and safety policy

☐

I know why I should keep the work area hygienic, safe and clean avoiding cross-infection and infestation

☐

I always explain technical terms eliminating misunderstanding

☐

I know how to achieve a variety of hair patterns by using clippers and other equipment

☐

I understand the necessity of personal, hygiene and presentation

☐

I know how to work with the natural hair textures, densities and growth patterns and how they influence the work

☐

I know that my posture and the client's seated position is important for accuracy and health and safety aspects

☐

I know the factors that affect the ways in which hair can be cut and shaped

☐

I know how to create, scale and transfer designs accurately to the hair

☐

I have built a portfolio of design work that I can use with clients to help them to get an idea of different patterned effects and what it will look like for them

☐

Assessment of knowledge and understanding

Project

For this project you will need to gather information from different sources.

Collect photos, digital images or magazine cuttings for different types of hair designs.

Include designs that are motivated by:

A modern music themes

B cultural or ethnic themes

C general artistic designs.

Give a brief description of each and reasons why you included it in your personal collection.

Revision questions

A selection of different types of questions to check your cutting knowledge.

Q1	Inverse clippering is a technique used to create _____ neck shapes.	Fill in the blank
Q2	Scissors should be sterilised in Barbicide™.	True or false
Q3	Select from the following list the items that are a type of machine clipper:	Multi selection

	Tram liner	☐ 1
	Steam liner	☐ 2
	Eye liner	☐ 3
	T liner	☐ 4
	Z liner	☐ 5
	White liner	☐ 6

Q4	Linear shapes are curved.	True or false
Q5	Which of the following is not a cutting term?	Multi choice

	Graduation	○ a
	Straightening	○ b
	Free hand	○ c
	Fading	○ d

Q6	Precision cutting is dependent upon cutting angles and even tension.	True or false
Q7	Which of the following are contra-indications for patterning hair?	Multi selection

	Bumps and lumps on the scalp	☐ 1
	Double crown	☐ 2
	Widow's peak	☐ 3
	Alopecia totalis	☐ 4
	Nape whorls	☐ 5
	High hairline	☐ 6

Q8	A _____ is a type of clipper with a tapered, narrow blade for detailing designs on hair.	Fill in the blank

Q9 Which of the following will affect the natural fall and the way that neck hair lies after it is cut?

Multi choice

Double crown ○ a
Cowlick ○ b
Nap whorl ○ c
Widow's peak ○ d

Q10 Clubbing is a technique of cutting that maximises the hair density.

True or false

Preparing for assessment checklist

Remember to:

✔	prepare clients correctly for the services you are going to carry out
✔	put on the protective wear available for styling and patterning hair
✔	listen to the client's requirements and discuss suitable courses of action
✔	adhere to the safety factors when working on clients' hair
✔	keep the work areas clean, hygienic and free from hazards
✔	promote the range of services, products and treatments within the shop
✔	clean and sterilise the tools and equipment before it is used
✔	work carefully and methodically through the processes of cutting hair
✔	place, position and direct the templates or hair appropriately to achieve the desired effect
✔	communicate what you are doing with the client and confirm their satisfaction

FELLOWSHIP FOR BRITISH HAIRDRESSING F.A.M.E. TEAM 2008

Chapter**sixteen**
Colouring hair

GH9

GH9.1/GB2.1
GH9.2/GB2.2
GH9.3/GB2.3
GH9.4/GB2.4

More information
See Unit G7 Advise and consult with clients
EKU GH 9.7

Unit G20 Make sure your own actions reduce risks to health and safety

See the appendices for Electricity at Work Regulations, COSHH regulations and Data Protection Regulations
EKU GH 9.8, EKU GH 9.9

Colouring hair: quick overview

Unit titles

GH9 Change hair colour and **GB2** Change men's hair colour

This is a **mandatory** unit for Hairdressing and an **optional** unit for Barbering at Level 2, it is made up of four main outcomes

Main outcomes

GH9.1 and GB2.1 Maintain effective and safe methods of working when colouring and lightening hair

GH9.2 and GB2.2 Prepare for colouring and lightening hair

GH9.3 and GB2.3 Colour and lighten hair

GH9.4 and GB2.4 Provide aftercare advice

What do I need to do for GH9.1 and GB2.1?

- Make sure that the client is adequately covered, protected and prepared for the service

- Make sure that the working position is comfortable and safe for both you and the client

- Keep the work area clean and tidy and that waste materials are disposed of properly

- Work without causing risks to you or your client's health and safety

- Work efficiently and effectively

- Accurately maintain the client's treatment records

What do I need to do for GH9.2 and GB2.2?

- Identify any contra-indications to colouring and/or lightening the client's hair

- Carry out tests and record the outcomes

- Seek assistance when you are unsure of results from tests or contra-indications

- Base your recommendations upon the evaluation of the client's hair and scalp

- Inform the client of the expected costs, duration and likely results

- Prepare the tools and equipment ready for use

What do I need to do for GH9.3 and GB2.3?

- Confirm the desired effect prior to starting

- Apply products safely, accurately, efficiently and in line with manufacturers' instructions

- Use appropriate techniques to achieve the desired result

- Remove the colouring and/or lightening products from the hair after development

- Identify and resolve problems where possible

- Achieve the desired effect

What do I need to do for GH9.4 and GB2.4?

- Give accurate constructive advice on how the client can maintain their hair colour

What aspects do I need to cover for GH9.1 and GB2.1, GH9.2 and GB2.2, GH9.3 and GB2.3, and GH9.4 and GB2.4?

- Semi, quasi and permanent hair colouring products and lighteners

- A variety of contra-indications to colouring services

- A range of factors that influence or limit the way in which colouring is done

- Different types of application such as regrowth, full head and partial colouring techniques

What aspects do I need to know for GH9.1 and GB2.1, GH9.2 and GB2.2, GH9.3 and GB2.3, and GH9.4 and GB2.4?

- Your salon's requirements for preparation, timings and standards of service

- How to work safely, effectively and hygienically when colouring hair

- The different factors that can affect or influence successful colouring services

- The tests that need to be done prior to and during the colouring services and the records that you must make

- The principles of basic colouring science and the effects of colouring products upon the hair

- How different strengths of hydrogen peroxide affect hair and how they can be diluted

- A range of different colouring tools and techniques and when and how they are used in colouring processes

- The aftercare advice and recommendations that you should give to clients

Keywords## Keywords

ICC (International Colour Chart) system
A tabular system for identifying hair colours made by different manufacturers by their depth and tone

Incompatibility test
A method of testing hair to see if previous chemical treatments are compatible with those used with professional salons

Contra-indications
These are the physical signs or information about a client's hair and skin that would stop you from carrying out the planned chemical services

Lighteners
Lighteners are products that remove natural tone from hair such as bleach, or high lift colour

Semi-permanent colour
A semi-permanent colour is not mixed with hydrogen peroxide. It only penetrates to the lower cuticle and therefore lasts for a few washes

Quasi-permanent colour
A quasi-permanent colour is mixed with hydrogen peroxide and must be treated like a permanent hair colour. Although it doesn't last quite as long as true permanent colours it penetrates deeper than semi-permanents and will alter natural pigments within the hair.

(continued)

NVQ2 Colouring hair GH9 and GB2

- Inform the client of the expected costs, duration and likely results
- Prepare the tools and equipment ready for use

What do I need to do for GH9.3 and GB2.3?

- Confirm the desired effect prior to starting
- Apply products safely, accurately, efficiently and in line with manufacturers' instructions
- Use appropriate techniques to achieve the desired result
- Remove the colouring and/or lightening products from the hair after development
- Identify and resolve problems where possible
- Achieve the desired effect

What do I need to do for GH9.4 and GB2.4?

- Give accurate constructive advice on how the client can maintain their hair colour

What aspects do I need to cover for GH9.1 and GB2.1, GH9.2 and GB2.2, GH9.3 and GB2.3, and GH9.4 and GB2.4?

- Semi, quasi and permanent hair colouring products and lighteners
- A variety of contra-indications to colouring services
- A range of factors that influence or limit the way in which colouring is done
- Different types of application such as regrowth, full head and partial colouring techniques

What aspects do I need to know for GH9.1 and GB2.1, GH9.2 and GB2.2, GH9.3 and GB2.3, and GH9.4 and GB2.4?

- Your salon's requirements for preparation, timings and standards of service
- How to work safely, effectively and hygienically when colouring hair
- The different factors that can affect or influence successful colouring services
- The tests that need to be done prior to and during the colouring services and the records that you must make
- The principles of basic colouring science and the effects of colouring products upon the hair
- How different strengths of hydrogen peroxide affect hair and how they can be diluted
- A range of different colouring tools and techniques and when and how they are used in colouring processes
- The aftercare advice and recommendations that you should give to clients

Keywords

ICC (International Colour Chart) system
A tabular system for identifying hair colours made by different manufacturers by their depth and tone

Incompatibility test
A method of testing hair to see if previous chemical treatments are compatible with those used with professional salons

Contra-indications
These are the physical signs or information about a client's hair and skin that would stop you from carrying out the planned chemical services

Lighteners
Lighteners are products that remove natural tone from hair such as bleach, or high lift colour

Semi-permanent colour
A semi-permanent colour is not mixed with hydrogen peroxide. It only penetrates to the lower cuticle and therefore lasts for a few washes

Quasi-permanent colour
A quasi-permanent colour is mixed with hydrogen peroxide and must be treated like a permanent hair colour. Although it doesn't last quite as long as true permanent colours it penetrates deeper than semi-permanents and will alter natural pigments within the hair.

(continued)

Keywords

Permanent colour

Permanent hair colours are mixed with hydrogen peroxide; they penetrate deeper to the cortex of the hair, where they alter the natural pigments within the hair providing a longer-lasting effect that grows out showing a regrowth at the roots.

Information covered in this chapter

- The preparations that you must make before carrying out any colouring service
- The tools and equipment used during colouring, their maintenance and the preparations that you should make before colouring hair
- The factors that influence successful results in colouring services
- A range of colouring techniques on differing hair lengths and types
- The aftercare advice that you should give

The colour triangle

Introduction

Colouring is arguably the most exciting and often the most difficult aspect of hairdressing. The increasing demands and expectations of clients have made colouring and in particular special colour effects the 'must have' of hairdressing. Our clients are better informed, have a better understanding, are more aware of what's on offer and are often keen to have a go themselves. This has led to a change in salon colouring. The amount of business done by the home colouring market is huge and this has had a particular impact on salon-based work. It is now more technically demanding than ever before, but this new challenge is not a threat. It now enables all hairdressers to be more professional in their role and create the effects that people can only dream about.

Colouring for men and women

The hairdressing unit for colouring GH9 and the barbering unit for men's colouring GB2 are very similar. Each one is made up of the same performance criteria and essential knowledge. The only differences that can be found are within their application, i.e. the range statements. Because of these similarities, this book combines the units and only draws attention to specific differences within the colouring processes themselves.

The principles of colour and colouring

Seeing colour

When you look at an object, what you are actually seeing is light reflected from it. White light is really a mixture of many colours – that is why sunlight refracted through falling rain can produce a rainbow. This splitting of white light creates what we see as seven different colours: red, orange, yellow, green, blue, indigo and violet. (Richard Of, York Gave Battle In Vain)

A white object reflects most of the white light that falls upon it; a black object absorbs most of the light falling on it. A red object reflects the red light and absorbs everything else.

Hair colour depends chiefly on the pigments in the hair, which absorb some of the light and reflect the rest. The colour that we see is also affected by the light in which it is seen, and (to a lesser extent) by the colours of clothes worn with it.

- White light from halogen bulbs and full daylight will show the hair's natural colour.
- Yellowish light emitted from standard electric light bulbs adds warmth to hair colour, but neutralises blue ash or ashen effects.
- Bluish/green light from fluorescent tubes reduces the warmth of red/gold tones in hair.

Mixing colours

The colours of the pigments in paints arise from three primary colours – red, blue and yellow. Pairs of these give the secondary colours – i.e. red and blue mixed together create violet, yellow and blue create green and yellow and red create orange. White and black can be added to vary the tone of the colour.

The primary colours in light are different – red, green and blue. (These are the three colours used in video cameras, computer screens and television.) The secondary colours are yellow, cyan and magenta.

The ways in which colour pigments are mixed together in paint to produce other new colours is similar to that used in hairdressing. Like paint, permanent hair colours can be mixed together to create different shades.

Natural hair colour

The natural colour of hair is determined by the colour of pigments within the hair's cortex. These are formed when the hair is in its germinating stage of growth.

Hair colour pigments – *melanin* – are deposited into the hair shaft at the region of the papilla and germinal matrix. The pigments responsible for black and brown hair are called *eumelanin*; those responsible for red and yellow hair are called *pheomelanin*. (There are in fact others, but these are the main pigments.) The hair colour you actually see is affected by the amount and proportion of the pigments present, by the light in which the hair is seen and – to a certain extent – by the colours of the clothes and make-up worn.

With age, or after periods of stress, the production of natural pigments may be reduced. The hairs already on the head will not be affected, but the new ones will. As hairs fall out and are replaced, the proportion that have the original pigmentation diminishes and the hair's overall colour changes. It may become lighter. If no pigment is produced at all, then the new hairs will be white.

The proportion of white hairs among the naturally coloured ones causes the hair to appear grey. Grey hair or greyness (*Canites*) is often referred to as a percentage; for example, '50 per cent grey' means that half of the hairs on the head are white and the rest are pigmented.

It is not uncommon for young people to exhibit some grey hairs – this does not necessarily mean that they will go grey, or completely white, at an early age.

The colour spectrum

The colour circle

Depth and tone

Hair science

When we talk about colour we often use the words depth and *tone*. Depth is used to describe how light or dark the colour is and tone is used to describe the colour or hue that we see such as brown, golden red etc. Depth = how light or dark it is. Tone = the colour or hue – ashen, golden, mahogany, etc.

These terms are easier to understand if we tabulate them in the following way.

Depth

Very light			
Light			
Medium			
Dark			
Very dark			
	Gold	Red	Violet

Tone ⟶

Remember

In vibrant red or bright auburn hair, nearly all the melanin is present in the form of pheomelanin; however, another alpha-amino pigment is present in a complex iron compound called *trichosiderin*. (In 100 g of red hair, there are 40 mg of trichosiderin.) The trichosiderin changes the colour make-up of hair, giving it the rich, attractive colour of a genetically Celtic origin.

Colouring this particular type of red hair is difficult because of this different pigmentation. Lightening red hair is especially hard as this compound is very difficult to remove.

WELLA

Depth and tones

Taking this principle further, the International Colour Chart (ICC) offers a way of defining hair colours systematically (although charts may vary between manufacturers). Shades of colour are divided and numbered, with black (1) at one end of the scale and lightest blonde (10) at the other. Tones of other colours (/1 /9 or also stated as .1 .9) are combined with these, producing a huge variety of colours. Charts are usually arranged with shades in rows down the side and tones in columns across the top. To use them, first identify the shade of your client's hair: that row of the chart then shows the colours you could produce with that hair.

For example, if your client has medium blonde hair (depth 7) and you colour with a copper tone (.4), the result should be a rich copper blonde (7.4). The possibilities are almost endless, as these examples indicate:

- to produce ash shades, add blue
- to produce matt shades, add green
- to produce gold shades, add yellow
- to produce warm shades, add red
- to produce purple or violet shades, add mixtures of red and blue.

EKU *statement*

GH9.35 and GB2.35) The principles of colour selection, including the International Colour Chart (ICC)

Activity

Depth and tone – warm and cool shades

The natural 'depth' of hair refers to how light or dark it is, whereas 'tone' refers to colouration e.g. red, blue or green.

Task 1. With your friends and using the salon shade chart, take it in turns to select the nearest natural shade for each of them. Don't make the mistake of looking at the rest of the chart, just keep to the natural bases.

Warm tones are yellow or golden based.

Cool tones are bluish or green based.

What tones are produced from red? Well, that depends on whether the red is orange based or pink based.

Task 2. Again in a group work through your salon's shade chart and for each shade note down its shade name, number or code, then decide as a group whether it is a warm tone or a cool tone.

Save the information from both of these tasks in your portfolio for future reference.

How many warm shades were there?

How many cool shades were there?

How many were neither warm nor cool?

Did you find any surprising results?

L'Oréal – Majirel

	Natural/Basic ,0	Ash ,1	Mauve ,2	Gold ,3	Copper ,4	Mahogany ,6	Red ,6	Metallic ,07
10	Lightest Blonde							
9	Very light Blonde	Very Light Natural Ash Blonde 9,1		Very Light Deep Golden Blonde 9,33	Very Light Natural Copper Blonde 9,04			Very Light Natural Cool Blonde 9,07
8	Light Blonde		Light Iridescent Blonde 8,2	Light Golden Blonde 8,3				
7	Blonde	Ash Blonde 7,1			Deep Copper Blonde 7,44		Extra Iridescent Red Blonde 7,62	
6	Dark blonde		Dark Deep Iridescent Blonde 6,22	Dark Natural Golden Blonde 6,03	Dark Copper Red Blonde 6,46	Dark Mahogany Golden Blonde 6,53	Dark Extra Red Blonde 6,66	Dark Natural Cool Blonde 6,07
5	Light brown	Light Deep Ash Brown 5,11			Light Extra Copper Red Blonde 5,46	Light Mahogany Iridescent Brown 5,52	Light Red Brown 5,6	Light Cool Ash Brown 5,71
4	Brown		Extra Burgendy Brown 4,20	Golden Brown 4,3		Mahogany Ash Brown 4,51		
3	Dark Brown							
1	Black							

In the table above we see how the L'Oréal shades are positioned within the colour table. Row 1, containing Black (1), denotes the *darkest* shades, gradually going up in numbers to Row 10, containing 'Lightest Blonde' (10.0). This denotes the *lightest* shades.

Within the table two shades, 'Dark Copper Red Blonde' (6.46) and 'Deep Copper Blonde' (7.44), are defined in blue. These two examples identify additional colour properties. These shades are denoted, as are many others in the table, with having a second number after the decimal point.

Shade	Depth	Primary tone	Secondary tone
Dark Copper Red Blonde	6 .	4	6

1 The primary tone denotes the range that the shade is in.

2 Secondary tone indicates the additional pigmentation within the shade. This provides lots of extra colouring permutations.

Sometimes colour manufacturers want to increase a shade's intensity and vibrancy. This is achieved by adding double the tone to the particular shade, doubling the tonal effect.

Shade	Depth	Primary tone	Secondary tone
Deep Copper Blonde	7 .	4	4

Types of synthetic hair colour

Temporary colour

Temporary colours are available in the form of lotions, creams, mousses, gels, lacquers, sprays, crayons, paints and glitter dust. On hair in good condition these do not penetrate the hair cuticle, nor do they directly affect the natural hair colour: they simply remain on the hair until washed off.

Temporary colours are ideal for a client who has not had colour before, as they are readily removed if not liked. They have subtle colouring effects, particularly on white hair. Hair condition, shine and control are enhanced.

If used on badly damaged or very porous hair, the temporary colour may quickly be absorbed into the cortex, producing uneven, patchy results.

Features and benefits

Feature	Benefits
Have large molecules and sit on the surface of the hair	Easy to remove as they are washed away during the next shampoo
Come in a variety of types as mousses, setting lotions, gels, creams, colour sprays and colour shampoos	Easy to apply as they can either be applied during the shampoo process or alternatively as a styling or finishing product
Come in a variety of shades and colours	Can be used as a fashion statement or alternatively to enhance natural tones by either adding depth to faded hair or neutralising unwanted tones from hair

Large colour granules adhere to the cuticle layer

Temporary hair colouring

Points to remember

- Temporary colours only last for one wash (unless the hair is porous).
- They are often difficult to remove totally from hair that is extremely porous or lightened.
- You cannot lighten hair with temporary colours.
- You cannot target a shade in the same way as you can with longer-lasting colours.
- They may not give you an even coverage on the hair.

Semi-permanent colour

Semi-permanent colours are made in a variety of forms – some ready-mixed for immediate use, others needing to be mixed and prepared before use as necessary. Always check the manufacturer's instructions to ensure that you know which type of colour you are going to use.

Semi-permanent colours contain pigments which are deposited in the hair cuticle and outer cortex. The colour gradually fades each time the hair is shampooed. Some colour will last through six washes, others longer.

Generally, these colours are not intended to cover large percentages of white hair – for instance, black used on white hair would not produce a pleasing result. Choose colours carefully.

Note Some permanent colour may be diluted for use as semi-permanents. These products may contain skin sensitisers, however, so skin tests must be performed before use in this way. Check manufacturer instructions for more information.

Features and benefits

Semi-permanent colours are ideal for those people who want to try colour but are not ready yet to take a big step forward into the maintenance of permanent colour effects. They last up to six or eight shampoos and do not produce any regrowth; the hair loses the colour on each subsequent shampoo so the effect fades over time. Conditioning agents form part of the colouring package to add shine and improve style manageability while the colour is deposited on to the hair.

COURTESY OF GOLDWELL UK

Semi-permanents also provide an ideal solution for livening up faded mid-lengths and ends for clients who have permanent colours; this is particularly useful if the hair is not really ready yet for another treatment of peroxide-based colours.

Semi-permanents will colour white/grey hair to some extent, although the penetration doesn't extend beyond the cuticle layer, so colour density is relatively poor. (White hair tends to have a very smooth cuticle so there are fewer spaces for the pigments to bond on to.) The colour range is varied, ranging from fashion effects to many of the shades you would expect to see in a standard shade chart. They are simple to use and require no developer and hence no mixing.

RUSH LONDON

Feature	Benefits
Have large molecules that sit on the surface of the hair whilst other smaller ones penetrate deeper into the hair	A great way to introduce clients to colour without long-term commitment. Fairly easy to remove as they are washed away in six or eight shampoos
Come in a variety of types as mousses, liquids, gels, creams	Easy to apply, normally requires no mixing, take a short time and leave no regrowth
Come in a variety of colours as fashion effects or as standard shade chart references	Can be used as a fashion statement or alternatively as a trial for a permanent colour effect.
(* At Level 3) Can be used in colour correction work	A simple and quick pre-filler and pre-pigmentation shade
Add tone to white/grey hair	Provide some masking/coverage for unwanted greys
Provide an alternative to permanent colour	Can provide a colour choice for those people who, because of sensitivity or allergy, may not be able to have permanent colours

Points to remember

- Semi-permanent colours only last for up to six or eight washes.
- They are often difficult to remove totally from hair that is extremely porous or lightened.
- You cannot lighten hair with semi-permanent colour.
- They will not colour white/grey hair with 100 per cent coverage.
- They cover with far better results than temporary colours.

Now that 'frequent use' shampoos have become popular, semi-permanent colours fade quickly. Therefore a new generation of longer-lasting, quasi-permanent colours have been introduced which are more practical and economical. These colours allow for a greater coverage of white hair and last for up to 12 washes.

Quasi-permanent colour

Quasi-permanent colours are nearly permanent – they last for a longer period of time than semi-permanent colour but not as long as the true permanent colour. When using them, follow the manufacturer's instructions carefully.

Features and benefits

Quasi-colours are used a lot in the home-retail sector. They are not true permanent colours but do require the mixing of colour with a low strength developer. They last for at least 12 washes and anything up to 24 and, regardless of advertisers' claims, *they do leave a regrowth*. These types of colours do have a better ability to cover white/grey hair and this is the main reason why they are so popular as home colours.

Quasi-colour should be treated like a permanent colour or lightener; they do require a skin test 24–48 hours beforehand.

Feature	Benefits
Are processed with a developer and have similar molecules that penetrate deeper into the hair	Easy solution for all-over colouring; last a long time, generally up to 12–24 shampoos
Come as gels or creams	Require mixing with developer and have been made easy to apply for home use. Leave a regrowth
Come in a variety of colours as fashion effects or as standard shade chart references (* At Level 3)	Can be used as a fashion statement or as an alternative to more permanent-based colour
Can be used in colour correction work	Are an alternative longer-lasting pre-pigmentation shade
Add depth and tone to white/grey hair	Provide up to 50 per cent coverage for unwanted greys
Provide a different alternative to permanent para dyes	Tend to be used regularly and more often than salon-provided treatments
Good conditioning properties, add shine and improve manageability	Leave hair in good condition, manageable and with added shine

Points to remember

- Quasi-permanent colours always require a skin test.
- They last for 12 washes, leaving a regrowth.
- They can only be removed by colour reduction (not by colour or lightener).
- They often provide the basis for colour correction work if wrongly used at home.
- They offer good coverage; colour white/grey with better saturation than semis.
- They have similar effects to permanent colours.

Permanent colour

Permanent colours are made in a wide variety of shades and tones. They can cover white and natural-coloured hair to produce a range of natural, fashion and fantasy shades.

Hydrogen peroxide is mixed with permanent colour. This oxidises the hair's natural pigments and joins the small molecules of synthetic pigment together, a process called *polymerisation*. The hair will then retain the colour permanently in the cortex. Hair in poor condition, however, will not hold the colour and colouring could result in patchy areas and colour fading.

The use of modern permanent colour can lighten or darken the natural hair colour, or both together in one process. This is achieved by varying the percentage strength of hydrogen peroxide.

Tiny colour granules are mixed with hydrogen peroxide – they pass through the cuticle layer into the cortex

Main points to remember

True permanent para-dyes are the only colours that cover white/grey hair with 100 per cent saturation/coverage. The colours tend to come in easy-to-dispense tubes as creams or gels which are then mixed with hydrogen peroxide, as the developer, to create lasting effects that grow out. Even if the colour used is darker than the natural depth and deposits only, the colour effect will remain until it is either cut or grows out.

The para dyes contain PPD (*para-phenylenediamine*). This is a known irritant and it is this compound that necessitates the need for conducting skin or sensitivity tests before any colouring service is carried out. There are other chemicals within para dyes and they all do different things:

- Ammonia/resorcinol is alkaline and when it comes into contact with the hair it swells the hair shaft in preparation for the pigmentation. It also acts as an activator or booster for the hydrogen peroxide by releasing oxygen and starting the oxidation process.
- Conditioning agents improve the hair during the colouring process, enabling it to be smoother and shinier as a result.
- During the process hydrogen peroxide oxidises the natural pigments of the hair and this enables the synthetic pigments to bond with them, creating a permanent change within the hair's cortex.

Artificial depth and tone are added. Lightening of the natural pigments can occur with some shades

The granules swell and join together becoming permently trapped

Vegetable-based colour

As well as being a popular source for conditioning agents, plant extracts have been used as dyeing compounds for thousands of years. These were the only sources of colour until chemists developed synthetic alternatives. Natural henna (Lawsonia) is

Remember

 Compound henna is *incompatible* with hairdressing materials. It should not be confused with natural (vegetable) henna which is compatible with other hairdressing services.

Remember

Metallic and compound dyes are incompatible with hairdressing materials. Always carry out a test before using a lightener, colour or perm on any new clients whom you do not know, or on clients who have been recently having their hair done overseas.

EKU *statement*

GH9.36 and GB2.36) How the natural pigment within hair affects the choice of colour and colouring products and the possible need to pre-lighten

GH9.38 and GB2.38) How the different strengths of hydrogen peroxide influence colouring and lightening

Remember

 Mixing colour

Don't mix permanent colours together until you are ready to use them. Mix the colours carefully, making sure that you measure the amounts accurately. If the proportions are wrong the final effect will be wrong!

still used widely today in many countries and it is used for dyeing skin as well as the hair. Natural plant-based dyes do not present any problems for hairdressing treatments; however, these ingredients are sometimes added to other elements to form compounds, mixtures of vegetable extracts and mineral substances. One that is still available is compound henna – vegetable henna mixed with metallic salts. This penetrating dye is incompatible with professional products used in hairdressing salons and will react with professional salon colours and perming products.

Metallic dyes

Metallic dyes are surface-coating colour. They are variously known as reduction, metallic, sulphide and progressive dyes. These types of dye are also incompatible with chemical hairdressing services and are still found in men's colour restorers; such as 'Just for Men' and 'Grecian 2000'.

Activity
Solve the following problems and record your answers in your portfolio. What could be the reasons for:

1 permanent colour fading on the ends of long hair?

2 permanent colour not taking properly on the roots?

3 grey/white hair resisting semi-permanent colour?

4 permanent copper red colour not taking on mid-brown hair?

5 blonde hair looking ashen or green?

The effects of hydrogen peroxide on hair

Hydrogen peroxide strength	Effect upon the hair
20 vol (or 6%)	• Assists the deposit of colour into the hair, adding depth, making it darker • Enables coverage of white/grey hair • Will lighten two levels above base 6 (on fine hair) • Will lighten one level below base 4
30 vol (or 9%)	• Will lighten hair three levels above base 6 • Will lighten hair two levels below base 4
40 vol (or 12%)	• Will lighten hair four levels above base 6 (with high lift colour)

Special note: When hydrogen peroxide lightens hair to any level it will remove the smaller pigments first. The larger, warmer pigments (*pheomelanin*) within the hair are more difficult to remove so unwanted golden or even orange tones are often left within the hair.

Diluting hydrogen peroxide

This illustration shows you how the strengths that you have in stock can be diluted to make lesser strength hydrogen peroxide.

The first column refers to the strength peroxide that you have, the second refers to the peroxide you want to create. The last three columns show you how many parts of the peroxide you need and how many parts of distilled water you need to add to it.

Diluting hydrogen peroxide

Strength you have	Strength you want to create	Peroxide	Add	Water
40 vol (i.e. 12%)	30 vol (i.e. 9%)	3	+	1
40 vol	20 vol (i.e. 6%)	1	+	1
40 vol	10 vol (i.e. 3%)	1	+	3
30 vol (i.e. 9%)	20 vol (i.e. 6%)	2	+	1
30 vol	10 vol (i.e. 3%)	1	+	2
20 vol (i.e. 6%)	10 vol (i.e. 3%)	1	+	1

Lightening hair

Lighteners and bleaches have alkaline chemicals within them that achieve lightened effects by dissolving the natural tones (pigments) within hair. Similar to para dyes, lightening products are mixed with hydrogen peroxide to activate the oxidising process, and they are used in three main forms:

- *high lift colour* – which is a non-bleach process for lightening hair partially or whole head
- *powder bleach* – which is used for highlighting and partial lightening techniques
- *gel/oil bleach* – which is suitable for whole-head applications including the scalp.

The alkaline compound acts upon the hair by swelling and opening up the cuticle. This enables the peroxide at six per cent or nine per cent to release oxygen and oxidise the natural pigments of melanin from within the cortex. This creates oxymelanin and is seen as it reduces the natural colour through the different degrees of lift.

The colour control during lightening is not the same as with colouring though. Often when full-head lightening is done the result is quite yellow (although the control of warm pigments during lightening is better with high lift colour).

Toning colours

Level of depth	Tone required	Tonal quality	Pre-lighten to
10	Silver, platinum, mauve/violet	Cool	Very pale yellow
9	Ashen blondes, light beige blonde	Cool	Pale yellow
8	Beige blonde	Cool	Yellow
8	Sandy blonde	Warm	
7	Golden blonde	Warm	
7	Chestnut, copper gold	Warm	Orange
6	Red copper	Warm	
5	Mahogany	Cool	Red/orange
4	Burgundy, plum	Cool	

VICKY TURNER@GOLDSWORTHY'S

IMAGE COURTESY OF GOLDWELL

EKU *statement*

GH9.45 and **GB2**.45) Why it is important to emulsify colour prior to removal

Toning is the process of adding colour to previously bleached or lightened hair. A variety of pastel shades, such as silver, beige and rose, are used to produce subtle effects. Different types of toners are available; read the instructions provided by their manufacturers to find out what is possible.

Choice of lightening method

High lift colour

All manufacturers produce a special range of colours that are used to lighten hair. As these are mixed with 6 per cent or 9 per cent volume peroxide their ability to achieve very high lift results are limited by the natural depth that you are starting with.

The colour control and condition of the hair is generally better than that produced by using bleach, since the colour can deposit ashen, beige or warm tones as the colour works and the hair lightens. And because you are using a hair colour and not bleach, less moisture is removed from the hair during the process, so a better condition is guaranteed at the end.

High lift colours are similar in composition to normal hair colours with one exception: they use an alkaline component (e.g. resorcinol) which swells the hair shaft enabling a better penetration of the chemicals into the cortex and hence able to lighten as well.

Removing high lift colour You can remove high lift colour by emulsifying the colour by adding a little warm water to the colour and gently massaging all over. This mixes the colour with the water and helps to release the products from the hair enabling you to use a lighter action within the shampooing process. The hair can be conditioned as normal at the end or an anti-oxidant can be applied to help close the cuticle and lock in the colour results.

Emulsion bleach

Emulsion bleach is slow acting. It is made up of two compounds that are added together and then mixed with hydrogen peroxide:

- oil or gel bleach
- activators, boosters or controllers.

This type of bleach is specially formulated for use directly onto the roots of the hair, and is suitable for contact with the scalp. It is kinder and gentler during the lightening process and is mixed with 20 vol. hydrogen peroxide for root, mid-length and ends application. The lift through the undertone shades is aided and controlled by the addition of activators. These boost the power of the bleach whilst maintaining relatively low hydrogen peroxide strength.

Emulsion bleaches also contain additives which control the resultant colour as the bleach lightens the hair. As mentioned earlier, these tend to make hair yellow, so they have matt emulsifiers which neutralise unwanted yellow tones whilst the lifting process takes place. Heat may be used during the development of the process, but the client must be monitored closely (particularly if a colour accelerator or steamer is used to aid development) as these types of bleach can often be more viscous and mobile and might drip!

Activity

Types of colour

Complete the table below by filling in the missing information.

Colour	How long does it last on hair?	What effect does it have on hair?
Semi-permanent colour		
Quasi-permanent colour		
Permanent colour		
Lightener		

Remember

The degree of lift required in emulsion bleach is controlled by the number of activators added into the mixing bowl with the oil. It is not boosted by stronger hydrogen peroxide levels. Always follow the manufacturer's instructions when using lightening products.

Removing emulsion bleach Make sure that when the bleach is removed you rinse without massaging with only tepid or warm water. The client's scalp has been subjected to chemicals and could be sensitive; the cooling action of the rinsing will stop the lightening process and make the client more comfortable. After the emulsion has been rinsed away the hair can be shampooed with a mild colour shampoo and conditioned with an anti-oxidising treatment.

Powder bleach

Powder bleach can be mixed with 6, 9 or 12 per cent hydrogen peroxide, depending upon the level of lift required. Powder bleaches are fast acting and are used for a variety of highlighting techniques. When they are mixed in the bowl the consistency is that of a thick, 'porridge-type' paste. The stiffness of the consistency prevents spillages and enables the bleach to work like a poultice. As the process continues the bleach/peroxide mix will expand. This action is speeded up more if accelerated by heat, so a careful eye should be kept on the development timings.

Removing powder bleach Again, as with emulsion bleach, make sure that when the bleach is removed from the hair you rinse it without massaging, using only tepid or warm water. The removal of powder bleach can be far more problematic than that of emulsion bleach and this has more to do with the colouring technique that has been used. If different coloured highlights have been done with Easi-Meche™, foil, wraps, etc. these need to be removed carefully and individually as one colour may affect another.

VICKY TURNER@GOLDSWORTHY'S

EKU *statement*

GH9. and GB2.18) The dangers associated with the inhalation of powder lighteners

Although the client's scalp has not been subjected to chemicals, it still might be sensitive from the colouring technique; again, the cooling action of the rinsing will stop the lightening process and make the client more comfortable. Afterwards the hair can be shampooed with a mild colour shampoo and conditioned with an anti-oxidising treatment.

Remember

Avoid inhalation of powder bleach

Be very careful when you dispense powder bleach into a bowl. The particles are very small and tend to 'dust' into the air very easily. This is a hazardous chemical compound which can cause respiratory conditions. You must avoid contact through inhalation; wherever possible only use 'dust-free' powder bleach.

Lightening service required	What you need to check for	Technique/application	Bleach type
Whole head (on virgin hair)	Test results: • (Skin tests etc). Natural hair depth: • Bleaches will lift five levels quite happily on hair with brown/ash pigments. However, strong red content will be difficult to remove. • Hair beyond base 5 will not lift safely beyond base 9. Suggest other colouring options. Hair length: • Lengths up to 10 cm lighten evenly, provided manufacturer's instructions are followed. • Lengths over 15 cm are not recommended, as evenness of colour will be difficult to guarantee. Hair texture: • Finer hair needs extra care and lower hydrogen peroxide strengths i.e. 6%. • Medium and coarser hair present fewer technical problems. Hair condition: • Only consider hair in good condition for lightening. (lightening removes moisture content during the process, hair that is porous or containing low moisture levels has insufficient durability for lightening).	Bleach mixture must be applied to mid lengths and ends first. A plastic cap should envelop the contents and can be developed with gentle heat until ready. When the bleached hair has lightened two to three levels of lift, the root application can be applied. • Always follow manufacturer's instructions.	Only emulsion bleach or cream is suggested for application to the scalp. These are used with 6% hydrogen peroxide and sachet controllers to handle levels of lift.

Lightening service required	What you need to check for	Technique/application	Bleach type
Full head (on previously coloured)	• Not recommended		
Root application (pre-lightened ends)	Existing client: • Yes, check previous records and current hair condition and carry out service. • No, new client: go through all the checks in the full head application table and find out the previous treatment history.	Roots only without overlapping previous lightened ends. • Always follow manufacturer's instructions.	Only emulsion bleach or cream is suggested for application to the scalp.
Highlights (fine even meshes on virgin hair) Note – The success of highlights on coloured hair is very poor in comparison. This work is often undertaken in salons, but ends seldom lighten effectively, whilst the roots lighten very quickly. (Colour should be removed with a synthetic colour remover-decolour)	Test results: • (Skin tests etc). Natural hair depth: • Bleaches will lift five levels quite happily on hair with brown/ash pigments. However, strong red content will be difficult to remove and require stronger developer and/or additional heat. • Hair beyond base 5 will not lift safely beyond base 9. Suggest other lightening technique. Hair length: • Hair length will have an impact on evenness of colour. However a small tolerance is acceptable, and 'visually' indistinguishable on longer hair lengths Hair texture: • Finer hair needs extra care and lower hydrogen peroxide strengths i.e. 6% • Medium and coarser hair present fewer technical problems but generally take longer. Hair condition: • Only consider hair in good condition for lightening. (Lightening removes moisture content during the process, hair that is porous or containing low moisture levels has insufficient durability for lightening.)	• Plastic self-grip meshes (e.g. Easi-Meche™ L'Oréal). • Foil meshes. • Colour wraps.	High lift powder bleach with suitable hydrogen peroxide developer at 6%, 9% or for highest lift 12% (providing no product is allowed to make contact with the skin/scalp).

Cap highlights

Highlight caps are a safe, simple and popular choice for cost-effective, single-colour or lightened highlights on short layered hair. Even with the application of a single colour a multi-toned effect can be achieved. The reason for this is more to do with the cut and

RUSH LONDON

styling though, rather than the introduction of a solitary tone. Highlight caps can produce basic effects, whilst more complex, technically involved, multicolour effects are achieved through other techniques.

Woven highlights

Woven highlights in foil, Easi-Meche™ or wraps are the preferred technique for multi-toning hair. The visual effects are unlimited and new exciting colour combinations and techniques are happening each year. The application of this type of colouring is both creative and artistic, and is only limited by the vision that the stylist has.

Activity

With your colleagues, each collect from styling magazines a selection of (say six) partial/highlight effects.

Now take it in turns to show the others each of your pictures and then explain how each effect was created, providing the technique, application and colours used. Record these details along with the relevant pictures for use in your portfolio. Check your assessment with your supervisor or a senior member of staff.

GH 9.1 and GB2.1

Maintain effective and safe methods of working when colouring and lightening hair

Remember

 Always follow the manufacturer's instructions when using any colouring products.

Safety and preparation

Although Chapter 1 covers much of the general aspects of heath and safety that you need to know, each technical procedure has specific things that relate to that area of hairdressing alone. Hair colouring is particularly problematic as it involves the application of a variety of potentially harmful chemicals. Therefore the care that you take in handling products and preparing yourself and the client is absolutely critical to safe and successful colouring.

Records   These should be found and put ready at the beginning of the day. The appointment book identifies all the expected clients, so all their treatment history – dates of visits, who provided the services, previous chemical services, records of any tests and any additional comments – can all be collated long before the clients arrive.

Similarly, when clients have been in, any results of tests or notes following treatments must always be updated as soon as practically possible. The records are essential for keeping things going smoothly; by maintaining services even if key staff are away. Let alone if things go wrong and they are needed in any pursuance by insurers.

Tests   Collect together the results of any tests carried out prior to the appointment. If there have been any adverse reactions or contra-indications no permanent colour service can be carried out. Have you made this clear to the client and made plans for alternative services such as temporary or semi-permanent colouring?

(For more information on tests see pages 395–398.)

Materials After the records have been found it is advisable to get all tubes, cans or bottles of colour put aside and ready along with the client's record information. Doing this earlier has several benefits. It can save valuable time later when you need to mix them, particularly if you are running on a tight schedule. But it has useful benefits for the salon's stock control systems too: when products are removed from stock you can see when certain colours are running low. These can be noted and the relevant person made aware.

Gowning Always make sure that the client and the client's clothes are adequately protected before any process is started. Most salons have special 'colour-proof ' gowns for colouring and lightening processes. These gowns are resistant to staining and are made from finely woven synthetic fabrics that will stop colour spillages from getting through onto the client's skin or clothes. When you gown the client, make sure that the free edges are closed and fastened together. On top of this and around the shoulders you can place a colouring towel and over this a plastic cape. This needs to be fastened but loose enough for the client to be comfortable throughout the service. Remember that this may be over an hour or so.

Using barrier cream Barrier cream can be used as physical barrier to prevent staining around the client's face/hairline. It is also particularly useful if the client has any general sensitivity to chemical based products. Remember it is not an excuse for poor slapdash application, allowing you to extend the colour application beyond the root area to the skin. But it will help in areas where colour seeps off the hair onto the skin.

Apply barrier cream to the skin with a finger or cotton wool close to the hairline, taking care not to get it onto the hair, as this could stop the colour from taking evenly.

It can be removed later after you have shampooed the colour from the hair and before any other services are conducted.

Seating position The chair back should be protected with a plastic cover. If this is not available a colouring towel can be folded lengthwise and secured with sectioning clips at either end. The client should be seated comfortably, in an upright position, with their back flat against the cushioned chair pad.

Trolley You should have your colouring trolley prepared and at hand with the materials you will need. Foils for highlighting should have been previously prepared to the right lengths and combs, brushes, sectioning clips etc. should be all cleaned and sterilised and ready for use.

Protecting yourself Your personal hygiene and safety are also important. The care you take in preparing for work should be carried through in everything you do and this is made even more important when you are about to handle hazardous chemicals. Put on a clean colouring apron and fasten the ties in a bow. Then take a pair of disposable non-latex gloves and put them on ready for the application. It is recommended as best practice to wear a glove of 30 cm length to offer protection to the wrist area. There should be a variety of sizes for staff to choose from to ensure best fit. (See reference below for preventing dermatitis.)

Use your time effectively; each salon allocates different times for different services. A retouch may only take 20 minutes to apply on shorter hair whereas a long hair set of full-head woven highlights could be booked for an hour.

Remember

When mixing colouring products, never add colour or developer together by guesswork. The amounts that have to be added together are critical to a successful outcome. Don't take unnecessary risks!

EKU *statement*

GH9.12 and GB2.12) The type of personal protective equipment available

GH9.13 and GB2.13) Why it is important to use personal protective equipment

EKU *statement*

GH9.11 and GB2.11) The range of protective clothing and products that should be available for clients

EKU *statement*

GH9.15 and GB2.15) Why it is important to position your tools and equipment for ease of use

EKU statement

GH9.2 and GB2.2) Your salon's expected service times for basic colouring work

GH9.4 and GB2.4) Your salon's and legal requirements for disposal of waste materials

GH9.10 and GB2.10) What is contact dermatitis and how to avoid developing it whilst carrying out colouring services

GH9.14 and GB2.14) How the position of your client and yourself can affect the desired outcome and reduce fatigue and the risk of injury

GH9.21 and GB2.21) Methods of working safely and hygienically and which minimise the risk of cross-infection and cross-infestation

GH9.22 and GB2.22) The importance of personal hygiene

GH9.24 and GB2.24) Methods of cleaning, disinfecting and or sterilisation used in salons

GH9.54 and GB2.54) The importance of using products economically

For more information about working position and efficiency, personal hygiene, avoiding dermatitis etc., see Unit G20 Make sure your actions reduce the risks to health and safety (pages 4–24).

For more information about using and checking electrical equipment during processing see Unit GH8 Shampoo, condition and treat the hair and scalp (page 146).

EKU statement

GH9.23 and GB2.23) Why it is important to check electrical equipment used to aid the colouring and lightening process

Activity
Make sure that you are up to speed with your colouring
You can always practise your timing for different colouring services by working on a modeling head and applying conditioner instead of colour. This allows you to get the feel of product application without any problems arising from uneven application.

Remember

 Dos and Don'ts

Dos	*Don'ts*
When a client's hair is developing under a Climazone, Rollerball or any other colour accelerator, do check at intervals during the processing to see that they are comfortable and that the equipment is not too hot.	Never handle electrical equipment with wet hands, always dry them first.
Do check the equipment controls so that the timing and temperature settings are correct.	Never leave colour spillages until later. Mop them up straight away while you still have your protective gloves on.
Do check the manufacturer's instructions before you mix any products. They will give you the recommended amounts and quantities to mix together.	Don't mix up too much product at one time, it is wasteful and expensive. If you need more you can always mix up more when you need it.

Dos

Always do a skin test on the client before any colouring process.

Do put screw tops and lids back on colouring products immediately. Their effectiveness will be impaired if they are exposed to the air for any longer than needed.

Do make a note of low levels of stock as product is removed from storage.

Do make good use of your time. Always prepare your work area and the materials you will need before the client arrives; this saves valuable time later.

Don'ts

Never mix products up before they are needed. Colour products have a set development time and oxidisation will start if they are exposed or mixed too soon.

Never attempt to do any colouring procedure without wearing the correct PPE.

Don't work in a cluttered environment. Always make sure that the work area is prepared properly and ready for use.

Don't forget to complete the client details/records after doing the service. Make sure that all aspects – dates, times, changes in materials etc. – are recorded accurately.

Remember

 Always follow the manufacturer's instructions for mixing the correct amounts together. If the proportions are wrong the colour will be wrong.

Remember

Colouring materials are expensive. The profitability of the job you are about to do relates directly to the amount of colour you use. Always mix a small amount up to work with. If you do run out you can always mix up some more.

Activity

Hair Tests

Complete this activity by filling in the missing information in the spaces provided

Type of test	What is the purpose of the test?	How is the test carried out?
Elasticity		
Porosity		
Incompatibility		
Patch		
Strand		

GH9.2 and GB2.2 — Prepare for colouring and lightening hair

Colour consultation

Before you start any colouring treatment there are a number of things that you should do.

EKU statement

GH9.40 and GB2.40) How the factors in the range can affect your choice of colouring and lightening products and application techniques

GH9.47 and GB2.47) How and why the contra-indications in the range can affect the delivery of colouring services to clients

Choosing colours

First of all	Things to consider
Does the client know of any reasons that would affect your choice of service?	Ask the client about their hair to find out if there are any known reasons why the service can not continue – are there any contra-indications?
What colour would be best to suit their needs?	Should you be using temporary, semi-permanent or permanent colouring?
How can the desired effect be best achieved?	Does the colour need to be applied to the roots first, the mid-lengths and ends, or can it be applied all over? Would the effect benefit more from partial colouring such as highlights or lowlights?
How long will it last?	Will the colour fade off or does it have to grow out?
How much will it cost?	Is this affordable and something that can be kept up in the future?
How will it affect the hair?	Will the long-term effects be what the client expects?
Is the hair suitable for colouring?	Have you tested the hair and skin beforehand to see if there are any contra-indications or hair condition issues that will affect the result?

Now consider

What are the client's expectations?	How will the colour enhance the style and natural colour of the hair? What are the benefits for them?
What are the results of your tests?	Examine the hair: does it present any limitations for what you intend to do?
What is the hair condition like?	Are there any factors that will change the way in which colouring will work on the hair?
	What previous information is available?
What do the client's records say?	Does this information influence the choice and colour process?
How will you show the effect to the client?	Have you got any illustrations of the finished effect? Does the colour chart give a clearer picture of the shade the hair will go?
How long will the process take?	Is there enough time to complete the effect? Has anything changed as a result of the consultation? Would this service now need to be rebooked or do you have the time to complete it still?

What contra-indications are you looking for?

Contra-indications are	How could you find out?	How else would you know?
Skin sensitivity	Ask the client if they have ever had a reaction to hair or skin products in the past	Patch test/sensitivity test.

Contra-indications are	How could you find out?	How else would you know?
Allergic reaction	Ask the client if they have ever had a reaction to hair or skin products in the past	Patch test/sensitivity test.
Skin disorder	Ask the client if they know about any current skin disorders	Examine the scalp to see if there are any physical signs of skin abrasions, discolouration, swellings, infestation or infections.
Incompatible products	If you see the results of any previous colour ask what type it was, how was it done?	Look for discolouration or unnatural colour effects on the hair. Test for incompatibles.
Medical reasons	Ask the client if there are any current medical reasons why colouring can not be performed	Examine the hair; look for signs of healthy active growth. If there are signs of weakened, damaged, broken or missing hair, ask for more information. Test for elasticity and porosity.
Damaged hair	Ask the client if there are any current known reasons why the hair is in its current state/condition?	Examine the hair; look for signs of healthy active growth. If there are signs of weakened, damaged, broken or missing hair, ask for more information. Test for elasticity and porosity.

EKU statement

GH9.52 and GB2.52) The types of tools, materials and equipment used for highlighting and lowlighting hair

GH9.53 and GB2.53) When and how shampoos and conditioners should be used when colouring and lightening hair

What sort of colour should I use?

Type, PPE and timings	Preparation	Suitability	Effects
Temporary colour PPE – wear gloves and apron. Whole head application done at workstation takes 5 mins.	No mixing required, colour applied straight from the can, bottle etc. as coloured mousses, setting lotions, hair mascara.	No skin test required. Most hair types (including coloured and permed) although it can be more difficult to remove from bleached hair. Colour control – poor, shade guide targeting can only be used as an approximation.	The colour only lasts until the next wash. Subtle toning on grey hair. Hair condition may be improved. Surface colour without chemical penetration. Does not lift natural colour, only deposits.
Semi-permanent colour PPE – wear gloves and apron. Whole head application done at workstation or at basin takes 5 mins. Left on up to 15 mins.	No mixing required, although transference to an applicator may be necessary.	Skin test may be required. Most hair types (including coloured and permed) often used as a colour refresher between permanent colour treatments. Can cover small amounts of graying hair. Colour control – poor, shade guide targeting can only be used as an approximation.	Lasts up to six shampoos. Colour fades/diffuses after each wash. Does not lift natural colour, only deposits. No regrowth, natural colour unaffected.

Type, PPE and timings	Preparation	Suitability	Effects
Quasi-permanent (longer-lasting) colour PPE – wear gloves and apron. Whole head brush application done at workstation, takes up to 25 mins. Alternatively, using an applicator bottle can save time and takes up to 15 mins. Left on up to 40 mins.	Mixed with developer or activators. These can be in liquid or crystal form. Measurement and mixing must be accurate.	Skin test required. Most hair types (including coloured and permed) often used as a colour refresher between permanent colour treatments. Will cover up to 30% grey hair. Colour control – good, will achieve shade guide targeting.	Lasts up to 12 shampoos. Colour fades a small amount after subsequent shampoos. Does affect natural colour, bonds with natural pigments. Can produce a regrowth.
Permanent colour (para dye) PPE – wear gloves and apron. Regrowth brush application done at workstation, takes up to 25 mins. Left on up to 40 mins. Whole head colouring will depend on length and order of application.	Mixed with hydrogen peroxide at 10, 20, 30 or 40 volumes (3%, 6%, 9%, or 12%). Measurement and mixing must be accurate.	Skin test required. All natural hair types and most coloured and permed hair (providing hair not too porous or damaged). Will cover all grey. Can lift up to two shades – high lift colour will lift three or four shades.	Permanent colour or para dyes are made in a wide variety of shades and tone. Long lasting and grows out. Will change natural hair pigments.

Note: All timings are approximated. Partial colouring techniques – highlights, slices, dip ends etc. – may take longer depending on operator experience, the amount of colour applied and the technique used.

EKU *statement*

GH9.50 and **GB2**.50) The importance of following manufacturers' instructions when measuring and mixing colouring and lightening products
GH9.51 and **GB2**.51) How to accurately measure and mix colour and lightening products to manufacturers' instructions

Measuring flasks and mixing bowls

Measurement of hydrogen peroxide at any strength must be accurate; the amount used in relation to colour is a critical factor to a successful outcome. Different types of colour are formulated to be used with particular developers. For example, a Wella Color Perfect should be mixed with Welloxon developer. If you use a different developer the consistency will be wrong and this will make the application difficult. All gel and cream colours, when mixed, will be stiff enough not to run or drip when either on the brush or on the hair. Using unmatched, alternative developers will do the opposite and could be a potential hazard for the client.

When you measure developer into a measuring flask you must make sure that your eye-line is at the same level as the liquid in the flask so that the measurement is accurate.

When you mix developer with colour from tubes, you will notice that all tubes have markings on the side showing the ¼, ½ and ¾ points. These enable you to squeeze from the bottom of the tube up to these points, knowing that your measurement will be accurate.

If you are mixing two or more shades of colour together, always mix these well in the bowl first before adding any developer. This allows the different pigments to be evenly distributed throughout the colour and also throughout the hair when it is applied!

Remember

 Never mix colour or put it into a bowl before you need to use it. Permanent colours will oxidise in the air; this expands the colour pigments and they will not be able to enter the hair shaft through the narrow cuticle layers, thus rendering the colour useless.

Remember

Always gown your client properly so that they are protected from spillages of chemicals.

Always wear the PPE provided by the salon every time you apply colour.

Always follow the manufacturer's instructions; never deviate from the tried-and-tested formulae.

Make sure that your work position is clear and that your posture is correct.

Make sure that the client is comfortable throughout as they will be sitting for some considerable time.

 Activity

What personal health and safety aspects must you consider before undertaking any colouring treatment?

What PPE must you wear when colouring hair?

What PPE must the client wear during colouring?

Record your answers in your portfolio.

Skin and hair tests

Skin or sensitivity test

The sensitivity test is used to assess the reaction of the skin to chemicals or chemical products. In the salon it is mainly used before colouring. Some people are allergic to external contact of chemicals such as PPD (found in permanent colour). This can cause dermatitis or, in even more severe cases, permanent scarring of skin tissue and hair loss. Some have an allergy to irritants to which they react internally.

To find out whether a client's skin reacts to chemicals in permanent colours, carry out the following test 24 to 48 hours prior to the chemical process.

Measuring tools

Carrying out a skin test

1 Mix a little of the colour to be used (with the correct amount of hydrogen peroxide – following recommendations by the manufacturer).

2 Clean an area of skin about 8 mm square, behind the ear. Use a little spirit on cotton wool to remove the grease from the skin.

3 Apply a little of the colour mixture to skin.

4 Cover the colour patch with a simple dressing to protect it. Ask your client to report any discomfort or irritation that occurs over the next 24 hours. Arrange to see your client at the end of this time so that you can check for signs of reaction.

5 If there is a positive response – a contra-indication, a skin reaction such as inflammation, soreness, swelling, irritation or discomfort – do not carry out the intended service. *Never* ignore the result of a skin test. If a skin test shows a reaction and you carry on anyway, there may be a more serious reaction that could affect the whole body!

EKU *statement*

GH9.28 and GB2.28) The types and purposes of tests

GH9.29 and GB2.29) The importance of following manufacturers' instructions for skin testing

GH9.30 and GB2.30) When and how tests should be carried out and the expected results

IMAGE COURTESY OF GOLDWELL UK

IMAGE COURTESY OF GOLDWELL

EKU *statement*

GH9.31 and GB2.31) How
the results of tests can
influence the colouring and
lightening service

GH9.32 and GB2.32)
Potential consequences of
failing to carry out tests

GH9.33 and GB2.33) The
courses of action to take in
the event of adverse reactions
to tests (e.g. what type of
reactions you must report to
other, more senior people)

GH9.34 and GB2.34) Why
it is important to record test
results

EKU *statement*

GH9.3 and GB2.3) How to
complete client records
effectively

GH9.25 and GB2.25) The
importance of questioning
clients to establish any
contra-indications to
colouring and or lightening
services

GH9.26 and GB2.26) Why
it is important to record
client responses to
questioning

GH9.27 and GB2.27) The
legal significance of client
questioning and the
recording of client's
responses to questioning

6 If there is a negative response – no reaction to the chemicals – then carry out the treatment as proposed.

7 Record the details of any tests on the client's treatment and service history.

Hair tests

Incompatibility test	When is it done	How is it done
This will show if there are any chemicals present, i.e. metallic salts or other mineral compounds, within the hair that will react against any new proposed services.	Prior to colouring, highlighting and perming treatments.	Place a small sample of hair in a mixture of 20 parts hydrogen peroxide (6%) and one part ammonium-based compound from perm solution. If the mixture bubbles, heats up or discolours do not carry out the service.

Elasticity test	When is it done	How is it done
This determines the condition of the hair by seeing how much the hair will stretch and return to its original length. Overstretched hair will not return to the same length and indicates weakness and damage.	Prior to chemical treatments and services. (Ideal for hair that has impaired elasticity, e.g. from lightening or colouring.)	Take a couple of strands of hair between your fingers, holding them at the roots and the ends. Gently pull the hair between the two points to see if the hair will stretch and return to its original length. (If the hair breaks easily it may indicate that the cortex is damaged and will be unable to sustain any further chemical treatment.)

Porosity test	When is it done	How is it done
This test also indicates the hair's current condition by assessing the hair's ability to absorb or resist moisture from liquids. (Hair in good condition has a tightly packed cuticle layer which will resist the ingress of products.) Hair that is very porous holds on to moisture; this is particularly evident when you try to blow-dry it. The hair takes a long time to dry.	Before chemical services. If the cuticle is torn or damaged, the absorption of moisture and therefore hydrogen peroxide is quicker, so the processing time will be shorter. Over-porous hair will quickly take in colour but will not necessarily be able to hold colour as the cuticle is damaged and allows the newly introduced pigments to wash away.	Rub strands of hair between your fingertips to feel how rough or smooth it is. If it feels roughened, as opposed to coarse, it is likely that the hair is porous.

Strand test	When is it done	How is it done
Most colouring products just require the full development time recommended by the manufacturer – check their instructions. (However, some hair conditions take on the colour faster than others. A strand test will check the colour development and see if it needs to come off earlier.)	A strand test or hair strand colour test is used to assess the resultant colour on a strand or section of hair after colour has been processed and developed. A strand test is also useful prior to lightening natural pigments from hair or prior to removing synthetic pigments (i.e. decolour or colour reducer) to see how the hair will respond.	1. Rub a strand of hair lightly with the back of a comb to remove the surplus colour. 2. Check whether the colour remaining is evenly distributed throughout the hair's length. If it is even, remove the rest of the colour. If it is uneven, allow processing to continue, if necessary applying more colour. If any of the hair on the head is not being treated, you can compare the evenness of colour in the coloured hair with that in the uncoloured hair.

Recording the results

Make sure that you record the details of any test that you conduct. Update the client's record card in full and immediately after you have done the test. Don't leave it until later, you might forget! These records are essential information that will be needed again and help to show that a competent service has been provided at that time.

This would be vitally important if there was a problem at some later stage, particularly if it involved any legal action taken against the salon.

Remember

Record the results
After any treatment or tests have been carried out always update the client's records immediately. These tests and the findings are critical to the client's well-being and the salon's good name. You should record the:

- date
- the test carried out
- development times
- results
- recommended home-care or follow-up advice given.

Remember

If you are not sure about the results of any tests that you perform, ask a senior member of staff for their second opinion.

Remember

Record the client's responses to your questions and the comments about how the results of any tests affected their hair and skin.

GH9.3 and GB2.3

Colour and lighten hair and GB2.3 Colour and lighten (men's) hair

Colour selection

Colour selection, i.e. the process you go through in choosing the right target shade for your client's hair and the correct mixture of products to achieve that target shade, is based upon:

- customer choice (initially)
- current state of your client's hair (i.e. if it has already undergone processes such as highlights)
- existing condition of your client's hair.

1 If the hair has been regularly coloured before and there is a clear regrowth, with ends that have faded, you may only need to do a straightforward regrowth application with the same colour. Then, later in the development process, the residual colour can be diluted and taken through to the rest to refresh the total effect. So in this instance a regrowth that takes 20 minutes to apply can be left for 30 minutes' development (depending on manufacturer/colour type). Then, in the last 15 minutes, it can be taken through to the ends, until it is ready to be removed.

 However, if your client's hair has been coloured before, you also need to remember that it will not be possible to make the hair lighter by colouring. Permanent colour does not reduce permanent (synthetic) pigments in the hair. (If this is required you will have to use a colour remover first.)

2 If you need or want to counteract and neutralise unwanted tones in the hair, you will need to apply the principles of the colour wheel. If the client wants to reduce or 'calm down' unwanted red tones then you will be choosing a colour slightly darker in depth but which has the matt tones capable of neutralising that effect. Conversely, if your aim is to eliminate ashen matt tones (e.g. the colour often seen on fairer hair colours that are regularly subjected to chlorinated swimming pools) then you will be introducing warmer tones to the hair. So in this situation a 'greeny'-looking base 6 blonde will be improved by a shade depth 6 but with a tone warmth .03 (for more information see the section on depth and tone earlier in this chapter).

 If you had to reduce a tonal effect that was too yellow, say on a head that had been lightened, then (although the principle of toning bleached hair is slightly different) you would still be applying the principles of the colour wheel. Therefore a violet-based ash colour should be used to neutralise the unwanted tones.

The colour wheel is set out with the three primary colours: red, yellow and blue. In between these three are the secondary colours: orange, green, and violet. These are a direct result of mixing the two adjacent primary colours.

Red + Yellow = Orange

Yellow + Blue = Green

Blue + Red = Violet

However, a colour's tonal hue is neutralised if it is mixed with a colour directly opposite in the circle. Hence:

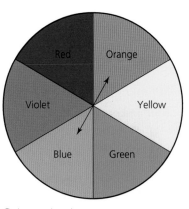

Colour wheel

Red tones are muted by *green*.

Orange tones are muted by *blue*.

Yellow tones are muted by *violet*.

3 If your client has never had any colour on their hair before (virgin hair) then colour targeting is easy. Your client will be able to choose practically any shade on the permanent shade chart, providing it is at the same depth or darker. (It is possible to lighten a shade or two with colour in certain situations.)

4 If your client has grey or greying (i.e. white) hair then you will have to decide and agree on what reduction of grey is necessary. If the client wants to cover all the grey, then this is only achievable by using or adding base shades to the target colour, i.e. a natural shade or a natural shade plus the target shade.

The amount of base added to the target shade is directly proportional to the amount of grey. Grey hair is referred to as a percentage of the whole head; therefore a client who has about a quarter of their hair that is grey is referred to as 25 per cent grey. Similarly, a client one tenth of whose hair is grey is 10 per cent grey.

So, the formula for mixing base shades works out like this:

● If a client has 25 per cent grey/white then you need ¼ of the base shade added to ¾ of the target shade.

● If a client has 50 per cent grey/white then you need ½ of the base shade added to ½ of the target shade.

● If a client has 75 per cent grey/white then you need ¾ of the base shade added to ¼ of the target shade.

Note: Different manufacturers have their own particular instructions for reducing/covering grey hair. Always check the instructions for the type of colour that you are using.

Existing hair condition

The hair's existing condition is a major contributing factor in the way in which it will respond when it is coloured. Hair that is too porous will absorb the colour differently. The porosity of hair is never even along the hair length, let alone across the hairs throughout the head. This is because the porosity of the hair is directly related to areas of damaged cuticle. Areas of high porosity occur at sites along the hair shaft where cuticle is torn or missing. At these points, moisture or chemicals can easily enter the inner hair without cuticle layer resistance.

This changes the rate of absorption, which ultimately affects the final evenness of the colour and the hair's ability to retain colour in subsequent washing etc. Ph balancing conditioners help to even out the hair's porosity and return chemically treated hair back to a natural pH 5.5.

During processing the only other factors that affect the achievement of an even and expected final colour result (providing your selection is correct) are:

● timing

● temperature.

Timing the colour development

The level of colour saturation is proportional to the length of time that the hair is exposed to colour. Under-processed hair will not achieve the same saturation as hair that has had full development. The longer that colour is left on, the more density the colour will have.

EKU *statement*

GH9.39 and GB2.39) How porosity levels can affect the choice and application of products and the results of the colouring process

GH9.43 and GB2.43) The importance of restoring the hair's pH balance after the colouring and lightening process

GH9.44 and GB2.44) Why it is important to avoid disturbing areas still processing when removing products from developed areas

EKU *statement*

GH9.46 and GB2.46) Why it is important to leave the hair and scalp free of colouring and lightening products

EKU *statement*

GH9.41 and GB2.41) Effects of temperature on the application and development of colouring and lightening products

Remember

 Always make sure that you remove all colouring products from the hair. This not only stops the action from developing further, but more importantly, it ensures that the client will not get any irritation or discomfort from chemicals deposited on the skin.

This can be explained in another way. Imagine that you wanted to redecorate a plain, smooth, white wall. First of all, you choose the colour and shade of paint that you want it to be. Then, after some preparation, you take a brush and start by applying the first coat. When this is dry you look at the colour, only to find that the effect is uneven and patchy. You can see that the tone you wanted is there but it is often thin and almost transparent in places. So you repaint the wall. When this extra layer of paint dries, the saturation of colour is better and more even, but still a little patchy in places. Finally you apply a third coat to the areas that are still patchy and when it dries the colour has an even density throughout. This effect is called *saturation*; it is achieved by the evenness of the density of the colour throughout the hair.

How temperature affects colouring

Temperature is also a contributing factor to colour development. The warmer the salon environment the quicker the colour processing will be. We know that when colour is introduced to heat it takes even more quickly; this can be localised to the client or relate to the whole salon. For instance, the salon temperature may be cool but the colour can be accelerated by putting the client under a Climazon or Rollerball.

But, remember, the human body produces heat too. In fact up to 30 per cent of body heat is emitted through the top of your head! (This is why wearing a hat in winter keeps you warm.) This heating effect has a dramatic impact on the development of colour and even more critical when lightening!

So with this extra heat around the scalp area, you can see there are potential problems in controlling the colour and aspects of the client's safety. To help control this process you must make sure that, when the colour is applied to the root area, the hair is lifted away from the scalp so that the air is able to circulate and ventilate the scalp evenly. This ensures that there are no 'hot spots' anywhere that might take more quickly or become a safety hazard to the client.

Remember

 Health and safety

When the scalp becomes warm during the processing of colour the skin attempts to regulate the overheating by producing sweat. At this point when the skin is moistened by sweat the colouring products become more viscous and spread more easily onto and even into the skin! This is extremely dangerous and will cause scalp burns as chemicals enter the skin through the hair follicles!

Initially, the client will not be able to distinguish between the heat from the processing and the burning sensation from the chemicals. By the time that they do, the longer-term damage is done. Chemical burns continue to act upon the skin long after the colour has been removed. You *must* avoid this happening.

If this does occur, the client must seek medical attention immediately at hospital.

Colour selection checklist

✔	What is the client's target shade?
✔	What is the percentage of white/grey hair?
✔	What is the difference in depth between the natural hair and the target colour?

✔	If the target shade is lighter than the natural shade, is it achievable by colouring alone?
✔	What colouring products would be needed to achieve the effect?
✔	What developer will be needed to achieve the effect?
✔	If the hair appears porous or porous in areas, do you need to do a test cutting first?
✔	If the hair has a small percentage of white/grey, what amount of base shade will you need to add to the target shade to stabilise the effect?

Activity

You have a client who has recently been on holiday in a hot country. The hair colour that you applied to her hair beforehand has now faded off. On questioning her, you find out that she has been swimming in the pool every day. You observe that her hair colour has taken on a greenish tone.

1   Why has the hair colour changed?

2   What is your recommended course of action to rectify this problem?

Record this case study and your response in your portfolio.

Remember

  If the hair is very porous the colour produced by temporary colours may be uneven or difficult to remove.

Remember

  Only work on manageable amounts of hair at any one time. Always secure the hair that you aren't working on out of the way with sectioning clips.

Remember

The higher the strength of the hydrogen peroxide, the more free oxygen is available and the more oxygen is released into the hair, the higher degree of lift that is achieved. When colour deposit only is required then a lower-strength hydrogen peroxide will suffice.

Refreshing the colour of the lengths and ends

When you are re-colouring the roots on longer hair you will often find that the ends of the colour need refreshing too. This doesn't mean that a full head colour is necessary: the refreshing can be done during the application

Appearance	1st step	2nd step	3rd step	4th step
When the colour looks the same at the ends as the target shade	Apply to regrowth	Allow to develop and then 15 minutes before full development time	Add 15–20 cc of tepid water to the mixture in	Leave for a further 5–10 minutes, to complete the development process

Appearance	1st step	2nd step	3rd step	4th step
			the bowl then apply this to the lengths and ends	
When the tonal quality has faded but the colour is still the same depth	Apply to regrowth	Allow to develop then 25 minutes before full development time	Add 15–20 cc of tepid water to the mixture in the bowl then apply this to the lengths and ends	Leave for a further 15–20 minutes, to complete the development process
When both the tonal quality and depth has faded on the ends	Apply to regrowth	Add 15–20 cc of tepid water to the mixture in the bowl then apply this to the lengths and ends immediately	Leave all the colour on for full development 35–40 mins	

Regrowth application: quick checklist

Remember

If you used dry heat to accelerate the development of permanent colours, don't let the heat dry out the products as this will stop the colour from developing further.

Consultation	– Find out what needs to be done.
	– Are there any modifications needed to do the regrowth?
Prepare the client	– Make the usual protective preparations.
	– Brush the hair through to remove the tangles.
	– Apply a barrier cream to the hairlines (if necessary).
Prepare the materials	– Make sure that you have everything you need at hand.
	– Put on your disposable gloves and apron.
	– Mix the products correctly.
Method/technique	– Divide the hair into four equal quadrants.
	– Start the application with a brush to the roots at the top of the head, working down and along each quadrant. – Pick up a horizontal section of hair within a back quadrant and with the tail of the brush.
	– Apply the colour/bleach to the regrowth evenly.
	– Repeat down the back of the head and through the sides.
Development	– Monitor the colour development throughout the processing.
	– Apply heat if needed to speed up the development process.
	– Check with the client throughout to ensure their comfort.
Removal	– When processing is complete, take the client to the basin and rinse the hair with tepid/warm water, gently massage to emulsify the colour.
	– Rinse thoroughly until the colour is removed.
	– Shampoo and condition with an anti-oxidising agent.

Step-by-step: Regrowth application

After the usual protective preparations for the client brush the hair through to remove the tangles. Apply a barrier cream to the hairlines (if necessary). Make sure that you have everything you need at hand. Put on your disposable gloves and apron. Mix the products correctly.

Step 1 Apply the colour carefully along the natural parting.

Step 2 Continue down the back and across from side to side which divides the hair into quadrants. Now sub-divide each quadrant into horizontal meshes and apply the colour as you work through each one.

Step 3 After the colour has developed, you can refresh the colour of the lengths by adding a little water to the remaining colour in the bowl and applying it to the lengths of the hair.

Step 4 Comb through each section to distribute the colour evenly.

Step 5 Leave for a further 10 minutes and then remove the colour in the usual way.

Step 6 Finished effect.

Full head: quick checklist

Consultation	– Find out what needs to be done. Are any modifications needed to the application, colour(s) or lightener?
Prepare the client	– Make the usual protective preparations.
	– Brush the hair through to remove the tangles.
	– Apply a barrier cream to the hairlines.
Prepare the materials	– Make sure that you have everything you need to hand.
	– Put on your disposable gloves and apron.
	– Mix the products correctly.
Method/ technique	– Divide the hair into four equal sections.
	– Start the application with a brush to the mid-lengths and ends at the top of the head, working down and along each quadrant.
	– Pick up a thin 5 mm horizontal section of hair within a back quadrant and with the tail of the brush.
	– Apply the colour/lightener to the mid-length and ends evenly.
	– Repeat down the back of the head and through the sides.
1st part of development	– Allow the mid-length and ends to develop sufficiently first.
	– Monitor the colour development throughout the processing.
	– Apply heat if needed to speed up the development process.
	– Check with the client throughout to ensure their comfort.

2nd part of development	– Pick up each of the horizontal sections of hair with the tail of the brush.
	– Apply the colour/lightener to the root area evenly.
	– Repeat down the back of the head and through the sides.
	– Monitor the colour development throughout the processing.
	– Apply heat if needed to speed up the development process.
	– Check with the client throughout to ensure their comfort.
Removal	– When processing is complete, take the client to the basin and rinse the hair with tepid/warm water, then apply gentle massage to emulsify the colour.
	– Rinse thoroughly until the colour is removed.
	– Shampoo and condition with an anti-oxidising agent.

Step-by-step: Full head application

Step 1 After the usual protective preparations for the client brush the hair through to remove the tangles. Apply a barrier cream to the hairlines (if necessary).

Step 2 Make sure that you have everything you need at hand. Prepare the client with a gown and a plastic cape to protect their clothes and salon chair. Put on your disposable gloves and apron. Mix the products correctly.

Step 3 Section off the lower hair at the nape and start to apply the colour to the mid-lengths and ends.

Step 4 Continue working up the back of the head; laying each section down on the previously coloured lengths.

Step 5 Work the colour through the lengths as you go.

Step 6 Comb through the lengths to distribute the colour evenly.

Step 7 Carefully secure the hair out of the way so that the colour doesn't fall over the client's face. Then leave the mid-lengths and ends to develop for the manufacturer's suggested timings.

Step 8 Take the lengths down and apply more colour to all of the roots.

EKU *statement*

GH9.57 and GB2.57)
Techniques for highlighting
and lowlighting hair

Step 9 Make sure that the colour application is even. Comb again if necessary.

Step 10 Finished effect.

Cap highlights: quick checklist

Consultation	– Find out what effect your client is trying to achieve.
	– How much lightened or coloured hair in relation to natural colour is expected – 5%, 10%, 25%?
	– How will you explain the effect to the client?
	– Do you have any visual aids to help?
	– Explain everything that you are going to do.
Prepare the client	– Make the usual protective preparations.
	– Brush the hair to examine the growth patterns and to remove any tangles. Look for areas where highlights would be conspicuous or unsightly.
	– Look for natural part/parting areas; confirm how the hair is to be worn.
	– If the hair has slightly longer layers or tends to tangle, apply some talcum powder to the hair and work through with your hands. This will help the hair to come through the holes, reducing any discomfort from tugging and picking the sections.
Prepare the materials	– Check the quality of the highlight cap. When a cap has previously been used for colouring it starts to wear.
	– Look for enlarged holes or splits where colour/lightener can seep through on to the hair.
	– Make sure that you have everything you need at hand.
	– Put on your disposable gloves and apron.
	– Mix the products correctly.
	– Ask the client to take hold of the front of the cap, ensuring it is centrally positioned at the forehead.
	– Pull the cap down smoothly, ensuring that the fit hugs the contour of the head correctly.
Pull the highlights through	– Start at the nape area.
	– Pull the highlights through by taking enough hair to complete each one in a single movement. Always pull through at an acute (narrow angle) to the cap.
	– Complete the pattern of repeated highlights, i.e. the percentage required, all over the head.
Apply the lightener or colour	– Carefully apply the mixture to all of the highlights evenly.
	– Lift the pasted hair slightly with the tail of a comb for even ventilation, so that no hair is trapped and can overheat or overdevelop.

Development	– Carefully place a clear, polyethylene cap on and around the highlights, to stop any spillages and to aid an even development.
	– Monitor the colour development throughout the processing.
	– Apply heat if needed to speed up the development process.
	– Check with the client throughout to ensure their comfort.
Removal	– When processing is complete, rinse thoroughly until all the product is removed (a slight shampoo may be needed).
	– Lift the flanges of the cap into the basin area and remove in one smooth and even pull.
	– Shampoo and condition with an anti-oxidising agent.

Step-by-step: Cap highlights

1 Check the quality of the highlight cap. A cap that has already been used for colouring hair starts to wear out. Look for enlarged holes or splits where colour/lightener can seep through on to the hair.

2 Prepare the client.

3 Put on your disposable gloves and apron.

4 Mix the products correctly.

5 Ask the client to take hold of the front of the cap, ensuring it is centrally positioned at the forehead. Pull the cap down smoothly, ensuring that it fits and hugs the contour of the head correctly.

6 Starting at the nape area, pull the highlights through by taking enough hair to complete each one in a single movement. Always pull through at an acute (narrow) angle to the cap.

7 Complete the pattern of repeated highlights, i.e. percentage required, all over the head.

8 Carefully apply the mixture to all of the highlights evenly. Lift the pasted hair slightly with the tail of a comb for even ventilation, so that no hair is trapped and can overheat or overdevelop.

Step 1 Check the cap for worn or torn areas.

Steps 2–3 Carefully mix the bleach and developer together.

Step 4 Ask the client to hold the front of the cap in position

Step 5 Start pulling through at the lowest part of the cap first

Step 6 Check that the highlights are evenly distributed

Step 7 Apply the bleach evenly to the hair.

Step-by-step: Men's partial colouring

Step 1 Before.

Step 2 Start by weaving out hair from a section that is long enough to hold (Note if the hair is not long enough to hold it may not be suitable for this colouring/lightening technique).

Step 3 Position a folded highlight foil beneath the hair and carefully apply the colour (The hair will become easier to handle as soon as the colour/lightener is applied).

Step 4 Continue working up the head; keeping the folded packets neat and tidy.

Step 5 Close up of the technique.

Step 6 The completed foils can be developed with or without heat.

Step 7 Final effect.

Step-by-step: Shoe shine colour

Step 1 Make sure that your client is adequately protected.

Step 2 A small amount of dry wax or hairspray can be worked into the ends at different positions on the head. (This helps it to stand away from the head).

Step 3 Then using a brush, apply a thin layer of colour/lightener to one side of a length of highlight foil.

Step 4 Very lightly, rub the surface of the foil across the tips of the client's hair (it's not essential to cover all of the hair).

Step 5 Keep the foil taught as you work across the client's hair.

Step 6 The optimum coverage should be no more than this. The colour can be left to develop with or without heat.

Step 7 The final effect.

Step-by-step: High light T section

Step 1 Before.

Step 2 Gown and protect the client. Look closely at the area that needs to be highlighted.

Step 3 Start at the back of the head– near, or below the crown. Secure the remainder of the top out of the way, now weave out an even mesh of hair from the section you are holding.

Step 4 Fold over the edge of a highlight foil across the stem of a pin-tail comb. Then using the comb as a guide, place the section of foil beneath the woven mesh.

Step 5 Apply the colour/lightener evenly to the hair. (Taking care not to overlap the colour).

Step 6 Work from the back of the head in small, narrow sections; through to the front.

Step 7 The foils should be neat and flat. This makes it easier to place subsequent foils so that they remain close to the head.

Step 8 Moving around to the side; start at the lowest point and secure the over falling hair out of the way.

Step 9 Keep an even tension on each section as you work up the sides.

Step 10 Repeat 8 and 9 on the opposite side.

Step 11 The final effect.

Woven highlights: quick checklist

Consultation	– Find out what effect your client is trying to achieve.
	– How much bleached and/or coloured hair in relation to natural colour is expected? What percentage of each is needed – 5%, 10%, 25%?
	– How will you explain the effect to the client?
	– Do you have any visual aids to help?
	– Explain everything that you are going to do.
Prepare the client	– Make the usual protective preparations.
	– Brush the hair to examine the growth patterns and to remove any tangles, look for areas where highlights would be conspicuous or unsightly.
	– Look for natural part/parting areas; confirm how the hair is to be worn.
Prepare the materials	– Make sure that you have everything you need at hand including foils cut to the required length.
	– Put on your disposable gloves and apron.
	– Mix the products correctly.
Method/technique	– Divide the hair into four equal sections.
	– Start at the back of the head at the nape.
	– Divide the remaining hair and section and secure it out of the way.
	– Pick up a horizontal section of hair and, with your pin-tail comb, weave out of the section a mesh of fine amounts of hair.
	– Place underneath the mesh a foil long enough to protrude beyond the hair length.
	– Apply the colour/lightener to the mesh evenly.

	– Fold in half and half again (fold the edges too, if required).
	– Continue on to next section with the alternating colour(s) or lightener.
	– Repeat up the back of the head and through the sides.
Development	– Monitor the colour development throughout the processing.
	– Apply heat if needed to speed up the development process.
	– Check with the client throughout to ensure their comfort.
Removal	– When processing is complete each foil must be removed individually by rinsing thoroughly until all the product is removed (this ensures that the colours do not run and bleed together).
	– Shampoo and condition with an anti-oxidising agent.

EKU *statement*

GH9.60 and GB2.60) How to handle the hair when weaving to maintain an even tension and to secure the materials to prevent seepage

EKU *statement*

GH9.61 and GB2.61) The types and causes of colouring and lightening problems that may occur during processing (e.g. skin staining, deterioration of hair condition and product seepage)

GH9.62 and GB2.62) Ways of resolving simple colouring and lightening problems that may occur during processing

GH9.63 and GB2.63) The potential risks of using lightening products on previously chemically treated hair

Step-by-step: Woven highlights

1 Brush the hair to examine the growth patterns and to remove any tangles. Look for areas where highlights would be conspicuous or unsightly. Look for the natural part/parting areas; confirm how the hair is to be worn.

2 Make sure that you have everything you need at hand including cut foils to the required length. Prepare the client then put on your disposable gloves and apron. Mix the products correctly.

3 Divide the hair into two equal sections. Start at the back of the head at the nape and divide and section and secure out of the way the remaining hair. Pick up a horizontal section of the hair and, with your pin-tail comb, weave out of the section a mesh of fine amounts of hair.

4 Place underneath the mesh, a foil long enough to protrude beyond the hair length. Apply the colour/lightener to the mesh evenly.

5 Fold in half and half again (possibly fold the edges too, if required). Continue on to next section with the alternating colour(s) or lightener.

6 Repeat up the back of the head and through the sides.

7 Monitor the colour development throughout the processing. Develop with heat if needed to speed up the development process. Check with the client throughout to ensure their comfort.

8 Each foil must be removed individually by rinsing thoroughly until all the product is removed (this ensures that the colours do not run and bleed together). Shampoo and condition with an anti-oxidising agent.

Colouring problems and corrective measures

Problem or fault	Possible reasons why	Corrective actions
Colour patchy or uneven	Insufficient coverage by colour	Spot colour the patchy areas
	Poor application	
	Poor mixing of chemicals	
	Sectioning too large	
	Overlapping, causing colour build-up	
	Under-processing (colour was not given full development)	
Colour too light	Incorrect colour selection	Choose a darker shade
	Peroxide strength too high causing lightening	Check strengths and re-colour
	Peroxide strength too low	Check strengths
	Under-processed	Re-colour
	Hair in poor condition	Apply restructurants
Colour fades quickly	Effects of sun or swimming	Recondition before next application
	Harsh treatment: over-drying, ceramic straighteners etc.	
	Hair in poor condition	
	Under-processing	Process correctly
Colour too dark	Incorrect colour selection	Senior assistance required
	Over-processing	
	Hair in poor condition	
	Metallic salts present	

Problem or fault	Possible reasons why	Corrective actions
Colour too red	Peroxide strength too high revealing undertone colour	Apply matt/green tones
	Hair not lightened enough	
	Under-processing	
Discolouration	Hair in poor condition	Use colour wheel to correct unwanted tones
	Undiluted colour repeatedly combed through	
	Incompatibles present	Senior assistance required
White hair not covered	Resistance to peroxide/colour	Pre-soften
	Lack of base shade within the mixed colours	Re-colour with correct amount of base and tones
Hair resistant to colouring	Cuticle too tightly packed	Pre-soften
	Under-processed	Recolour
	Incorrect colour selection	Senior assistance required
	Poor mixing/application	Senior assistance required
Scalp irritation or skin reaction	Chemicals not removed from hair properly after processing	Wash hair again and condition with anti-oxidants
	Peroxide strength too high	
	Poor quality materials causing abrasions to the scalp	Senior assistance required
	Client allergic to chemicals	Refer to doctor/hospital
Breakage	Lightening/highlighting hair that has previously had lightener on it before	Use restructurant on remaining hair to strengthen the weakened hair

GH9.4 and GB2.4 Provide aftercare advice

EKU statement

GH9.64 and GB2.64) Products for home use that will benefit the client and those to avoid and why

GH9.65 and GB2.65) How the continual use of heated equipment can affect the hair colour

GH9.66 and GB2.66) Recommended time intervals between colouring and other services

GH9.67 and GB2.67) How lifestyle can affect colour choice and the maintenance of colour

GH9.68 and GB2.68) How to give effective advice and recommendations to clients

Clients need your help to look after their hair at home, you need to give them the right advice so that they can make the most of their new colour and style between visits.

You should tell them what sorts of products that they could use that would make their colour last and reduce the risk of fading. Also make a point of telling them what they should avoid, as some products will reduce the effects of your colouring, causing it to fade prematurely or lose its intensity or vibrancy.

Explain the benefits of maintaining their hair in good condition, as hair in good condition is easier to manage, it looks better and is noticeable to everyone else as well.

Finally, if you would like to see more information on aftercare advice, see Units GH8 Shampoo, condition and treat the hair and scalp (pages 168–169) and GH12 Cut hair using basic techniques (pages 300–301).

Checkerboard

I know how to prepare clients before undertaking any chemical service

I know how to prepare the equipment and materials before they are used upon the client

I can carry out colour consultation and understand the colour selection process

I know and understand the science in respect to colouring and lightening

I always carry out tests prior to any new colouring treatment

I know and understand the health, safety and hygiene risks that clients are exposed to in chemical work

I know and understand the potential problems and risks of not testing hair before chemicals are introduced

I know and understand the effects that colouring products have upon the hair

I know when and to whom to refer clients in situations where external assistance is required

I know how to recognise and implement colour correction procedures by countering unwanted tones

I know and understand the ways of diluting hydrogen peroxide to make other strengths

I know how to carry out a variety of full head and partial colouring techniques on a variety of hair lengths

I always carry out working practices according to the salon's health and safety policy

Assessment of knowledge and understanding

Project 1

For this project you will need to collect and test a range of hair samples. You will need to create three sets of sample batches of:

- grey/white hair
- coloured hair (with high lift colour)
- lightened hair
- coloured hair (base 6)
- natural virgin hair (base 6).

Each of the different types listed above will be coloured with

a a base shade 8

b a copper shade 8

c an ash/beige shade

Mark each hair sample so that you know which one is which. Now mix up your three selected shades with 6 per cent (20 vol) hydrogen peroxide, then apply a little of each colour to each of the three collected sample batches. Allow time for the full development, then rinse each one and dry it off.

Record the changes for each sample:

- Which ones reached target shade?
- Which ones had no effect?
- Which ones have little or no coverage?
- Which ones have discoloured?

Write up the findings of your project in your portfolio. (If you have enough of each sample repeat the exercise again but now with 3 per cent (10 vol) hydrogen peroxide for a differing set of results.)

Case study

Your salon is recommended to a client who has moved to the area. She walks into the salon with lightened hair and requests a root retouch. The hair is coarse, dry and below the shoulders.

She says that her work had tended to move her around and previous attempts by other salons have resulted in inconsistent colouring.

How would you deal with this?

List the process of events that should take place in your portfolio. Include in your responses:

- consultation aspects, questions, examination and tests
- selection of suitable products and equipment
- the precautions you would take
- the advice and conclusion you would provide.

Project 2

For this project you will need to collect and test a range of hair samples.

You will need to create sample batches of:

- grey/white hair
- coloured hair (base 6)
- natural virgin hair (base 7)
- natural virgin hair (base 6)
- natural virgin hair (base 5).

Each of the different types listed above will be lightened to test the effects upon each prior to highlighting.

Mark each hair sample so that you know which one is which. Now mix up your lightener with 9 per cent (30 vol) hydrogen peroxide, and then apply a little lightener to each of the sample batches.

Allow time for the full development, then rinse each one and dry it off.

Record the changes for each sample:

- Which ones reached a suitable shade for highlights?
- Which ones were unsuitable for highlights?
- Which ones had no effect?

Write up the findings of your project in your portfolio.

Case study

Your client recently had her hair highlighted at another salon whilst on holiday. The client did not think that the result was at all satisfactory. The resultant highlight effect was uneven, and also patchy in places that were too gold.

How would you deal with this situation?

Make notes of what you would say and do. List the questions you would ask, and the order in which you would ask them. Retain notes for your portfolio.

Here are some things you should consider:

- Find out why the hair was not successfully treated at the other salon.
- Find out whether the client returned there to complain and what the outcome was.
- Record what you think might have caused the unsatisfactory results.
- Record what you think would have been a successful course of action.
- Find out whether the hair is in a fit state for further treatment.
- Record the results of your discussion with your client, and what you have agreed.

Revision questions

A selection of different types of questions to check your colouring knowledge.

Q1	A _____ test will identify a client's sensitivity to colour products.	Fill in the blank
Q2	A quasi-permanent colour lasts longer than semi-permanent colour.	True or false

Q3   Which of the following products are likely to be an incompatible?   Multi selection

Permanent colour containing PPD   ☐ 1
Retail permanent colour containing PPD   ☐ 2
Vegetable henna   ☐ 3
Compound henna   ☐ 4
Single step applications for covering grey i.e. "Just for men"   ☐ 5
Single step toners for application to bleached hair   ☐ 6

Q4   Bleaches and high lift colours are the same.   True or false

Q5   Which of the following tests do not apply to colouring services?   Multi choice

Skin test   ○ a
Incompatibility test   ○ b
Porosity test   ○ c
Development test curl   ○ d

Q6   Permanent colours alter the pigmentation of hair within the cuticle.   True or false

Q7   Which of the following colour products do not require the addition of hydrogen peroxide as a developer?   Multi selection

Powder bleach   ☐ 1
Semi-permanent colour   ☐ 2
Quasi-permanent colour   ☐ 3
Temporary colour   ☐ 4
Vegetable henna   ☐ 5
High lift colour   ☐ 6

Q8   Green tones within hair are neutralised by adding ____ tones.   Fill in the blank

Q9   Hair lightened from natural base 7 should be capable of maximum lift to: Multi choice

Red   ○ a
Pale yellow   ○ b
Yellow   ○ c
Yellow/orange   ○ d

Q10   Lightened hair that appears too yellow can be neutralised by adding mauve.   True or false

Preparing for assessment checklist

Remember to:

✔	prepare clients correctly for the services you are going to carry out
✔	check the results of any tests that have been undertaken
✔	put on the protective wear available for colouring and lightening
✔	listen to the client's requirements and discuss suitable courses of action
✔	adhere to the safety factors when working on clients' hair
✔	keep the work areas clean, hygienic and free from hazards
✔	promote the range of services, products and treatments within the salon

✔	clean and sterilise the tools and equipment before they are used
✔	apply the science aspects you have learnt relating to colouring and lightening
✔	work carefully and methodically through the chemical processes
✔	time the development of any chemical processes carefully
✔	communicate what you are doing with the client as well as your fellow staff members
✔	record the processes in the client's treatment history.

FELLOWSHIP FOR BRITISH HAIRDRESSING F.A.M.E. TEAM 2008

Chapter**seventeen**
Perming hair

GH14

GH14.1

GH14.2

GH14.3

GH14.4

More Information
See Unit G7 Advise and consult with clients

Unit G20 Make sure your own actions reduce risks to health and safety

See the appendices for Electricity at Work Regulations, COSHH Regulations and Data Protection Regulations
EKU GH14.7,
EKU GH14.9

Perming: quick overview

Unit title

GH14 Perm and neutralise hair

This is an **optional** unit for Hairdressing and Barbering at Level 2, it is made up of four main outcomes

Main outcomes

GH14.1 Maintain effective and safe methods of working when perming hair

GH14.2 Prepare for perming and neutralising hair

GH14.3 Perm and neutralise hair

GH14.4 Provide aftercare advice

What do I need to do for GH14.1?

- Make sure that the client is adequately covered, protected and prepared for the service
- Make sure that the working position is comfortable and safe for both you and the client
- Keep the work area clean and tidy and that waste materials are disposed of properly
- Work without causing risks to you or your client's health and safety
- Work efficiently and effectively
- Accurately maintain the client's treatment records

What do I need to do for GH14.2?

- Identify any contra-indications to perming the client's hair
- Carry out tests and record the outcomes
- Seek assistance when you are unsure of results from tests or contra-indications
- Inform the client of the expected costs, duration and likely results
- Prepare the tools and equipment ready for use

What do I need to do for GH14.3?

- Confirm the desired effect prior to starting

- Apply products safely, accurately, efficiently and in line with manufacturers' instructions

- Use winding techniques carefully and accurately to achieve the desired result

- Monitor and check the curl development

- Neutralise the hair correctly after development

- Identify and resolve problems where possible

- Achieve the desired effect

What do I need to do for GH14.4?

- Give accurate constructive aftercare advice on how the client can maintain their hair and perm

What aspects do I need to cover for GH14.1, GH14.2, GH14.3 and GH14.4?

- A variety of perm and neutralising products

- A variety of contra-indications to perming services

- A range of factors that affect or influence perming

- A variety of hair tests

- Different types of winding techniques

What do I need to know for GH14.1, GH14.2, GH14.3 and GH14.4?

- Your salon's requirements for preparation, timings and standards of service

- How to work safely, effectively and hygienically when perming and neutralising hair

- The different factors that can affect or influence successful perming and neutralising services

- The tests that need to be done prior to and during the perming services and the records that you must make

- The basic science of perming and neutralising and the effects of the chemicals upon the hair

- A range of different perming and neutralising products; how they work and when they are used

- The aftercare advice and recommendations that you should give to clients

Keywords

pH
The presence of positive hydrogen ions with a compound which denotes its levels of acidity or alkalinity

Pre-damping and post-damping
The application of perming lotion to the hair either before or after winding; depending upon style or hair requirements

Nine-section wind
A classic technique for perming that starts by sectioning and securing the hair into nine pre-defined workable areas

Brick wind
A technique of winding rods into the hair so that there aren't any uniform divisions or 'roller marks' after the perm is finished When the hair has been wound in this formation it looks like a brick wall.

Directional wind
A technique of winding rods in, so that when finished, the hair will move in a particular direction

Pre-perm treatment
A special treatment that balances the porosity of the hair prior to perm application so that an even perm result can be achieved throughout the hair

Disulphide bonds
The chemical bonds within the hair that are re-arranged during perming in order to give hair movement or curl.

(continued)

Information covered in this chapter

- The preparations that you must make before carrying out any perming and neutralising service
- The tools and equipment used during perming and neutralising, their maintenance and the preparations that you should make
- The factors that influence successful results in perming and neutralising services
- A range of perming techniques on different hair lengths
- The aftercare advice that you should give

CORTEX
Contains natural colour pigments

CUTICLE
Can be many layers thick

MEDULLA
Not always present

Cross-section of hair

Introduction

Ask a hundred clients with finer hair what they really want and you will get a unanimous response: lasting volume. Only one service in hairdressing or barbering can deliver this and that is the permanent wave.

Perming is a complex technical operation that involves the careful and accurate application of potentially damaging chemicals to the client's hair. If you get it right then quite possibly no-one will ever know that the hair has been permed (except the client that is.)

Successful perming relies heavily upon having a sound knowledge and the experience in knowing what different hair textures, types and densities will react like when the movement is added. Without this knowledge the only thing that can be guaranteed is failure. But like many things in life it is easy when you know how. This chapter provides you with all the essential information you need in the future to get it right every time.

How perms work

Science

The chemical changes that take place within the hair

'Perming' is the term given to the physical and chemical processing of hair, changing it into waves or curls. Unlike the movement and curl or smoothness produced by blow-drying or setting, the adding of movement to hair produced by perming is permanent: the hair does not return to its previous state when it is dampened. However, hair continues to grow and the new hair retains its natural shape. So, the waves and curls produced by perming gradually get further and further away from the scalp as the hair grows. To keep the same style the hair will, at some point, need to be permed again.

Because perming really does make a permanent change to the hair, you cannot easily correct mistakes (as you can with blow-styling, for example). The process also involves a variety of chemicals. It is therefore important that you make sure you understand what you are doing.

EKU *statement*

GH14.31) The effects of perm lotions and neutralisers on the hair structure

Changing the keratin

Before going ahead with this section, refer to 'the physical properties of hair' in Unit G7 (Chapter 5, page 105).

Of the cross-links between the polypeptide chains of hair keratin, the disulphide bonds or bridges give hair its shape. Each disulphide bridge is a chemical bond linking two sulphur atoms, between two polypeptide chains lying alongside each other. During perming some of these links or bridges are chemically broken, making the hair softer and more pliable, allowing it to be moved into a new position of wave or curl. Only 10–30 per cent (depending on lotion strength) of the disulphide bridges are broken during the action of perming. If too many are broken, the hair will be damaged beyond repair. You need to keep a check on the progress of the perm to ensure that:

● perm movement is optimised
● the chemical action is stopped at the right time.

You do this by rinsing away the perm lotion and neutralising the hair. During neutralising, pairs of broken links are joined up again at different sites along the hair. The newly formed cross-links hold the permed hair firmly into its new shape.

Changing the bonds

The hair is first wound with tension on to some kind of former, such as a curler or rod. This is the *moulding* stage. Then you apply perm lotion to the hair, which makes it swell. The lotion flows under the cuticle and into the cortex. Here it reacts with the keratin, breaking some of the disulphide bonds between the polypeptide chains. This *softening* stage allows the tensioned hair to take up the shape of the former: you then rinse away the perm lotion and neutralise the hair. This fixing stage permanently rearranges the *disulphide bonds* into the new shape.

This process can also be described in chemical terms. The softening part that breaks some of the cross-links is a process of reduction. The disulphide bridges are split by the addition of hydrogen from the perm lotion. (The chemical in the perm lotion that supplies the hydrogen is called a 'reducing agent'.) The keratin is now stretched: it is in a beta-keratin state.

The final part of the process, the *fixing* stage, re-creates bonds at different positions between polypeptide chains. It occurs by an oxidation reaction. New disulphide bridges form and the hydrogen that was previously introduced as hydrogen peroxide is chemically changed. The hydrogen reacts with the oxygen in the neutraliser, forming water. (The chemical in the neutraliser that supplies the oxygen is called an 'oxidising agent' or 'oxidiser'.) The keratin is now in a new, unstretched form: it is alpha-keratin state again.

EKU statement

GH14.1) Your salon's requirements for client preparation
GH14.2) Your salon's expected service times for basic perming and neutralising
GH14.11) The range of protective clothing and products that should be available for clients
GH14.12) The type of personal protective equipment available
GH14.13) Why it is important to use personal protective equipment
GH14.14) How the position of you and your client can affect the desired outcome and reduce fatigue and the risk of injury
GH14.15) Why it is important to position your tools and equipment for ease of use
GH14.17) Why it is important to keep your work area clean and tidy
GH14.18) Methods of working safely and hygienically and which minimise the risk of cross-infection and cross-infestation
GH14.19) The importance of personal hygiene
GH14.20) Why it is important to check electrical equipment used to aid the perming process
GH14.21) Methods of cleaning, disinfecting and/or sterilisation used in salons

Disulphide bridges

Reduction: Breaking disulphide bridges

Oxidation: Forming new disulphide bridges

Remember

Always bear in mind how your perm will affect the client's hair structure.

Maintain effective and safe methods of working when perming hair

Protect the client

Gowning

Because of the way that perms are generally applied to hair – by post-damping (where the lotion is applied and easily absorbed into previously wound sections of hair) – the solutions tend to be very watery and mobile. This, potentially, could be a hazard to the client unless you take adequate precautions. The majority of perm lotions are alkaline. If they drip or soak into textiles they will be held against the skin like a poultice. This is potentially very dangerous as it could cause irritation, swelling and even burns! This is also a problem if it does go onto the client's clothes as it may even discolour the fabrics to.

Make sure that you protect your client well so that this never happens. Put on a chemical-proof gown and secure into place, a clean, fresh towel around their shoulders. On top of this you should fix a plastic cape, ensuring that it is comfortable around the neck.

Barrier cream

After gowning, you can now apply the barrier cream to the hairline.

Protect yourself

Your salon must provide all the personal protective equipment (PPE) that you may need in routine daily practices. Perming involves the handling and application of chemicals, so this is one of those occasions where you must protect yourself from their caustic effects. Always read the manufacturer's instructions and follow the methods of practice that they specify. You are obliged to wear and use the PPE provided for you, these being disposable non-latex gloves, a waterproof apron and barrier cream.

The Control of Substances Hazardous to Health Regulations (COSHH) 2003 lay out the potential risks that hairdressing chemicals can have. You need to make yourself aware of the information provided by the manufacturers about their handling, storage and safe disposal. Generally, perm solutions should be stored in an upright position, in a cool, dry place away from strong sunlight. When they are used they should be applied in a well-ventilated area and if there is any waste (materials that cannot be saved and used another time) it should be disposed of by flushing down the basin with plenty of cold water.

For more information on work flow, work position, personal health and hygiene see Unit G20 (pages 6–21).

Remember

Barrier cream is a thick protective cream, ideally suited for wearing on your hands as an invisible coating to help prevent the action of chemicals causing you any harm.

It is equally important for the client. Barrier cream applied around the hairline will also help prevent the action of chemicals harming them during processing.

EKU statement

GH14.8) Your own responsibilities under the current Control of Substances Hazardous to Health Regulations in relation to the use of perming and neutralising products

EKU statement

GH14.4) Your salon's and legal requirements for disposal of waste materials
GH14.43) The importance of using products economically

Remember

Disposable gloves
Your salon will provide non-latex disposable gloves for your personal safety when you are handling any chemicals in the workplace. It is recommended that these are of the vinyl variety, only used once and then discarded. If your gloves tear or stretch during use change them immediately as their protection will be impaired.

Working effectively

Experienced hairdressers work in a way that makes the most out of the time available: they optimise the way in which they work. You need to learn the ways in which you can optimise your time and effort so that your work is both productive and effective. There are a number of ways that you can make this happen.

Minimise waste

Get into the habit of eliminating waste. All the resources that you use cost money and the only way that you can be more effective is to maximise your time and effort whilst minimising the cost of carrying out your work. This can be illustrated further by thinking about what goes down the sink. Water is the first thing that comes to mind; cold water is a costly but essential part of hairdressing. All business premises have metred water so, in principle, every shampoo and conditioning rinse can be a calculated cost. But sometimes people rinse far longer than they need to or leave taps running between shampoos and that's where the additional cost is incurred. This is made even worse if the water is hot! We know that cold water is metred, now we've got the additional cost of heating it too!

Maximise your time: always make good use of your time. There are always things to do in a hairdressing salon and most of them relate to preparation.

- Prepare the salon by cleaning work areas so that it is ready to receive the clients.
- Prepare the materials, look out for stock shortages and report them.
- Prepare the equipment, cleaning and washing the brushes, combs and curlers.
- Prepare client records, and get things ready for when they arrive.
- Prepare the trolleys, get the right curlers ready, make sure that the rubbers haven't perished and the end papers are at hand.

Activity
Minimising waste

How can you minimise wastage?

Have a look around your salon and see what things you can do to reduce the waste of resources.

Create a table for the information, recording what things you can find and how they could be used in the most effective way.

EKU *statement*

GH14.36) How the factors in the range can affect your choice of perming and neutralising products
GH14.38) The types of equipment used during the perm development process
GH14.39) The manufacturers' instructions for the specific perming and neutralising products in your salon
GH14.41) The different types and uses of available perm lotions and neutralisers

Types of perm

For the client a perm is a major step – they will have to live with the result for several months. They may not be familiar with the range of perming solutions available so you will need to explain what the differences are and what is involved in each.

Remember

Making the most out of the salon's resources should be second nature. Don't throw away what's left in the perm bottle after application. You can use the cold wave type perms another time.

Remember

Remove and dispose of waste items as soon as possible. Don't leave cotton neck wool, plastic caps etc. around at the basins. Put them into a covered bin. Wash, dry and replace perm curlers back into the trays as soon as possible.

EKU *statement*

GH14.10) What is contact dermatitis and how to avoid developing it whilst carrying out perming services (See Unit G20 page 14).

Remember

Dermatitis is an occupational hazard for hairdressers; you reduce the risk by wearing vinyl gloves when using chemicals. The gloves provide you with a guaranteed barrier against the action of harsh chemicals upon the skin.

For more information on dermatitis see Unit G20, page 14.

TRACEY DEVINE @ ANGELS

- Cold permanent wave solutions, such as L'Oréal's Dulcia or Synchrone, are mild alkaline perms. These types of perm are most widely available and simplest to use with applications for all hair types and tendencies and most conditions. These solutions tend to have a pH at around 9.5 so they are a fairly strong alkali that will swell the hair and affect around 20 per cent of the disulphide bridges. They reduce the natural moisture levels within the hair and are therefore better on normal to greasy hair types. They are particularly good for achieving strong, pronounced movement and curl and therefore create lasting effects that can withstand the high maintenance of regular blow-drying, setting etc.

- Acid wave solutions – such as Zotos's Acclaim – provide alternatives for perming when the hair is particularly delicate and needs to retain higher moisture levels or requires softer, gentler movement. They have lower pH values at around 6–7 and are therefore much gentler in the way that they work. They are suited to dryer, more porous hair types too. Acid perms are two-part solutions and require the components to be mixed together just before application so that the perm is self-activated. Any residual lotion left over after application will not last and must be discarded.

- Exothermic perming systems – such as Zotos's Warm and Gentle – tend to be similar to acid waves in their chemical composition and therefore can have similar benefits. The only difference is that these perms need heat to be activated and will self-generate this when the two chemical parts (*reagents*) are added together, without the need for accelerators or hood dryers.

GH14.2   Prepare for perming and neutralising hair

Remember

 Acid and exothermic perms require the mixing of parts A and B together before the perms are applied to the curlers. This starts a chemical reaction, enabling the perm to work on the hair. Make sure that you protect yourself and your client by wearing disposable gloves and an apron and applying barrier cream and moistened cotton wool around the client's hairline, so that any drips do not cause any irritation or burning of the skin. It is advisable to check that the client is comfortable during processing and, if necessary, change the cotton wool again with more moistened cotton wool.

Remember

Contra-indications for perming

 The following list indicates situations when perming should not be undertaken

- when the hair is particularly porous (possibly over-bleached)
- when the scalp has abrasions or sensitive areas
- when the hair is weakened, broken or damaged
- when the hair is inelastic (does not have any ability to stretch and return to same length)
- when incompatible chemicals have been used on the hair (Just for Men, Grecian 2000, compound henna etc.)
- when the hair has varying levels of porosity throughout the lengths (poorly coloured or lightened)
- when there is any evidence of physical or chemical changes on the hair or scalp and the client is unable to provide you with a full, satisfactory account of what actions have been taken
- when there is any evidence of scalp disease or disorder.

HAIR BY MOSKO, WISHAW, PHOTOGRAPHY BY JOHN RAWSON@TRP

Activity
Types of perm

Many clients are uncertain about the types of perms and the effects that they will achieve. This activity will review your knowledge about the different perm types and what is involved in each.

Complete the table below.

Type of perm	Features
Cold wave	
Acid wave	
Exothermic	

EKU *statement*

GH14.22) The importance of questioning clients to establish any contra-indications to perming services

Consultation

Find out your client's requirements – what they expect from perming – and determine whether this is the best solution bearing in mind the added maintenance, care and attention needed to achieve the desired effect.

- Consider the style and cut, together with your client's age and lifestyle.
- Examine the hair and scalp closely. If there are signs of inflammation, disease or cut or grazed skin, do not carry out a perm. If there is excessive grease or a coating of chemicals or lacquer you will need to remove these by washing with a pre-perm shampoo first. Previously treated hair will need special consideration.
- Analyse the hair texture, condition and porosity.
- Carry out the necessary tests to select the correct perm lotion.
- Always read manufacturer's instructions carefully.
- Determine the types of curl needed to achieve the chosen style.
- If this is a regular client, refer to the records for details of previous work done on their hair.
- Advise your client of the time and costs involved. Summarise what has been decided to be sure there aren't any misunderstandings.
- Minimise combing and brushing to avoid scratching the scalp before the perm.
- Update the client's treatment records for future reference.

Analysis/examination

It is important to make sure you choose the most suitable perm lotion, the correct processing time and the right type of curl for the chosen style. Consider the following factors.

- *Hair texture* – For hair of medium texture, use perm lotion of normal strength. Fine hair curls more easily and requires weaker lotion; coarser hair can often be more

HAIR BY MOSKO, WISHAW, PHOTOGRAPHY BY JOHN RAWSON@TRP

EKU *statement*

GH14.37) How and why the contra-indications in the range can affect the delivery of perming services

difficult to wave and may require a stronger lotion for resistant hair. (Although this is not true for oriental hair types.)

- *Hair porosity* – The porosity of the hair determines how quickly the perm lotion is absorbed. Porous hair in poor condition is likely to process more quickly than would hair with a resistant, smooth cuticle. See the section on pre-perming treatments later in this chapter.

- *Previous treatment history* – 'Virgin' hair – hair that has not previously been treated with chemicals – is likely to be more resistant to perming than hair that has been treated. It will require a stronger lotion and possibly a longer processing time.

- *Length and density of hair* – Longer heavier hair requires a tighter curl than shorter hair because the hair's weight will cause it to stretch. Short, fine hair may become too tightly curled if given the normal processing time.

- *Style* – Does the style you have chosen require firm curls or soft, loose waves? Do you simply wish to add body and bounce?

- *Size of rod, curler or other former* – Larger rods produce larger curls or waves; smaller rods produce tighter curls. Longer hair generally requires larger rods. If you use very small rods in fine, easy-to-perm hair, the hair may frizz; if you use rods that are too large you may not add enough curl. To check, make a test curl before you start (see hair tests, pages 428–429).

- *Incompatibility* – Perm lotions and other chemicals used on the hair may react with chemicals that have already been used – for example, in home-use products. Hair that looks dull may have been treated with such chemicals. Ask your client what products are used at home, and test for incompatibility.

What should you find out before you start?

First of all	Things to consider
Does the client know of any reasons that would affect your choice of service?	Ask the client about their hair to find out if there are any known reasons why the service can not continue – are there any contra-indications?
What type of perm would be best to suit their needs?	Should you be using a cold wave, acid or exothermic?
How can the desired effect be best achieved?	What type of wind should you use: conventional, brick, directional? What size curlers should you use, what curl or movement is required?
How long will it last?	Is perming suitable for the hair type, condition and texture?
How much will it cost?	Is perming a cost effective solution for the client?
How will it affect the hair?	Will the long-term effects be what the client expects?
Is the hair suitable for perming?	Have you tested the hair and skin beforehand to see if there are any contra-indications or hair condition issues that will affect the result?

Now consider

What are the client's expectations?	How will the perm enhance or support the style and the hair? What are the benefits for them?
What are the results of your tests?	Examine the hair: does it present any limitations for what you intend to do?
What is the hair condition like?	Are there any factors that will change the way in which perming will work on the hair?
	What previous information is available?
What do the client's records say?	Does this information influence the choice and perm process?
How will you show the effect to the client?	Have you got any illustrations of the finished effect?
How long will the process take?	Is there enough time to complete the effect? Has anything changed as a result of the consultation? Would this service now need to be rebooked or do you have the time to complete it still?

What contra-indications are you looking for?

Contra-indications are	How could you find out?	How else would you know?
Skin sensitivity	By asking the client if they have ever had a reaction to hair or skin products in the past	Patch test/sensitivity test
Allergic reaction	By asking the client if they have ever had a reaction to hair or skin products in the past	Patch test/sensitivity test
Skin disorder	Ask the client if they know about any current skin disorders	Examine the scalp to see if there are any physical signs of skin abrasions, discolouration, swellings, infestation or infections
Incompatible products	If you see the results of any previous colour ask what type it was, how was it done?	Look for discolouration or un-natural colour effects on the hair, test for incompatibles
Medical reasons	Ask the client if they are any current medical reasons why perming can not be performed	Examine the hair; look for signs of healthy active growth. If there are signs of weakened, damaged, broken or missing hair; ask for more information and test for elasticity and porosity

EKU *statement*

GH14.25) The types and purposes of tests

GH14.26) When and how tests should be carried out and the expected results

GH14.27) How the results of tests can influence the perming service

GH14.28) Potential consequences of failing to test the courses of action to take in the event of adverse reactions to tests (e.g. the type of reactions you need to report to another, more senior person)

GH14.29) Why it is important to record test results

Contra-indications are	How could you find out?	How else would you know?
Damaged hair	Ask the client if there are any current known reasons why the hair is in its current state/condition	Examine the hair; look for signs of healthy active growth. If there are signs of weakened, damaged, broken or missing hair; ask for more information and test for elasticity and porosity

Hair tests

- *Skin test* – The skin sensitivity test is used to assess the reaction of the skin to chemicals or chemical products. Some people are allergic to external contact of chemicals such as Ammonium thioglycolate which is found in perm solutions. This can cause dermatitis or, in more severe cases, burning, permanent scarring and even hair loss.

To find out whether a client's skin reacts to chemicals in permanent colours, the following test should be carried out at least 24 hours prior to the chemical process.

Note: Skin testing is not just for new clients, it has now been found that clients can develop sensitivity to chemicals through prolonged use of the same or similar products. Therefore periodic testing for adverse reactions is essential and should be carried out routinely from time to time.

1 Clean an area of skin about 8 mm square behind the ear or in the fold of the arm. Use a little spirit on cotton wool to remove the grease from the skin.

2 Apply a little of selected perm solution to a simple dressing and apply it to the prepared area of skin.

3 Ask your client to report any discomfort or irritation that occurs over the next 24 hours. Arrange to see your client at the end of this time so that you can check for signs for reaction.

4 If there is a *positive response*, i.e. a skin reaction such as inflammation, soreness, swelling, irritation or discomfort, do not carry out the intended service. Never ignore the result of a skin test. If a skin test showed a reaction and you carried on anyway, there may be a more serious reaction which could affect the whole body.

5 If there is a *negative response*, i.e. no reaction to the chemicals, then carry out the treatment as proposed.

Warning: In recent years there have been a growing number of successful personal injury claims made against salons where the necessary precautions have not been taken.

- *Elasticity test* – This tests the tensile strength of the hair. Hair in good condition has the ability to stretch and return to its original length, whereas hair in poor or damaged condition will stretch and will not return to original length. This lack of elasticity will make the hair difficult to manage and maintain. A clear indication for this would be to ask the client how long their set or blow-dry lasts after it has been done. When the styling drops or can't be sustained in the hair, it is a clear indication that the hair has lost this vital attribute of elasticity. Take a single hair

HAIR BY RICHARD WARD

strand and hold firmly at either end then stretch between your fingers. If it breaks easily the cortex may be damaged and perming could be harmful.

- *Porosity test* – The purpose of this test is to find out how well protected the inner cortex is by the cuticle layers. Porous hair has a damaged cuticle layer and readily absorbs moisture; this presents a problem when drying, as this hair takes longer to dry and often lacks the ability to hold a style well. This can be done by taking a small section of hair and sliding from the root, through to the points, between your fingertips. From this you can feel how rough or smooth it is. Rougher hair (as opposed to coarse hair) is likely to be more porous, and will therefore process more quickly.

- *Incompatibility test* – Hairdressing products are based upon organic chemistry formulations. These are incompatible with inorganic chemistry compositions and will cause damage to the client's hair. This test will identify whether metallic salts are present within the hair, a clear contra-indication that the perm may be carried out. Protect your hands by wearing disposable gloves. Place a small cutting of hair in a mixture of hydrogen peroxide and ammonium hydroxide. Watch for signs of bubbling, heating or discolouration: these indicate that the hair already contains incompatible chemicals. The hair should not be permed, nor should it be coloured or bleached. Perming treatment might discolour or break the hair, and might burn the skin.

- *Pre-perm test curl* – If you are unsure about how your client's hair will react under processing you could conduct a pre-perm test curl. Sometimes this can be done on the head and in other situations where there isn't sufficient time etc. you will need to cut your sample for testing. Wind, process and neutralise one or more small sections of hair. The results will be a guide to the optimum rod size, the processing time and the strength of lotion to be used. Remember, though, that the hair will not all be of the same porosity.

- *Development test curl* – This test is always carried out after the hair has been damped with perm solution and during the processing time. It will determine the stage of curl development so that the processing is not allowed to continue beyond the optimum. Unwind – and then rewind – rods during processing, to see how the curl is developing. If the salon is very hot or cold this will affect the progress of the perm: heat will accelerate it, cold will slow it down. When you have achieved the 'S' shape you want, stop the perm by rinsing and then neutralising the hair.

Recording the results

Make sure that you record the details of any test that you conduct. Update the client's record card in full and immediately after you have done the test. Don't leave it until later, you might forget! These records are essential information that will be needed again and help to show that a competent service has been provided at that time.

This would be vitally important if there was a problem at some later stage, particularly if it involved any legal action taken against the salon.

EKU *statement*

GH14.3) When and how to complete client records

GH14.23) Why it is important to record client responses to questioning

GH14.24) The legal significance of client questioning and the recording of clients' responses to questioning

GH14.30) Why it is important to record test results

Remember

Record the results
After any treatment or tests have been carried out always update the client's records immediately. These tests and the findings are critical to the client's well-being and the salon's good name. You should record the:

- date
- the test carried out
- development times
- results
- recommended home care or follow-up advice given.

Remember

Record the client's responses to your questions and the comments on how any tests affected their hair and skin.

Remember

Temperature has a major impact on perming. This could be general salon temperature or by added heat from a hood dryer. In either case remember that processing times will be *reduced* considerably.

EKU *statement*

GH14.40) When and why it is important to use pre-perm treatments

GH14.42) The types and uses of post-perm conditioners

Pre-perm and post-perm treatments

Matching the correct perm lotion to hair type is an essential part of the hair analysis. However, many perming solutions come in only a tinted, normal or resistant formula and this alone will not cater for all hair conditions. Dry, porous hair will absorb perming solutions more readily; therefore special attention needs to be given to it. Pre-perming treatments are a way to combat these conditioning issues. Porous hair that is suitable for perming will have an uneven porosity throughout the lengths. Hair that is nearer the root will have a different porosity level to that at mid-length hair, or that of the ends. Therefore the hair's porosity levels will need to be evened out, i.e. balanced before the perm lotion is applied. This enables the hair to absorb perm lotion at the same rate, evening out the development process and ensuring that the perm doesn't over-process in certain areas. A pre-perming treatment is applied before winding on damp hair and combed through to the ends. Any excess is removed and the hair is wound as normal.

After perming and neutralising it is also necessary to rebalance the hair's pH value back to that of 5.5. Post-perm treatments do this by removing any traces of residual oxygen from the neutralising process.

Activity

Hair tests

Complete this activity by filling in the missing information in the spaces provided

Type of test	What is the purpose of the test?	How is the test carried out?
Elasticity		
Porosity		
Incompatibility		
Development test curl		
Pre-perm test curl		

GH14.3 Perm and neutralise hair

Step-by-step: Perm preparation

1 Prepare your trolley. You will need:

- rods or curlers of the chosen sizes
- end papers, for use while winding
- a tail comb and clips, for sectioning and dividing
- cotton wool strips, to protect your client

- vinyl gloves, to protect your hands
- perm lotion and a suitable neutraliser/normaliser (read the instructions carefully)
- a water spray, to keep the hair damp
- a plastic cap and a timer for the processing stage.
- barrier cream for the hairline
- tensioning strips to bridge between curlers under the rubbers.

2 Protect your client with a gown and towels.

3 Shampoo the hair to remove grease or dirt with a pre-perming, soapless shampoo (failure to remove build-up of styling products could block the action of the perm lotion).

4 Towel-dry the hair. (Excess water dilutes the lotion, but if the hair is too dry the perm lotion won't spread evenly through the hair.)

5 If you are going to use a pre-perm lotion to help even out porosity apply it now. Make sure you have read the instructions carefully. Too much pre-perm lotion may block the action of the perm itself.

6 Check that your client's skin and clothing are adequately protected.

EKU *statement*

GH14.45) The factors that influence the use of different sized perm rods

GH14.47) Methods of application of perming lotions and neutralising agents

Winding techniques

Sectioning/sequence of winding

First of all divide the hair into workable sections. This makes the hair tidier, easier to control and looks professional. Done properly, sectioning makes the rest of the process simple and quick. If it's not done well, you will have to resection the hair during the perm, and this may spoil the overall result.

Step-by-step: Nine-section perm wind

1 Following shampooing and towel drying, comb the hair to remove any tangles.

2 Make sure you have the tools you will need, including a curler to check the width of the section size.

3 Now divide the hair into nine sections, as follows (use clips to secure the hair as you work): divide the hair from ear to ear to give front hair and back hair

- divide the back hair into lower, nape hair and upper top back hair
- divide the front hair, approximately above the mid-eyebrow, to give a middle and two sides
- divide the top section along the same lines, to give a middle and two sides
- divide the nape section likewise, to give a middle and two sides.

Sectioning nine-section wind

Once the hair has been divided into the nine sections and firmly secured with clips you can start to wind in the perm rods. The diagram on sectioning shows these sections, the numbering refers to the order in which the sections are wound. You start winding at the occipital area down the back of the head in an organised and controlled way.

Note. The sectioning techniques for perming can be adapted and used for many other techniques. For more information on directional and brick-type winds see the section on winding techniques below.

Remember

Note that the tension of the held section is even throughout. There is no slack or pulling from one side to the other.

Winding: Depth section

Winding: Width section

Six-section wind

The National Occupational Standards for hairdressing S/NVQ Level 2 require the learner to demonstrate the nine-section wind technique. There is another, quicker version of this that is more commonly used in salons and that is the six-section wind.

In the diagram on the previous page – the six-section winding technique amalgamates the zones 5 and 2, 4 and 1, and 6 and 3, to form only three rear panels at the back of the head. This means that the wind is started centrally, at the top rather than halfway down the back. This is easier to manage than the nine-section wind, although it will take a little more care in sectioning accurately.

Winding the rods into the hair

Winding is the process of placing sections of hair onto a variety of rods or curlers. There are various winding techniques, designed to produce different effects, but the method is basically the same in each case. In modern perming systems you need to wind the hair finely and evenly, but without stretching the hair or leaving it in tension.

Activity
Practise your winding

Practise winding a nine-section wind on wet hair on a modelling block. It should be dampened with water rather than perm lotion, as this gives you more time.

When you can do this regularly in around 30 minutes, you're ready for trying it for 'real' on a model.

Step-by-step: Winding

1 Divide off a section of hair, of a length and thickness to match the curler being used (see the diagram on the previous page).

2 Comb the hair firmly, directly away from the head. Keep the hair together, so that it doesn't slip.

3 Place the hair points at the centre of the curler. Make sure the hair isn't bunched at one side and loose at the other.

4 Hold the hair directly away from the head. If you let the hair slope downwards, the curler won't sit centrally on the base section: hair will overlap, and the curler will rest on the skin.

5 Before winding, make sure the curler is at an angle suited to the part of the head against which it will rest when wound.

6 Hold the hair points with the finger and thumb of one hand. The thumb should be uppermost.

7 Direct the hair points round and under the curler. Turn your wrist to achieve this. The aim is to lock the points under the curler and against the main body of hair – if they don't lock, they may become bucked or 'fish-hooked'. Don't turn the thumb too far round or the hair will be pushed away from the curler and won't lock the points.

8 After making the first turn of the curler; pass it to the other hand to make the next turn. The hands need to be in complete control: uncontrolled movement, or rocking from side to side, may cause the ends to slip, the hair to bunch or the firmness to slacken.

9 After two or three turns the points will be securely locked. Wind the curler down to the head. Keep the curler level – if it wobbles from side to side, the hair may slip off or the result may look uneven.

10 At the end, the curler should be in the centre of the section. If it isn't, unwind it and start again,

11 Secure the curler. Don't let the rubber fastener press into the hair – it might damage it.

EKU *statement*

GH14.44) When to use the types of sectioning techniques listed in the range and why

Remember

Wear gloves from the beginning. It is inconvenient to have to put them on later.

Before.

Make sure you have everything to hand.

Step 1–2 Divide the hair into nine secured sections or more conveniently, into six sections.

Step 3 Start at the top, take a section no wider or deeper than the curler being put in.

Step 4 Wind down the curler with even tension.

Step 5 Position the curler so that it sits upon its own base and doesn't impede the next curler's positioning.

Step 6 Continue down the back until all of the curlers have been placed, then move on to the sides.

Step 7 With the first back section wound, start the sides ensuring that the remainder hair on the top is no wider than the width of a curler.

Step 8 With the sides and back completed and bridging strips in place, finish off the top working forwards from the crown.

Step 9 Apply lightly dampened cotton wool around the hairline and then apply the perm lotion to each curler.

Step 10 Apply just enough lotion to each curler so they are moisturised but not saturated. Then a plastic cap can be placed around all of the curlers for the development process.

Step 11 Finished effect.

Activity
Winding techniques

Complete the chart below by explaining the effect on the hair for each of the listed winding techniques.

Draw diagrams or add pictures of the different winding techniques into the first column.

Technique	Effect that it has upon the hair
Nine-section wind	
Brick wind	
Directional wind	

Directional winding

Other techniques

There are various winding techniques, used to produce varied effects. The following are the most commonly used.

Directional winding The hair is wound in the direction in which it is to be finally worn. This technique is suitable for enhancing well-cut shapes. The hair can be wound in any direction required, and the technique is ideal for shorter hairstyles.

Brick winding The wound curlers are placed in a pattern resembling brickwork. By staggering the partings of the curlers, you avoid obvious gaps in the hair. This technique is suitable for short hairstyles.

Perming tools and equipment

- The pin-tail comb is useful for directing small pieces of hair onto the curler. The pin-tail comb is narrower than a plastic tail comb so you can guide the wound hair around the wound section to make sure that all the hair has an even tension.

- End papers or wraps are specially made for winding perms. Very few hairdressers would consider winding without them as they ensure control of the hair when it is wound. Fold them neatly over the hair points (never bundle them). The wrap overlaps the hair points and prevents fish-hooks. For smaller or shorter sections of hair, half an end wrap is sufficient – a full one would cause unevenness. Other types of tissue may absorb the perm lotion and interfere with processing, and these are best avoided.

- Many kinds of curler are suitable for perm winding. Plastic, wood and PVC foam are amongst the commonest materials used. The manufacturer uses different colours to indicate size. The greater the diameter or the fatter the curler, the bigger the wave or curl produced. The smallest curlers are used for short nape hair or for producing tight curls. Most curlers are of smaller diameter at the centre: this enables the thinner, gathered hair points to fill the concave part evenly and neatly as the hair is wound, widening out to the shoulder of the curler as you wind closer to the head.

Staggered or brick winding

WELLA

Weave winding

Activity

Try out different curlers, rods and winding shapes. Note the varied effects they produce. Practise the different curler positions for perming. Try these out on blocks or models to appreciate the differences. On a practise block, experiment with the effects produced by different incorrect forms of winding. This will help you to recognise and avoid these effects.

Spiral winding

Processing and development

Perm lotion may be applied before winding (pre-damping) or when winding is complete (post-damping). Pre-damping is often used on long hair to ensure the solution penetrates evenly through the hair length. When pre-damping, you have to work quickly to avoid over-processing the hair. Your work should be complete within 35 minutes. Follow the manufacturer's instructions on the type of application to use. Post-damping is perhaps more convenient as you can wind the hair without wearing gloves and the time taken in winding doesn't affect the overall processing time.

Applying the perm lotion

Most modern perming systems come in individually packed perm lotions, ready for application. Others may need to be dispensed from a litre-size bottle to a bowl, before applying to the wound head using cotton wool, a sponge or a brush.

- Underlying hair is often more resistant to perming (e.g. at the nape of the neck), so you could apply lotion to those areas first (see the diagram on sectioning on page 431).

Weave winding

Double winding

Piggyback winding

Stack winding

- Keep lotion away from the scalp. Apply it to the hair section, about 12 mm from the roots.
- If post-damping, apply a small amount of the perm lotion to each rod; do not over-saturate as the lotion will flood onto the scalp and will drip on to the client. This could cause either irritation or burning on the scalp or skin.
- It is better to apply the lotion again once the first application has started to absorb into the hair.
- Don't overload the applicator, and apply the lotion gently. You will be less likely then to splash your client.
- If you do splash the skin, quickly rinse the lotion away with water.

Processing time

Processing begins as soon as the perm lotion is in contact with the hair. The time needed for processing is critical. Processing time is affected by the hair texture and condition, the salon temperature and whether heat is applied, the size and number of curlers used and the type of winding used.

The perm needs to be checked during the development so that over-processing is avoided. The optimum processing ensures that the curl is maximised whilst there is no detrimental effect to the hair condition.

The figure below shows two intersecting lines; both have a time element, but each one has a different resultant effect. The green line has an increase in curl development over time, where the red line has a decrease in hair condition/damage over time. Ideally, where the two lines cross; it will denote the optimum perm processing. At this point a curl development check will show a good 'S' movement without loss of essential hair moisture/ and subsequent impaired condition.

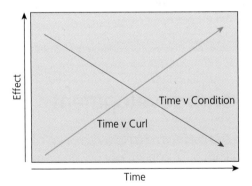

Hair texture and condition Fine hair processes more quickly than coarse hair and dry hair more than greasy hair. Hair that has been processed previously will perm faster than virgin hair.

Temperature A warm salon cuts down processing time; in a cold salon it will take longer. Even a draught will affect the time required. Usually the heat from the head itself is enough to activate perming systems. Wrap your client's head with plastic cap to keep in the heat. Don't wrap the hair in towels: these will absorb the lotion and slow down the processing.

Some perm lotions require additional heat from computerised accelerators, roller balls or dryers. Don't apply heat unless the manufacturer's instructions tell you to – you might damage both the hair and the scalp. And don't apply heat unless the hair is wrapped; the heat could evaporate the lotion or speed up the processing too much.

Curlers Processing will be quicker with a lot of small sections on small curlers than with large sections on large curlers. (The large sections will also give looser results.)

Winding The type of winding used, and the tension applied, can also affect processing time. Hair wound firmly processes faster than hair wound slackly – in fact, if the winding is too slack it will not process at all. Hair wound too tightly may break close to the scalp. The optimum is a firm winding without tension.

Development test curl This involves testing the curl during processing. As processing time is so critical, you need to use a timer. You also need to check the perm at intervals to see how it's progressing. If you used the pre-damping technique, check the first and last curlers that you wound. If you applied the lotion after winding, check curlers from the front, sides, crown and nape.

- Unwind the hair from a curler. Is the 's' shape produced correct for the size of curler used?
- If the curl is too loose, rewind the hair and allow more processing time. (But if the test curl is too loose because the curler was too large, extra processing time will damage the hair and won't make the curl tighter.)
- If the curl is correct, stop the processing by rinsing.

Remember

Health and safety
Don't pack curlers with dry cotton wool. This absorbs the perm lotion; it also keeps it in direct contact with the skin, causing irritation.

Remember to use a barrier cream across the hairline. Don't let barrier cream get on the hair, however, as it will prevent the lotion from penetrating into the hair.

EKU *statement*

GH14.32) How temperature affects the perming process

EKU *statement*

GH14.46) Method of checking curl development

Activity

Preparing and planning for perming

Making the right preparations and taking appropriate action is an essential part of any hairdressing service. Complete the table below to review this chapter.

Task	How do you do this?	Why do you do this?
Prepare materials		
Prepare the client		
Prepare yourself		
Update records		

Remember

Health and safety
Take care not to splash your client's face while rinsing. Even dilute perm lotion can irritate the skin. If perm lotion enters the client's eye, flush out immediately with cold running water. Ensure the water drains downwards away from the face. Seek help from a qualified first aider.

EKU statement

GH14.16) The safety considerations which must be taken into account when perming and neutralising

Remember

Read labels and check contents of boxes – before use.

EKU statement

GH14.34) The importance and effects of restoring the hair's pH balance after the perming and neutralising process

EKU statement

GH14.35) The importance of considering water temperature during the neutralising process

Neutralising

Introduction

The successful outcome of a perm is dependent on the correct processing and the way the hair is rebalanced during the action of neutralising.

In this section we will look at:

- the principles of neutralising perms
- how neutralising works
- choosing a neutraliser
- neutralising techniques
- what to do after perming.

Rebalancing the hair

Neutralising is the process of fixing the curl or movement into the hair, whilst returning the hair back to a balanced chemical state. An industry term, 'neutralising' is a little misleading. In chemistry, a 'neutral' chemical condition is neither acidic nor alkaline (pH 7.0).

Conversely', during the hairdressing treatment of 'neutralising', the previously processed hair is returned to the skin's healthy, slightly acidic natural state of pH 4.5–5.5. Rebalancing the pH value of the hair is essential for maintaining hair in good condition, if the hair is not rebalanced the hair will be dry, porous and the perm will be very difficult to manage afterwards.

How neutralising works

As described earlier, perm lotion acts on the keratin in the hair. The strongest bonds between the polypeptides are the disulphide bridges. Perm lotion breaks some of these, allowing the keratin to take up a new shape. This is how new curls can form.

What neutralising does is to make new disulphide bridges. If you didn't neutralise the hair it would be weak and likely to break, and the new curls would soon fall out. Neutralising is an oxidation process – a process that uses oxidising agents such as hydrogen peroxide, sodium bromate and sodium perborate.

Choosing a neutraliser

Manufacturers of perm lotions usually produce matching neutralisers. These are designed to work together. Always use the neutraliser that matches the perm lotion you've used. As most perms are individually packed you will find a perm lotion and its matched neutraliser in the box.

A neutraliser may be supplied as an emulsion cream, a foam or a liquid. Always follow the manufacturer's instructions. Some can be applied directly from the container, others are applied with a sponge or a brush.

Neutralising technique

Neutralising follows directly on from perming. Imagine that you have shampooed, dried and wound the hair. The hair is now perming, and you are timing the perm carefully and making tests to check whether it is complete. You will also be reassuring the client that they have not been forgotten! As soon as the perm is finished, you need to be ready to stop the process immediately.

Preparation

1 Gather together the materials you will need.

2 Make sure there is a back wash basin free. (This makes it easier for you to keep chemicals away from the client's eyes.)

First rinsing

1 As soon as the perm is complete, move your client immediately to the back wash basin. Make sure they are comfortable.

2 Carefully remove the cap. The hair is in a soft and weak stage at this point, so don't put unnecessary tension on it. Leave the curlers in place.

3 Run the water. You need an even supply of warm water. The water must be neither hot nor cold as this will be uncomfortable for the client. Hot water will also irritate the scalp and could burn. Check the pressure and temperature against the back of your hand. Remember that your client's head may be sensitive after the perming process.

4 Rinse the hair thoroughly with the warm water. This may take about five minutes or longer if the hair is long. It is this rinsing that stops the perm process – until you rinse away the lotion, the hair will still be processing. Direct the water away from the eyes and the face. Make sure you rinse *all* the hair, including the nape curlers. If a curler slips out, gently wind the hair back onto it immediately.

Applying neutraliser

1 Make sure your client is in a comfortable sitting position.

2 Blot the hair thoroughly using a towel (you may need more than one). It may help if you pack the curlers with cotton wool.

3 When no surplus water remains, apply the neutraliser. Follow the manufacturer's instructions. These may tell you to pour the neutraliser through the hair, or apply it with a brush or sponge, or use the spiked applicator bottle. Some foam neutralisers need to be pushed briskly into the hair. Make sure that neutraliser comes into contact with all of the hair on the curlers.

4 When all the hair has been covered, time the process according to the instructions. The usual time is five to ten minutes. You may wrap the hair in a towel or leave it open to the air – follow the manufacturer's instructions.

5 Gently and carefully remove the curlers. Don't pull or stretch the hair. It may still be soft, especially towards the ends, and you don't want to disturb the curl formation.

6 Apply the neutraliser to the hair again, covering all the hair. Arrange the hair so that the neutraliser does not run over the face. Leave for the time recommended, perhaps another five to ten minutes.

Second rinsing

1 Run the water, again checking temperature and pressure.

2 Rinse the hair thoroughly to remove the neutraliser.

Remember

 When applying a conditioner apply to the palms of the hands first and gently work the conditioner through the hair. Do not massage the scalp or pull or comb the hair as it may soften the newly formed curl.

3 You can now treat the hair with an after-perm (anti-oxidant) or conditioner. Use the one recommended by the manufacturer of the perm and neutraliser, to be sure that the chemicals are compatible.

Perm aids or conditioner and balanced conditioners (anti-oxidants) help neutralise the effect of the chemical process by helping to restore the pH balance of the hair to pH 4.4–5.5 and smooth down the hair cuticle improving the hair's look, feel, comb-ability and handling.

After neutralising

At the end of the neutralising process, you will have returned the hair to a normal, stable state.

- The reduction and oxidation processes will have been completed.
- The hair will now be slightly weaker – fewer bonds will have formed than were broken by the perm.
- Record any hair or perm faults on the client's record card. Correct faults as appropriate.
- Under-neutralising – not leaving neutraliser on for long enough – results in a slack curls or waves.
- Over-oxidising – leaving the neutraliser on too long or using oxidants that are too strong – results in weak hair and poor curl.

The hair should be ready for shaping, blow-drying or setting.

After the perm

1 Check the results of perming.

- Has the scalp been irritated by the perm lotion?
- Is the hair in good condition?
- Is the curl even?

2 Dry the hair into style.

- Depending on the effect you want, you may now use finger-drying, hood-drying or blow-drying technique.
- Treat the hair gently as the hair may take a few washes to settle in. If you handle it too firmly the perm may relax again.

3 Advise the client on how to manage the perm at home.

- The hair should not be shampooed for a day or two.
- The manufacturer of the perm lotion may have supplied information to be passed to the client
- Discuss general hair care with your client.

4 Clean all tools thoroughly so that they are ready for the next client.

5 Complete the client's record card.

- Note details of the type of perm, the strength of the lotion, the processing time, the curler sizes and the winding technique.
- Record any problems you have had. This information will be useful if the hair is permed again.

EKU *statement*

GH14.5) Your own limits of authority for resolving perming and neutralising problems

GH14.6) The person to whom you should report problems you cannot resolve

GH14.48) Types and causes of problems that can occur during the perming and neutralising processes

GH14.49) Methods of resolving perming problems

Fault	Action now	Possible cause	In future
The perm is slow to process	Increase warmth but do not dry out; check the winding tension and the number of curlers	Winding was too loose	Wind more firmly or use smaller curlers
		The curlers were large, or too few were used	Use smaller curlers and more of them
		The wrong lotion was used	Double-check labels on bottles
		The sections were too large	Take smaller sections
		The salon is too cold	The temperature should be comfortable
		Lotion was absorbed from the hair	Don't leave cotton wool on the hair
		Too little lotion was used	Don't skimp on the lotion or miss sections
The scalp is tender, sore or broken	Seek advice from a qualified first aider	The curlers were too tight	Don't apply too much tension when winding
		The wound curlers rested on the skin	Curlers should rest on the hair
		Lotion was spilt on the scalp	Keep lotion away from the scalp
		There was cotton wool padding soaked with perm lotion between the curlers	Renew the cotton wool as necessary or don't use it
		The hair was pulled tightly	Don't overstretch it
		The perm was over-processed	Time perms accurately
There are straight points or roots	Re-perm, if the hair condition permits*	The curlers or sections were too large	Take sections no longer or wider than the curler used
		Sections were overlooked	Check that all hair has been wound
		Too few curlers were used	Put curlers closer together
		The winding was too loose	Be a little firmer next time
		Lotion was applied unevenly	Take care to apply it evenly
There are fish-hooks	Remove by trimming the ends	The hair points were not cleanly wound	Comb the hair cleanly
		The hair points were bent or buckled	Place hair sections evenly on to the curlers
		The hair was wrapped unevenly in the end papers	Curl from the hair points
		Winding aids were used incorrectly	Take more care; practise winding

Fault	Action now	Possible cause	In future
Hair is broken	Nothing can be done about the broken hair. After discussion with your senior or trainer, condition the remaining hair	The hair was wound too tightly	Wind more loosely next time
		The curlers were secured too tightly	Secure them more loosely next time
		The curler band cut into the hair base	Keep it away from the hair base
		The hair was over-processed	Follow the instructions more carefully
		Chemicals in the hair reacted with the lotion	Test for incompatibility beforehand
The hair is straight	Re-perm, if the hair condition permits*	The wrong lotion was used for hair of this texture	Choose the lotion more carefully
		The hair was under-processed	Time perms accurately
		The curlers were too large for the hair length	Measure the curlers beforehand
		The neutralising was incorrectly done	Follow the instructions more carefully
		Rinsing was inadequate	Rinse more thoroughly
		Conditioners used before perming were still on the hair	Prepare the hair more carefully
		The hair was coated and resistant to the lotion	Check for substances that block the action of perm lotion, shampoo if necessary
The hair is frizzy	Cut the ends to reduce the frizziness	The lotion was too strong for hair of this texture	Assess texture correctly; select suitable lotions; read manufacturer's instructions
		The winding was too tight	Practise and experiment to avoid this
		The curlers were too small	Choose more suitable curlers
		The hair was over-processed	Time perms accurately
		The neutralising was incorrectly done	Follow the instructions more carefully
		There are fish-hooks	Avoid bending hair points when winding
The perm is weak and drops**	Re-perm, if the hair condition permits*	Lotion was applied unevenly	Apply lotion more evenly
		The neutraliser was dilute	Follow the instructions more carefully
		Neutralising was poorly done	Be more careful
		The hair was stretched while soft	Handle the hair gently
		The curlers or sections were too large	Use more curlers

Fault	Action now	Possible cause	In future
Some hair sections are straight	Re-perm if the hair condition permits*	The curler angle was wrong	Wind correctly
		The curlers were placed incorrectly	Wind correctly
		The curlers were too large	Use smaller curlers
		Sectioning or winding was done carelessly	Practise before perming again
		Perm lotion or neutraliser was not applied correctly	Make sure that all curlers get the correct application of chemicals
The hair is discoloured		Metallic elements or compounds present	Test for incompatibility
Unknown/ unexpected result	Seek assistance from a senior operator/follow their instructions		Learn from this experience and modify your process accordingly

* Don't re-perm the hair unless its condition is suitable. For example, you should not re-perm if the hair is over-processed. Conditioning treatments and/or cutting may help. Discuss the problem with a senior or your trainer.

** Before attempting to correct this fault make sure that the hair is not over-processed. Dampen the hair to see how much perm there is.

EKU *statement*

GH14.50) Products for home use that will benefit the client and those to avoid and why

GH14.51) How the continual use of heated equipment can affect permed hair

GH14.52) Recommended time intervals between perming and other services

GH14.53) How lifestyle factors can affect the hair (e.g. swimming, time necessary for hair maintenance)

GH14.54) How perming can affect other services (e.g. the need for regular cutting, effect on colour services)

GH14.55) How to give effective advice and recommendations to clients

GH14.4   Provide aftercare advice

Clients need your help to look after their hair at home, you need to give them the right advice so that they can make the most of their new perm and style between visits.

Remember to tell them how a new perm needs particular care in the way that it is handled and that stretching during styling will weaken the result and could even cause the perm to fail prematurely.

You should tell them what sorts of products that they could use that would benefit the condition and manageability of their hair. You should also make a point of telling them what they should avoid, as some products will work against the new perm.

Explain the benefits of maintaining their hair in good condition, as hair in good condition is easier to manage, it lasts longer, looks better and is noticeable to everyone else as well.

Finally, if you would like to see more information on aftercare advice, see Units GH8 Shampoo, condition and treat the hair and scalp (pages 168–169), and GH12 Cut hair using basic techniques (pages 300–301).

RAE PALMER FOR SCHWARZKOPF

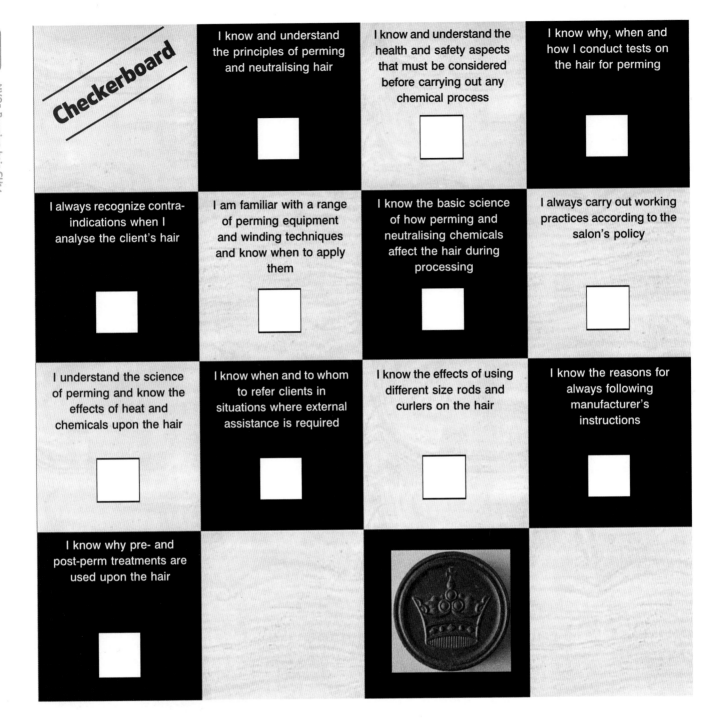

Checkerboard

I know and understand the principles of perming and neutralising hair

I know and understand the health and safety aspects that must be considered before carrying out any chemical process

I know why, when and how I conduct tests on the hair for perming

I always recognize contra-indications when I analyse the client's hair

I am familiar with a range of perming equipment and winding techniques and know when to apply them

I know the basic science of how perming and neutralising chemicals affect the hair during processing

I always carry out working practices according to the salon's policy

I understand the science of perming and know the effects of heat and chemicals upon the hair

I know when and to whom to refer clients in situations where external assistance is required

I know the effects of using different size rods and curlers on the hair

I know the reasons for always following manufacturer's instructions

I know why pre- and post-perm treatments are used upon the hair

Assessment of knowledge and understanding

Project 1

For this project you will need to collect and test a range of hair samples.

Over a period of time, collect and fix together a variety of different hair samples.

You will need to create three batches of:

- grey/white hair
- coloured hair
- double processed hair
- bleached hair
- previously permed hair
- natural virgin hair.

For each type, record the differences in tendency, texture and condition.

Use a little perm lotion in each scenario.

1   Perm your first batch of samples with the correct/matched lotion for the correct length of development time with a medium size curler.

2   After you have rinsed and neutralised each one, note any changes in tendency, texture and condition in your portfolio.

3   Repeat the process again with a second batch of samples using:

- tinted lotion on the grey/white hair
- normal lotion on the tinted, bleached and double processed hair
- resistant lotion on the previously permed and virgin hair.

Now record your findings again after over-processing the samples and see the differences.

Note: Keep your third batch for a later project with neutralising.

Project 2

Use the remainder of your hair samples from project 1. Perm them and prepare them, ready for neutralising.

Try out different ways of neutralising. Note the different effects produced and record them for your portfolio. Carry out this project in the following ways:

1   Without rinsing the hair sample, apply the neutraliser and time as directed by the instructions. What are the effects produced when the hair is still wet and the effects when it has been dried?

2   Using another permed hair sample, rinse the hair but do not apply any neutraliser. What are the effects produced when the hair is still wet and the effects when it has been dried?

3   On the third sample, leave out both rinsing and neutralising phases. What are the effects produced when the hair is still wet and the effects when it has been dried?

4   Rinse and neutralise the fourth sample as directed by the perm manufacturer. What are the effects produced when the hair is still wet and the effects when it has been dried?

5   Retain these samples and compare the results when the hair has dried out. Then check again after 12, 24 and 48 hours.

6   List and try out different types of neutraliser, with varying times of application. Compare the results.

7   Repeat these experiments using hair of different textures. Make sure that you have a correctly permed and neutralised sample with which to compare your results.

Revision questions

A selection of different types of questions to check your knowledge.

Q1   A development test _____ will identify when optimum movement is achieved.

Fill in the blank

Q2   Cold wave perms are usually post-damped.

True or false

Q3   Which of the following factors are likely to be affected by perming?

Multi selection

Elasticity	☐ 1
Natural colour	☐ 2
Thickness	☐ 3
Texture	☐ 4
Porosity	☐ 5
Abundance	☐ 6

Q4   Neutralisers contain hydrogen peroxide.

True or false

Q5   Which of the following chemical bonds are permanently rearranged during perming?

Multi choice

Salt bonds	○ a
Hydrogen bonds	○ b
Disulphide bonds	○ c
Oxygen bonds	○ d

Q6   Time and temperature have a direct impact upon perm development.

True or false

Q7   Which of the following tests are *not* applicable to perming?

Multi selection

Strand test	☐ 1
Incompatibility test	☐ 2
Peroxide test	☐ 3
Porosity test	☐ 4
Elasticity test	☐ 5
Skin test	☐ 6

Q8   The rearrangement of chemical bonds takes place within the _____.

Fill in the blank

Q9   The chemical compound responsible for modifying the hair's structure during perming is?

Multi choice

Hydrogen peroxide	○ a
Ammonium hydroxide	○ b
Ammonium thioglycolate	○ c
Sodium perborate	○ d

Q10   Smaller perming rods produce tighter curl effects.

True or false

Preparing for assessment checklist

Remember to:

✔	prepare clients correctly for the services you are going to carry out
✔	check the results of any tests that have been undertaken
✔	put on the protective wear available for perming and neutralising
✔	listen to the client's requirements and discuss suitable courses of action
✔	adhere to the safety factors when working on client's hair
✔	keep the work areas clean, hygienic and free from hazards
✔	promote the range of services, products and treatments within the salon
✔	clean and sterilise the tools and equipment before they are used
✔	apply the science aspects you have learnt relating to perming and neutralising hair
✔	work carefully and methodically through the chemical processes
✔	time the development of any chemical processes carefully
✔	communicate what you are doing with the client as well as your fellow staff members
✔	record the processes in the client's treatment history.

KEN PICTON@KEN PICTON

Appendix 1 Health and safety legislation

This section will provide you with an outline of the main health and safety regulations that affect hairdressers and their work. The Health and Safety at Work Act 1974 is the legislation that covers a variety of safe working practices and associated regulations. You do not need to know the contents of this Act, but you should at least be aware of the existence of relevant regulations made under its provisions. They cover the following aspects at work:

- management of safety at work (assessing risk in the workplace)
- safe equipment and systems of work
- protective equipment
- handling chemicals and substances
- electricity
- first aid
- handling and moving objects
- fire precautions.

HSE information Go online for more information at www.hse.gov.uk and www.hsedirect.gov.uk

COSHH A brief guide to the regulations

What you need to know about the Control of Substances Hazardous to Health Regulations 2002 (COSHH): INDG136(rev3) is available free as a single copy (from HSE books and on the www.hse.gov.uk website), or in priced packs of ten (ISBN 0 7176 2982 1) for £5.00.

The Management of Health and Safety at Work Regulations 1999

The main regulation requires the employer to appoint competent personnel to conduct risk assessments for the health and safety of all staff working on the premises as well as other visitors to the business premises. Staff must be adequately trained to take appropriate action, eliminate or minimise any risks. Other regulations cover the necessity to set up procedures for emergency situations, reviewing the risk assessment processes. In salons where five or more people are employed, there is the added obligation to set up a system for monitoring health surveillance, should the risk assessments identify a need.

The main requirements for management of health and safety are:

- identify any potential hazards
- assessing the risks which could arise from these hazards identifying who is at risk

- eliminating or minimising the risks
- training staff to identify and control risks
- regular reviewing of the assessment processes.

Young workers at risk

There is also a requirement to carry out a risk assessment for young people. Any staff member who is under school-leaving age must have a personalised risk assessment kept on file. This would be applicable for those on work experience or Saturday staff.

- Easy online steps to control health risks from chemicals
- COSHH Essentials has been developed to help firms comply with the COSHH regulations. The COSHH Essentials Website is easy to use and is available free as part of hsedirect – a database of all health and safety legislation and HSE's priced guidance (http://www.coshhessentials.org.uk/).

The Workplace (Health, Safety and Welfare) Regulations 1992

These regulations supersede the Offices, Shops and Railway Premises Act 1963 (OSRPA) and cover the following workplace key points:

- maintenance of the workplace and the equipment in it
- ventilation, temperature and lighting
- cleanliness
- sanitary and washing facilities
- drinking water supply
- rest, eating and changing facilities
- storage of clothing
- glazing
- traffic routes
- work space.

Amendments and additions in this regulation provide new requirements for employers with particular attention for glazed areas such as windows and doors etc. Any transparent and translucent partitions must be made of safe materials and if they could cause injury to anyone, they should be appropriately marked. Other amendments have particular rules for rest rooms and rest areas. These must include suitable alternative arrangements to protect non-smokers from the effects caused by tobacco smoke and suitable rest facilities for any person at work who is either pregnant or a nursing mother.

The Health and Safety (First-Aid) Regulations 1981

The Health and Safety (First-Aid) Regulations 1981 require the employer to provide adequate and appropriate equipment, facilities and personnel to enable first aid to be given to their employees if they are injured or become ill at work.

The minimum first-aid provision on any work site is:

- a suitably stocked first-aid box
- an appointed person to take charge of first-aid arrangements

It is also important to remember that accidents can happen at any time. *First-aid* provision needs to be available at all times people are at work.

The Personal Protective Equipment (PPE) at Work Regulations 1992

These relate to the requirement of employers to provide suitable and sufficient protective clothing and equipment for all employees to use. The PPE Regulations 1992 require managers to make an assessment of the processes and activities carried out at work and to identify where and when special items of clothing should be worn. In hairdressing environments, the potential hazards and dangers revolve around the task of providing hairdressing services – that is, in general, the application of hairdressing treatments and associated products.

Potentially hazardous substances used by hairdressers include:

- acidic solutions of varying strengths
- caustic alkaline solutions of varying strengths
- flammable liquids, which are often in pressurised containers, vapours and dyeing compounds.

There are also potentially hazardous items of equipment and their individual applications, such as:

- electrical appliances
- heated/heating instruments
- sharp cutting tools.

All these items require correct handling and safe usage procedures, and for several of them this includes the wearing of suitable items of protective equipment.

Control of Substances Hazardous to Health Regulations 2003 (COSHH)

Hairdressing employers are required by law to make an assessment of the exposure to all the substances used in their salon that could be potentially hazardous to themselves, their employees and other salon visitors, who may be affected by the work activity. The purpose of COSHH regulations is to make sure that people are working in the safest possible environment and conditions.

A substance is considered to be hazardous if it can cause harm to the body. It only presents a risk if it is:

- in contact with the skin or eyes
- absorbed through the skin or via the eyes (either directly or from contact with contaminated surfaces or clothing)
- inhaled (breathed in from the atmosphere)
- ingested via contaminated food or fingers
- injected
- introduced to the body via cuts and abrasions.

Cosmetic Products (Safety) Regulations 1989

These regulations lay down the recommended volumes and percentage strengths of different hydrogen-based products. The strength will vary depending on whether it has been produced for professional or non-professional use. It is important that the manufacturer's guidance material and current legislation is checked when using or selling products.

Health and Safety (Information for Employees) Regulations 1989

The regulation requires the employer to make available to all employees, notices, posters and leaflets either in the approved format or those actually published by the HSE.

The Health and Safety (Display Screen Equipment) Regulations 1992

These regulations cover the use of computers and similar equipment in the workplace. Although not generally a high risk, prolonged use can lead to eye strain, mental stress and possible muscular pain. As more hairdressing salons use information technology and computers this is becoming a major consideration for hairdressing employees.

It is the employer's duty to assess display screen equipment and reduce the risks that are discovered. They will need to plan the scheduling of work so that there are regular breaks or changes in activity and provide information training for the equipment users. Computer users will also be entitled to eyesight tests which will be paid for by the employer.

Manual Handling Operations Regulations 1992

These regulations apply in all occupations where manual lifting occurs. They require employers to carry out a risk assessment of the work processes and activities that involve lifting. The risk assessment should address detailed aspects of the following:

- any risk of injury
- the manual movement that is involved in the task
- the physical constraints the loads incur
- the work environmental constraints that are incurred
- the worker's individual capabilities
- steps and/or remedial action to take in order to minimise the risk.

Provision and Use of Work Equipment Regulations (PUWER) 1998

These regulations refer to the regular maintenance and monitoring of work equipment. Any equipment, new or second-hand, must be suitable for the purpose that it is intended. In addition to this they require that anyone using this equipment must be adequately trained.

Electricity at Work Regulations 1989

This requires employers to maintain electrical equipment in a safe condition and to have them checked by a suitably qualified person. A written record of testing must be kept and made available for inspection. It is the employees' responsibility for reporting any known faulty equipment to their employer or supervisor. The following information must be kept:

- the electrician's/contractors name, address, contact details

- an itemised list of salon electrical equipment along with serial number (for individual identification)
- the date of inspection
- the date of purchase/disposal.

The Reporting of Injuries, Diseases and Dangerous Occurrences Regulations 1995 (RIDDOR)

Under these regulations there are certain diseases and groups of infections that, if sustained at work, are noticeable by law. So if any employees suffer a personal injury at work which results in one of the following:

- death
- major injuries including; fractures, (not fingers and toes) amputation, dislocation, loss of sight and other eye injuries
- more than 24 hours in hospital
- an incapacity to work for more than three calendar days

they must be reported to the appropriate authority.

Appendix 2 Infections, accidents and emergencies

Preventing infection

A warm, humid salon can offer a perfect home for disease-carrying bacteria. If they can find food in the form of dust and dirt, they may reproduce rapidly. Good ventilation, however, provides a circulating air current that will help to prevent their growth. This is why it is important to keep the salon clean, dry and well aired at all times – and this includes clothing, work areas, tools and all equipment.

Some salons use sterilising devices as a means of providing hygienically safe work implements. 'Sterilisation' means the complete eradication of living organisms. Different devices use different sterilisation methods, which may be based on the use of heat, radiation or chemicals.

Chemical sterilisation/disinfection

Chemical sterilisers are widely used within salons and you should only handle them when wearing gloves. These solutions are hazardous to health and should not come into contact with the skin. The most effective form of sterilisation is achieved by the total immersion of the contaminated implements into a bath of fluid. This is how babies' feeding utensils are usually sterilised.

Disinfectants reduce the probability of infection and are widely used in general day-to-day hygienic salon maintenance. Antiseptics are used specifically for treating wounds. Many pre-packaged first-aid dressings are impregnated with antiseptic fluids.

All tools must be cleaned to remove visible debris prior to sterilisation/disinfecting.

Ultraviolet radiation

Ultraviolet (UV) radiation cabinets may be utilised to store previously sterilised or disinfected tools and equipment.

Autoclaves

The autoclave provides a very efficient way of sterilising using heat. It is particularly good for metal tools although the high temperatures are not suitable for plastics such as brushes and combs. Items placed in the autoclave take around 20 mins to sterilise. (Check with manufacturer instructions for variations.) Autoclaves must be regularly checked by a competent person under the Pressure Systems Safety Regulations 2000.

Fire

Fires occurring in salons are more likely to arise from electrical faults, gas leaks, or smoking. Faulty or badly maintained electrical equipment, such as hand dryers or hood dryers, may malfunction and overheat, and even ignite! Gas appliances, such as ovens or hobs, present a possible risk if they are left unattended. Staff cooking facilities need to be closely monitored to prevent gas being left on, whether lit or not. Your salon will have set fire safety procedures, which must always be followed.

Your salon premises will have been assessed for fire risk and a written policy will exist, if five or more people are employed there. The fire risk assessment will take into account all other people on the premises, clients and visitors as well as other entities on a shared occupancy basis, if other firms occupy other parts of the building.

Emergency evacuation

All premises must have a designated means of escape from fire. This route must be kept clear of obstructions at all times and during working hours the fire doors must remain unlocked. The escape route must be easily identifiable, with clearly visible signs. In buildings with fire certificates, emergency lighting must be installed. These lighting systems automatically illuminate the escape route in the event of a power failure and are operated by an independent battery back-up.

In the event of fire breaking out the main consideration is to get everybody out:

- *Raising the alarm* – Anyone discovering a fire must immediately raise the alarm by operating the nearest alarm. Staff and customers must be warned, and the premises must be evacuated.
- *On hearing the alarm* – All people must exit the building via the designated fire exits and proceed to the designated assembly point. Doors should be closed on exiting the building and designated staff may assist the less able.
- *Assembly point(s)* – Everyone must remain at the assembly point, away from danger whilst awaiting further instruction.
- *Call the fire brigade* – After exiting the building, call the emergency services. Dial 999, ask the operator for the fire service, and give your telephone/mobile number. Wait for the transfer to the fire service and then tell them your name and the address of the premises that are on fire. Do this even if you believe that someone else has already phoned.

Firefighting

Under the Regulatory Reform (Fire Safety) Order 2005, all premises are required to have firefighting equipment, which must be suitably maintained in good working order. However, *only* those people with adequate training can attempt to put a fire out.

Extinguisher	Type	Colour	Used on	Must not be used on
Non-electrical fires	Water	Red marking	wood, paper and textiles and other similar materials	burning liquids and flammable metal fires
	Foam	Cream marking	burning liquids	electrical fires or flammable metal fires
	Chemical	Yellow marking	wood, paper, cooking oils, fats and other organic solids	electrical fires or flammable metal fires
Electrical fires	Dry Powder	Blue marking	burning liquid, electrical fires and flammable liquids	flammable metal fires
	Carbon dioxide	Black marking	Safe on electrical fires and burning and flammable liquids	flammable metal fires
	Vaporising liquids	Green marking	Safe on electrical fires and burning and flammable liquids	flammable metal fires

Fire safety training

It is essential for staff to know the following fire procedures:

- fire prevention
- raising the alarm

- evacuation during a fire
- assembly points following evacuation.

Training is given to new members of staff during their induction period. This training must be regularly updated for all staff, and fire drills must be held at regular intervals.

Accidents (first aid)

The Health and Safety (First Aid) Regulations 1981 require the employer to provide equipment and facilities which are adequate and appropriate for providing first aid. In the event of an accident the 'Appointed Person' should be notified. This person takes control in these situations and will, if necessary, call an ambulance. There is also an appointed first aider who is qualified to administer first aid within the salon.

What is an Appointed Person?

An Appointed Person is someone who:

- takes charge if someone is injured or falls ill including calling an ambulance if required
- looks after the first aid equipment; e.g. restocking the first-aid box.

They should not attempt to provide first aid unless they have received appropriate training.

Every salon must have a first-aid kit in accordance with the regulations and, in the event that materials have been used, they must be replaced as soon as possible. All accidents and emergency aid given within the salon must be documented in the accident book.

Minimum contents of a typical first-aid box

1   first-aid guidance notes (HSE leaflet *Basic Advice on First Aid at Work*)

20   individually wrapped sterile adhesive dressings

2   sterile eye pads

4   individually wrapped sterile triangular bandages

6   safety pins

6   medium size (12 cm × 12 cm approx) sterile unmedicated dressings

2   large size (18 cm × 18 cm approx) sterile unmedicated dressings

1   pair of disposable gloves

What is a first aider?

A first aider is someone who has undergone a training course in administering first aid at work and holds a current first aid at work certificate. A first aider can undertake the duties of an appointed person. (Lists of approved first-aid training organisations in your area are available from HSE.)

Recording accidents and illness

All accidents must be recorded in the accident book. The recording system should always be kept readily available for use and inspection. When you are recording accidents, you will need to document the following details:

- date, time and place of incident or treatment
- name and job of the injured or ill person
- details of the injury or of the ill person and what treatment given
- what happened to the person immediately afterwards (e.g. went home, or went to hospital) were they taken in an ambulance?
- name and signature of the person providing the treatment and record entry.

Under the Reporting of Injuries, Diseases and Dangerous Occurrences Regulations 1995 major occurrences of injury or disease need to be reported to the National Incident Centre. More information is available from HSE.

General guidance on first aid

The following basic information is available in leaflet form from HSE, ISBN 0 7176 1070 5 in priced packs of 20.

Remember

You should not attempt to give anything more than basic first aid!

What to do in an emergency

Priorities Your priorities are to:

- assess the situation – do not put yourself in danger;
- make the area safe;
- assess all casualties and attend first to any unconscious casualties;
- send for help – do not delay.

Check for a response Gently shake the casualty's shoulders and ask loudly, 'Are you all right?' If there is no response, your priorities are to:

- shout for help;
- open the airway;
- check for normal breathing;
- take appropriate action.

Unconsciousness In most workplaces expert help should be available fairly quickly, but if you have an unconscious casualty it is vital that their airway is kept clear. If you cannot keep the airway open as described above, you may need to move the casualty into the recovery position. *The priority is an open airway.*

A = Airway

To open the airway:

- place your hand on the casualty's forehead and gently tilt the head back;
- lift the chin with two fingertips.

B = Breathing

Look, listen and feel for normal breathing for no more than ten seconds:

- look for chest movement;

- listen at the casualty's mouth for breath sounds;
- feel for air on your cheek.

If the casualty is *not* breathing normally:

- place in the recovery position;
- get help;
- check for continued breathing.

If the casualty is *not* breathing normally:

- get help;
- start chest compressions (see CPR).

C = CPR

To start chest compressions:

- lean over the casualty and with your arms straight, press down on the centre of the breastbone 4–5 cm, then release the pressure;
- repeat at a rate of about 100 times a minute;
- after 30 compressions open the airway again;
- pinch the casualty's nose closed and allow the mouth to open;
- take a normal breath and place your mouth around the casualty's mouth, making a good seal;
- blow steadily into the mouth while watching for the chest rising;
- remove your mouth from the casualty and watch for the chest falling;
- give a second breath and then start 30 compressions again without delay;
- continue with chest compressions and rescue breaths in a ratio of 30:2 until qualified help takes over or the casualty starts breathing normally.

Wounds and bleeding

Open wounds should be covered – *after you have put on sterile gloves*. Apply a dressing from the first-aid box over the wound and press firmly on top of it with your hands or fingers. The pad should be tied firmly in place. If bleeding continues another dressing should be applied on top. *Do not remove the original dressing.* Seek appropriate help.

Severe bleeding If there is severe bleeding:

- apply direct pressure to the wound;
- raise and support the injured part (unless broken);
- apply a dressing and bandage firmly in place.

Minor injuries

Minor injuries, of the sort which the injured person would treat themselves at home, can be treated from the contents of the first-aid box. The casualty should wash their hands and apply a dressing to protect the wound and prevent infection. In the workplace special metallic and/or coloured or waterproof dressings may be supplied according to the circumstances. Wounds should be kept dry and clean.

Broken bones and spinal injuries

If a broken bone or spinal injury is suspected, obtain expert help. Do not move casualties unless they are in immediate danger.

Burns

Burns can be serious – if in doubt seek medical help. Cool the part of the body affected with cold water until the pain is relieved. Thorough cooling may take ten minutes or more, but this must not delay taking the casualty to hospital.

Certain chemicals may seriously irritate or damage the skin. Avoid contaminating yourself with the chemical. Treat in the same way as for other burns but flood the affected area with water for 20 minutes. Continue treatment even on the way to hospital, if necessary. Remove any contaminated clothing which is not stuck to the skin.

Eye injuries

All eye injuries are potentially serious. If there is something in the eye, wash out the eye with clean water or sterile fluid from a sealed container, to remove loose material. Do not attempt to remove anything that is embedded in the eye.

If chemicals are involved, flush the eye with water or sterile fluid for at least ten minutes, while gently holding the eyelids open. Ask the casualty to hold a pad over the injured eye and send them to hospital.

Suggested numbers of first aid personnel

Here is a guide to the numbers of first aiders you should have, however the onus is on the employer to undertake a risk assessment to determine the requirements.

Category of risk	Number employed at one location	Suggested number of first aid personnel
Low risk:	Fewer than 50	At least one Appointed Person
shops, offices	50–100	At least one first aider
	100+	One additional first aider for every 100 people employed

Special hazards

Electrical and gassing accidents can occur in the workplace. You must assess the danger to yourself and not attempt assistance until you are sure it is safe to do so. If the casualty has stopped breathing and you are competent to give artificial ventilation and cardiac resuscitation, do so. Otherwise send for help without delay.

Appendix 3 People's rights and consumer legislation

People's rights and consumer legislation

Equal opportunities

The Equal Opportunities Commission (EOC) has the statutory duty to:

- ✔ work towards the elimination of discrimination
- ✔ promote equality of opportunity between men and women (and in relation to persons undergoing gender reassignment)
- ✔ keep the relevant legislation under review.

The legislation within the remit of the EOC is wide ranging; however, the main considerations are:

- ✔ equal pay
- ✔ sex discrimination
- ✔ disability discrimination (summary below).

In general, the Sex Discrimination Act (SDA) requires goods, facilities and services, whether for payment or not, which are offered to the public to be provided on the same basis for both sexes. The SDA prohibits direct and indirect sex discrimination.

Direct sex discrimination is treating a woman less favourably than a man because of her sex (or vice versa).

Indirect sex discrimination occurs when a condition or requirement is applied equally to both women and men but, in fact, it affects more women than men (or vice versa) and is not justifiable on objective grounds unrelated to sex. The Act provides for exceptions but unless a relevant exception to the requirements of the SDA can be used, facilities and services should be open to both sexes in the same way.

For more information visit www.eoc.org.uk/index.asp.

Disability Discrimination Act 2005 (DDA 2005)

The Act makes it unlawful to discriminate against disabled persons in connection with employment, the provision of goods, facilities and services or the disposal or management of premises; to make provision about the employment of disabled persons; and to establish a National Disability Council.

The Act protects the rights of disabled people and new revisions in 2005 have particular relevance to the business proprietor. For more information on this or accessibility issues visit www.disability.gov.uk/legislation.

Data Protection Act (1998)

Your clients have the following rights which can be enforced through any county court:

✔ *Right of subject access* – This is the right to find out what information about them is held on computer and in some paper records.

✔ *Correcting inaccurate data* – They have the right to have inaccurate personal data rectified, blocked, erased or destroyed. If your client believes that they have suffered damage or distress as a result of the processing of inaccurate data they can ask the court to award compensation.

✔ *Preventing junk mail* (from salons that market to their customer base) – Your client has the right to request in writing that a data controller does not use your personal data for direct marketing by post (sometimes known as 'junk mail'), by telephone or by fax.

For more information on consumer rights in relation to the Data Protection Act visit www.informationcommissioner.gov.uk/

The Data Protection Act (DPA) applies to any business that uses computers or paper-based systems for storing personal information about its clients and staff.

It places obligations on the person holding the information (data controller) to deal with it properly.

It gives the person that the information concerns (data subject) rights regarding the data held about them.

The duties of the data controller There are eight principles put in place by the DPA to make sure that data is handled correctly. By law, the data controller must keep to these principles. The principles say that the data must be:

1 fairly and lawfully processed

2 processed for limited purposes

3 adequate, relevant and not excessive

4 accurate

5 not kept for longer than is necessary

6 processed in line with your rights

7 secure

8 not transferred to other countries without adequate protection.

For more information see http://www.ico.gov.uk/

The Sale of Goods Act (1979) and Sale and Supply of Goods Act (1994)

The Sale of Goods Act 1979 and the later Sale and Supply of Goods Act (1994) are the main legal instruments helping buyers to obtain redress when their purchases go wrong. It is in the interest of anyone who sells goods or services to understand the implications of these Acts and the responsibilities they have under them. Essentially, these Acts state that what you sell must fit its description, be fit for its purpose and be of satisfactory quality. If not, you – as the supplier – are obliged to sort out the problem.

Briefly these Acts requires the vendor:

● To make sure that goods '*conform to contract*'. This means that they must be as you describe them e.g. highlight shampoo – it stops your highlights from fading.

- The goods must also be of '*satisfactory quality*', meaning they should be safe, work properly, and have no defects.
- You must also ensure the goods are '*fit for purpose*'. This means they should be capable of doing what they're meant for. For example, in the case of a brush it shouldn't fall apart when it is first used.

The Consumer Protection Act (1987)

This Act follows European laws to protect the buyer in the following areas:

- *product liability* – a customer may claim compensation for a product that doesn't reach general standards of safety
- *general safety requirements* – it is a criminal offence to sell goods that are unsafe; traders that breach this conduct may face fines or even imprisonment
- *misleading prices* – misleading consumers with wrongly displayed prices is also an offence.

The Act is designed to help safeguard the consumer from products that do not reach reasonable levels of safety. Your salon will take adequate precautions in procuring, using and supplying reputable products and maintaining them so that they remain in good condition.

The Prices Act (1974)

The price of products has to be displayed in order to prevent a false impression to the buyer.

The Trades Descriptions Act (1968 and 1972)

Products must not be falsely or misleadingly described in relation to their quality, fitness, price or purpose, by advertisements, orally, displays or descriptions. And since 1972 it has also been a requirement to label a product clearly, so that the buyer can see where the product was made.

Briefly, a retailer cannot:

- mislead consumers by making false statements about products
- offer sale products at half price unless they have been offered at the actual price for a reasonable length of time.

The Resale Prices Act (1964 and 1976)

The manufacturers can supply a recommended price (MRRP or manufacturers' recommended retail price), but the seller is not obliged to sell at the recommended price.

Appendix 4 Answers to end of chapter revision questions

Chapter**one**

Health and safety quiz (pages 22–23)

Q1	Hazard	Q2	True
Q3	1 3 6	Q4	False
Q5	C	Q6	False
Q7	2 4	Q8	First aid
Q9	D	Q10	True

Chapter**two**

Personal effectiveness quiz (pages 42–43)

Q1	Harmony	Q2	True
Q3	2 4 6	Q4	False
Q5	B	Q6	True
Q7	2 4	Q8	Thinking
Q9	C	Q10	True

Chapter**three**

Customer care quiz (pages 61–62)

Q1	Hygiene	Q2	True
Q3	1 4 5	Q4	True
Q5	D	Q6	True
Q7	3 4	Q8	body
Q9	B	Q10	True

Chapter**four**

Reception quiz (pages 91–92)

Q1	Credit	Q2	False
Q3	2 5	Q4	B
Q5	True	Q6	2 3
Q7	Home care	Q8	A
Q9	False		

Chapter**five**

Consultation and advice quiz (page 131)

Q1	Catagen	Q2	False
Q3	1 2 4	Q4	True
Q5	D	Q6	True
Q7	2 3	Q8	Dermis
Q9	C	Q10	True

Chapter**six**

Promotion and sales quiz (pages 142–143)

Q1	Benefits	Q2	False
Q3	4 5 6	Q4	True
Q5	C	Q6	True
Q7	1 3 5	Q8	Satisfactory
Q9	D	Q10	True

Chapter**seven**

Shampooing and conditioning quiz (page 171)

Q1	Dry	Q2	False
Q3	2 4 5	Q4	False
Q5	C	Q6	True
Q7	2 4	Q8	Ends
Q9	B	Q10	False

Chapter**eight**

Styling and finishing hair quiz (page 200)

Q1	Radial	Q2	True
Q3	1 3 6	Q4	True
Q5	A	Q6	True
Q7	1 2 3 5	Q8	Flat
Q9	B	Q10	True

Chapter**nine**

Men's styling and finishing quiz (pages 213–214)

Q1	Finger	Q2	True
Q3	2 3 5	Q4	True
Q5	C	Q6	True
Q7	3 4 6	Q8	Diffuser
Q9	B	Q10	True

Chapter**ten**

Styling, dressing and longer hair quiz (page 250)

Q1	Velcro	Q2	False
Q3	2 4 6	Q4	True
Q5	B	Q6	False
Q7	1 5	Q8	Pleat
Q9	B	Q10	False

Chapter**eleven**

Adding/extending hair quiz (pages 269–270)

Q1	Man	Q2	False
Q3	2 3 4	Q4	False
Q5	A	Q6	True
Q7	2 5 6	Q8	Wefts
Q9	B	Q10	False

Chapter**twelve**

Cutting quiz (pages 303–304)

Q1	Holding	Q2	False
Q3	1 2 4	Q4	True
Q5	D	Q6	True
Q7	3 5	Q8	Baseline
Q9	C	Q10	True

Chapter**thirteen**

Cutting quiz (page 333)

Q1	Holding	Q2	False
Q3	1 2 4	Q4	True
Q5	D	Q6	True
Q7	3 5	Q8	Baseline
Q9	C	Q10	True

Chapter**fourteen**

Cutting facial hair quiz (page 352)

Q1	Grades	Q2	False
Q3	1 5	Q4	True
Q5	D	Q6	True
Q7	4 6	Q8	Towels
Q9	B	Q10	False

Chapter**fifteen**

Creating patterns in hair quiz (pages 370–371)

Q1	Outline	Q2	False
Q3	1 4	Q4	False
Q5	B	Q6	True
Q7	1 4	Q8	Tramliner
Q9	C	Q10	True

Chapter**sixteen**

Colouring hair quiz (pages 416–417)

Q1	Skin	Q2	True
Q3	4 5	Q4	False
Q5	D	Q6	False
Q7	2 4 5	Q8	Red
Q9	B	Q10	True

Chapter**seventeen**

Perming hair quiz (pages 446–447)

Q1	Curl	Q2	True
Q3	1 5	Q4	True
Q5	C	Q6	True
Q7	1 3	Q8	Cortex
Q9	C	Q10	True

Useful addresses and websites

Business

Arbitration, Conciliation and Advisory Service (ACAS)

Head Office
Brandon House
180 Borough High Street
London, SE1 1LW

T: 020 7210 3613

www.acas.org.uk

Helpline 08457 47 47 47

Hairdressing Employers Association (HEA)

10 Coldbath Square
London, EC1R 5HL

T: 020 7833 0633

Training and Education

Hairdressing and Beauty Industry Authority (Habia)

Oxford House
Sixth Avenue
Sky Business Park
Robin Hood
Airport
Doncaster, DN9 3GG

T: 08452 306080

www.habia.org

Salon Studies (Online Learning NVQs and Diploma)

www.salonstudies.co.uk

Best4Hair (Online Hairdressing Consultation)

www.best4hair.co.uk

Association of Hairdressing Teachers (AHT)

5 Viscount Gardens
Byfleet
Surrey, KT14 6HE

City and Guilds (C and G)

1 Giltspur Street
London, EC1A 9DD

T: 020 7294 2800

www.city-and-guilds.co.uk

Department for Education and Skills

www.dfes.gov.uk

Lifelong Learning

www.lifelonglearning.co.uk

Qualifications and Curriculum Authority (QCA)

83 Piccadilly
London, W1J 8QA

T: 020 7509 3097

www.qca.org.uk

The Institute of Trichologists

Ground Floor Office
24 Langroyd Road
London, SW17 7PL

T: 08706 070602

www.trichologists.org.uk

Vocational Training Charitable Trust (VTCT)

46 Aldwick Road
Bognor Regis
West Sussex, PO21 2PN

www.vtct.org.uk

World Federation of Hairdressing and Beauty Schools

PO Box 367
Coulsdon
Surrey, CR5 2TP

T: 01737 551355

World Federation of Hairdressing Schools

73 Marlpit Lane
Coulsdon
Surrey, CR5 2HF

Publication

Hairdressers Journal International (HJ)

Quadrant House
The Quadrant, Sutton
Surrey, SM2 5AS

T: 020 8652 3500

www.reedbusiness.com

Creative Head

Mallan House,
Bridge End,
Hexham,
Northumberland, NE46 4DQ

www.head1st.net

Black Beauty and Hair

Culvert House
Culvert Road
London, SW11 5DH

T: 020 7720 2108

www.blackbeauty.co.uk

Trade associations

British Association of Beauty Therapy and Cosmetology Limited (BABTAC)

Meteor Court
Barnett Way
Barnwood
Gloucester, GL4 3GG

Caribbean and Afro Society of Hairdressers (CASH)

42 North Cross Road
East Dulwich
London, SE22 8PY

T: 020 8299 2859

Commission for Racial Equality

Elliot House
10–12 Allington Street
London, SW1E 5EH

T: 020 7828 7022

www.cre.gov.uk

Cosmetic, Toiletry and Perfumery Association (CTPA)

Josaron House
5–7 John Princes Street
London, W1G 0JN

T: 020 7491 8891

www.ctpa.org.uk

Fellowship for British Hairdressing

Bloxham Mill
Barford Road
Bloxham
Banbury
Oxon, OX15 4FF

T: 01295 724579

Freelance Hair and Beauty Federation

6 Warleigh Road
Brighton
East Sussex, BN1 4TN

T: 01273 604556

www.fhbf.org.uk

Guild of Hairdressers (GUILD)

Unit 1E
Redbrook Business Park
Wilthorpe Road
Barnsley, S75 1JN

T: 01226 730112

Hairdressing and Beauty Suppliers' Association (HBSA)

Bedford Chambers
The Piazza,
Covent Garden
London, WC2E 8HA

T: 020 7836 4008

Hairdressing and Beauty Suppliers Association

1st Floor, Manfield House
1 Southampton Street
Covent Garden
London, WC2R OLR

Hairdressing Council (HC)

12 David House
45 High Street
South Norwood
London, SE25 6HJ

T: 020 8771 6205

www.haircouncil.org.uk

Health and Beauty Employers Federation (part of the Federation of Holistic Therapists)

18 Shakespeare Business Centre
Hathaway Close
Eastleigh Hampshire, SO50 4SR
www.fht.org.uk

Incorporated Guild of Hairdressers, Wigmakers and Perfumers

Unit 8, Vulcan Road
M1
Distribution Centre
Meadowhall
Sheffield, S9 1EW

National Hairdressers' Federation (NHF)

One Abbey Court
Fraser Road
Priory Business Park
Bedford, MK44 3WH

www.the-nhf.org

Legal and regulatory

Health and Safety Executive

Publications
PO Box 1999
Sudbury
Suffolk, CO10 6FS
(HSE) Infoline
T: 0845 345 0055
www.hse.gov.uk

Equal Opportunities Commission

Arndale House
Arndale Centre
Manchester, M4 3EQ
T: 0161 833 9244

Union of Shop, Distributive and Allied Workers (USDAW)

188 Wilmslow Road
Fallowfield
Manchester, M14 6LJ
T: 0161 224 2804

Key skills information

Key skills are the fundamental skills that are most commonly needed to succeed in a range of work- or training-related activities. Key skills are for everyone under the age of 19 years. If you have already achieved these skills prior to your vocational training, e.g. at school within a GNVQ, you will not be required to do them again.

However, if you haven't covered these before you will be working towards the achievement of these during your training towards Hairdressing S/NVQ Level 2.

Don't panic, this is your lecturer's responsibility. Whilst you are training, your lecturer will recognise the opportunities that provide potential evidence. These will be during the everyday tasks that arise during your work and will be linked to your personal training programme.

Key skill and qualification level	These key skills enable people to:
Application of number L.1	Use numbers with confidence
Communication L.2	Communicate effectively with others
Information and communication technology L.1	Use computers at work
Working with others L.2	Work together well with others
Problem solving L.2	Make informed decisions
Improving own learning and performance L.2	Develop themselves further

The following key skills provide summary information of what is needed and the references to the individual standards. (Credit: Qualification Curriculum Authority; QCA 2004.)

Application of number at Level 1

To achieve this, you must be able to apply your number skills to suit different purposes. You will show that you can:

1 interpret information from two sources
2 carry out and check calculations
3 interpret the results of your calculations and present your findings.

Interpret information

- Read and understand tables, charts, graphs and diagrams.
- Read and understand numbers used in different ways (e.g. large numbers in figures or words, simple fractions, decimals, percentages).

- Read scales on familiar measuring equipment (e.g. watch, tape measure, measuring jug, weighing scales, thermometer) using everyday units (e.g. minutes, millimetres, litres, grams, degrees).

- Make accurate observations (e.g. count number of people or items).

- Identify suitable calculations to get the results you need for your task.

N1.1 Interpret information from two different sources. At least one source must include a table, chart, graph or diagram.

1.1.1 Obtain the information you need to meet the purpose of your task.

1.1.2 Identify suitable calculations to get the results you need.

Carry out calculations

- Add and subtract, with whole numbers and simple decimals with or without a calculator (e.g. using money or length).

- Work to the level of accuracy you have been told to use (e.g. round to the nearest whole unit, nearest 10, two decimal places).

- Multiply and divide a simple decimal by a whole number with and without a calculator (e.g. using money or length).

- Understand and find simple fractions and percentages (e.g. $\frac{2}{3}$ of £15 is £10, 75 percent of 400 is 300).

- Work out areas of rectangular spaces (e.g. floor area).

- Work out volumes of rectangular-based shapes (e.g. a box).

- Use scales on diagrams such as 20 mm to 1 m (e.g. finding distances from maps).

- Use ratios and proportion (e.g. three parts to one part).

- Find the average (mean) of up to ten items (e.g. temperatures, prices, time).

- Find the range for up to ten items (e.g. temperature range from highest to lowest was 16°C).

- Make sure your answers make sense and use different methods to check your calculations (e.g. estimate to reject impossible answers, check a subtraction by 'adding back').

N1.2 Carry out and check calculations to do with:

    a amounts or sizes

    b scales or proportion

    c handling statistics.

1.2.1 Carry out calculations to the levels of accuracy you have been given.

1.2.2 Check your results make sense.

Interpret results and present your findings

- Use suitable ways of presenting information, including a chart or diagram.

- Use the correct units (e.g. for area, volume, weight, time, temperature).

- Label your work correctly (e.g. use a title or key).

- Describe what your results tell you.

N1.3 Interpret the results of your calculations and present your findings – in two different ways using charts or diagrams.

1.3.1 Choose suitable ways to present your findings.

1.3.2 Use more than one way of presenting your findings.

1.3.3 Present your findings clearly using a chart or diagram.

1.3.4 Describe what your results tell you.

Communication at Level 2

To achieve this, you must be able to apply your communication skills to suit different purposes. You will show that you can:

1 take part in a group discussion

2 read and summarise at least two documents

3 give a short talk

4 write two types of document, each giving different information.

Discuss

- Use varied vocabulary and expressions to suit your purpose.
- Adapt what you say to suit different situations.
- Listen carefully to what others say.
- Identify the speaker's intentions.
- Move the discussion forward.

C2.1a Take part in a group discussion.

C2.1a.1 Make clear and relevant in a way that suits your purpose and situation.

C2.1a.2 Respond appropriately to others.

C2.1a.3 Help to move the discussion forward.

Give a short talk

- Prepare for the talk.
- Adapt your language to suit your subject, purpose and situation.
- Structure what you say to help listeners follow a line of thought or series of events.
- Use a variety of ways to support the main points of your talk including using images.

C2.1b Give a talk of at least four minutes.

2.1b.1 Speak clearly in a way that suits your subject, purpose and situation.

2.1b.2 Keep to the subject and structure your talk to help listeners follow what you are saying.

2.1b.3 Use appropriate ways to support your main points.

Read and summarise information

- Select and use different types of documents to obtain relevant information.
- Skim documents to gain a general idea of content.
- Scan documents to identify the information you need.
- Recognise the writer's intentions.
- Identify the main points, ideas and lines of reasoning from text and images.
- Summarise information for a purpose.

C2.2 Read and summarise information from at least two documents about the same subject. Each document must be a minimum of 500 words long.

2.2.1 Select and read relevant documents.

2.2.2 Identify accurately the main points, ideas and lines of reasoning.

2.2.3 Summarise the information to suit your purpose.

Write documents

- Use different formats for presenting information, including essays, reports and articles.
- Structure your writing to help readers follow and understand your main points.
- Use different styles of writing to suit different purposes.
- Proof-read and where necessary redraft your documents so that:
  - spelling is accurate including familiar technical words
  - sentences are formed correctly with accurate use of conjunctions
  - punctuation is accurate including use of commas, apostrophes and inverted commas.

C2.3 Write two different types of documents each one giving different information. One document must be at least 500 words long.

2.3.1 Present relevant information in a format that suits your purpose.

2.3.2 Use a structure and style of writing to suit your purpose.

2.3.3 Spell, punctuate and use grammar accurately.

2.3.4 Make your meaning clear.

Information and communication technology at Level 1

You need to know how to use ICT to help you in different tasks:

- save information so it can be found easily
- minimise health risks
- know how to get help when dealing with errors
- send and receive e-mail.

To achieve this level, you must be able to apply your ICT skills to suit different purposes. You will show that you can:

1 find, enter, explore and develop relevant information
2 present information, including text, images and numbers, using appropriate layouts and save information.

Find information

- Find different types of information from ICT sources (e.g. files, CD-ROMs, the Internet) and non-ICT sources (e.g. written notes, price lists, diagrams).
- Select information relevant to your purpose.

ICT1.1 Find and select relevant information.

1.1.1 Choose information that is relevant to your tasks.

Develop information

- Enter information (e.g. copy and paste text, import images) using formats that help development (e.g. tabs, tables, format of numbers).
- Develop information in the form of text, image and numbers (e.g. structure information, carry out calculations using suitable software, move and resize images).

ICT1.2 Enter and develop information to suit the task.

1.2.1 Enter information using formats that help development.

1.2.2 Save information so it can be found easily.

Present information

- Use layouts and techniques to suit different purposes (e.g. select page layouts for different types of document such as letters or invoices, organise the presentation by moving, copying, deleting or inserting information).

- Present information in a consistent way (e.g. fonts, bulleted lists, alignment) making sure it is accurate and clear (e.g. ask others, proofread, use a spell-checker, highlight information to improve its clarity).

ICT1.3 Develop the presentation so that the final output is accurate and fit for purpose.

1.3.1 Use appropriate layouts for presenting information in a consistent way.

Working with others at Level 2

To achieve this, you must be able to apply your skills to suit different purposes. You will show that you can:

1 identify what you need to achieve together

2 organise and carry out tasks to meet your responsibilities

3 identify your role in helping to achieve things together.

Plan work with others

- Make sure you understand what makes groups or teams effective.

- Identify what you need to achieve together (from the objectives suggested by your supervisor, tutor, yourself or others).

- Contribute and use relevant information to identify tasks, resources (materials, equipment and/or tools) and time-scales.

- Suggest ways you could help and find out what others would like to do.

- Identify individual responsibilities:

  - who will be responsible for organising and carrying out each task

  - the ground rules for working together (ways of behaving that show respect for each other's rights, feelings, ideas and contributions, what you and others should and should not do).

- confirm the arrangements for working together:

  - with whom you will be working, where and when

  - health and safety procedures

  - the appropriate people to go to for advice and support when needed.

WO2.1 Plan work with others.

2.1.1 Identify what you need to achieve together.

2.1.2 Share relevant information to identify what needs to be done and individual responsibilities.

2.1.3 Confirm the arrangements for working together.

Work cooperatively towards achieving the identified objectives

- Organise and carry out tasks so you can meet your responsibilities.

- Get and make the best use of resources.

- Pace your work to meet deadlines.

- Work safely to avoid accidents, health risks, offending others or disrupting their work.
- Use correct techniques and approaches to help you produce the quality of work required.
- Support cooperative ways of working.
- Anticipate the needs of others for information and support.
- Avoid actions that offend or discriminate against others.
- Act assertively, when needed, to protect your own rights.
- Show willingness to sort out disagreements or other problems.
- Check progress towards the objectives, seeking advice from an appropriate person to help resolve any conflicts or other problems.

WO2.2 Work cooperatively towards achieving the identified objectives.

2.2.1 Organise and carry out tasks safely using appropriate methods, to meet your responsibilities.

2.2.2 Support cooperative ways of working to help achieve the objectives for working together.

2.2.3 Check progress, seeking advice from an appropriate person when needed.

Review your contributions and agree ways to improve work with others

- Contribute information and listen to others on what went well and less well, including tasks and working relationships.
- Identify and describe your role in helping to achieve things together.
- Agree ways of improving your work with others, including interpersonal skills.

WO2.3 Review your contributions and agree ways to improve work with others.

2.3.1 Share relevant information on what went well and less well in working with others.

2.3.2 Identify *your* role in helping to achieve things together.

2.3.3 Agree ways of improving your work with others.

Problem solving at Level 2

To achieve this, you must be able to apply your skills to suit different purposes. You will show that you can:

1 accurately describe the problem

2 plan what you need to do to solve the problem

3 identify ways of improving your problem-solving skills.

Help identify a problem and identify different ways of tackling it

- Work with an appropriate person, such as your tutor or supervisor, to help identify a problem, by providing an accurate description of its main features:
  - what is known and not known about the problem
  - how it affects you and other people.
- Identify how you will know the problem has been solved:
  - find out the results people expect from tackling the problem
  - find out about methods you could use to check it has been solved.

- Come up with different ways of tackling the problem:
  - learn about different methods for solving problems and how similar problems have been solved
  - find out about the risks (the likelihood of things going wrong) and other factors that might affect the way you tackle the problem (time and expertise needed, health and safety rules)
  - decide what could help to solve your problem.

PS2.1 Identify a problem, with help from an appropriate person, and identify different ways of tackling it.

2.1.1 Provide information to help identify a problem, accurately describing its main features.

2.1.2 Identify how you will know the problem has been solved.

2.1.3 Come up with different ways of tackling the problem.

Plan and try out a way of solving the problem

- Confirm with an appropriate person, such as your tutor, supervisor or other person in authority, how you will try to solve the problem, adapting your ideas if necessary to meet rules and regulations.
- Plan what you need to do, identifying:
  - resources you will use (materials, tools, equipment, information and support from others)
  - the methods, steps and time-line for working through the problem, including ways of overcoming difficulties
  - health and safety procedures.
- Use your plan effectively, taking responsibility, when needed, for:
  - health and safety
  - getting support from your supervisor or other person with relevant expertise
  - keeping track of the steps taken in tackling the problem and
  - revising your plan to deal with unexpected events.

PS2.2 Plan and try out at least one way of solving the problem.

2.2.1 Confirm with an appropriate person how you will try to solve the problem.

2.2.2 Plan what you need to do, identifying the methods and resources you will use.

2.2.3 Use your plan effectively, getting support and revising your plan when needed to help tackle the problem.

Check if the problem has been solved and identify ways to improve problem solving

- Learn how to use the methods you have been given for checking if the problem has been solved and use these accurately.
- Describe clearly the results of your checking, including the strengths and weaknesses of how you tackled the problem at each stage.
- Identify ways of improving your problem-solving skills.

PS2.3 Check if the problem has been solved and identify ways to improve problem-solving skills.

2.3.1 Check if the problem has been solved by accurately using the methods you have been given.

2.3.2 Describe clearly the results, including the strengths and weaknesses of how you tackled the problem.

2.3.3 Identify ways of improving your problem-solving skills.

Improving own learning and performance at Level 2

To achieve this, you must be able to apply your skills to suit different purposes. You will show that you can:

1 plan your time well to meet your targets

2 identify when you need support to help you meet targets

3 identify ways you learn best and how to improve your performance.

Help set targets and plan how these will be met

- Work with an appropriate person, such as your tutor, supervisor or adviser, to make sure you understand how planning and reviewing your learning can help to improve your performance and what is meant by learning styles and evidence of achievement.

- Develop an individual learning plan that includes:

  - targets that say exactly what you want to achieve and how you will prove you have met them

  - provide information to make sure they are realistic, including what might affect your chances of success

  - the action you will take (action points) for each target and dates (deadlines) to help you manage your time

  - how to get the support you need, including who will review your progress, and where and when this will take place.

LP2.1 Help set targets with an appropriate person and plan how these will be met.

2.1.1 Provide information to help set real targets for what you want to achieve.

2.1.2 Identify clear action points for each target and how you will manage your time.

2.1.3 Identify how to get the support you need and arrangements for reviewing your progress.

Take responsibility for some decisions about your learning

- Work through your action points to complete these on time, revising your plan when needed to overcome unexpected events or problems.

- Choose different ways of learning (learning styles) and decide on the methods that best suit you (e.g. pictures/diagrams, reading/talking/writing, listening to others, watching or doing something practical).

- Work for short periods without close supervision so you have to take some decisions about your learning.

- Identify when you need support and use this effectively to help meet your targets.

LP2.2 Take responsibility for some decisions about your learning, using your plan to help meet targets and improve your performance.

2.2.1 Use your action points to help manage your time well; revising your plan when needed.

2.2.2 Choose ways of learning to improve your performance, working for short periods without close supervision.

2.2.3 Identify when you need support and use this effectively to help you meet targets.

Review progress and provide evidence of achievements

Work with an appropriate person, such as your tutor, supervisor or adviser, to:

- identify what you learned and how you used learning from one task to meet the demands of another task

- identify the targets you have met, by checking your plan to see if you have done what you set out to do

- identify evidence of your achievements

- identify ways you learn best (your preferred learning style/s and methods of learning) and how to improve your performance (the quality of your work, the way you work).

LP2.3 Review progress with an appropriate person and provide evidence of your achievements.

2.3.1 Identify what you learned, and how you have used your learning in another task.

2.3.2 Identify targets you have met and evidence of your achievements.

2.3.3 Identify ways you learn best and how to further improve your performance.

Glossary and key terms

Activators or boosters Products used to maintain curl in permed or naturally curly hair.

Adverse hair and scalp conditions Limiting factors that have an effect on what and how services are delivered to clients, e.g. head lice, psoriasis, alopecia, cysts, impetigo, scars, moles etc.

Alpha keratin The normal, coiled form of keratin.

Appointment system The system which organises the volume of work (client services or treatments) undertaken by a salon. This may be manual or computerised.

Appraisal The system of reviewing your past and planning your future work objectives.

Assessment An evaluation or judgement of input, value and/or attainment.

BD Appointment abbreviation for blow dry.

Benefits The ways in which the functions provide advantages.

Beta keratin The form keratin takes when it has been stretched, set and dried.

Bleach A hairdressing product that dissolves/removes natural colour pigments from hair.

Body language A non-verbal form of communication that reveals the way a person is thinking or feeling.

Booster An activator or colour development accelerator.

Brick wind A technique of winding rods into the hair so that there aren't any uniform divisions or 'roller marks' after the perm is finished When the hair has been wound in this formation it looks like a brick wall.

Case study A study, examination or evaluation of specific event(s) either factual or hypothetical.

CBD Appointment abbreviation for cut and blow dry.

Chemical sterilizers A form of sterilization.

Chemically damaged hair Hair conditioned worsened by the effects of chemical processing.

Chemically treated hair Hair that has been previously permed, coloured, bleached or relaxed.

Client care Providing service to salon customers in a way that promotes goodwill, comfort, satisfaction and interest, which ultimately results in regular return visits from clients.

Client consultation A service which is usually provided before the client has anything done to their hair. Consultation will find out what the client wants, identify any styling limitations, provide advice and maintenance information and formulate a plan of action.

Clip on extensions Pre-coloured wefts of hair that have clips or combs attached to them so that they can be affixed to the hair.

Clipper over comb A technique of cutting hair with electric clippers, using the back of the comb as a guide, especially on very short hair and hairline profiles.

Club cutting or clubbing hair The most basic and most popular way of cutting sections of hair straight across, parallel to the index and middle finger.

Col (Rt or Fh) Appointment abbreviation for colouring, either root application or full head.

Cold and hot bonded hair extensions cold bonding systems are used at level 2 to add hair to enhance a hair style. Hot bonding systems are used at level 3 in different ways and incorporate the use of heat to affix the hair extension to the hair.

Communication Listening, hearing and responding to the client.

Confidential information May include personal aspects of conversations with clients or colleagues, contents of client records, client and staff personal details (e.g. address, telephone numbers etc.) financial aspects of the business, hearsay/gossip.

Confidentiality The professional way of handling client information.

Consumer and Retail Legislation.

Consumer Protection Act (1987) This Act follows European directives to protect the buyer from unsafe products. The Act is designed to help safeguard the consumer from products that do not reach reasonable levels of safety.

Consumer Protection (Distance Selling) Regulations 2000 These are derived from a European Directive and cover the supply of goods and/or services made between suppliers acting in a commercial capacity and consumers, i.e. an individual acting outside a trade business or profession. The regulations should be of concern to any individual purchasing goods or services by telephone, using the Internet, digital TV or mail order catalogues and conversely be of concern to any suppliers dealing with consumers.

Consumer Safety Act (1978) There is a requirement to reduce the possible risk to consumers from any product that may be potentially dangerous.

Contrasts A marked difference (e.g. between colours, say black and white).

Control The ways in which risks identified are eliminated or reduced to an acceptable level.

Contra-indication Something that signifies that an adverse reaction has occurred.

Cortex The inner part of the hair where permanent colour is deposited and where perms make physical changes to the hair.

Cross-infection The passing on of disease from one person to another, either by contact or proximity, caused by poor hygiene and sanitation.

Cuticle The outer protective layers of the hair shaft.

Data Protection Act Under this Act, you must not pass on any client- or salon-related information without the permission of the person involved. You have a duty of care to keep any such information safe and secure.

Database An archive of information, usually held on computer, relating to business records: clients, staff, sales, products etc.

Depth The lightness or darkness of a hair.

Dermatitis A skin condition which results in a red, sore, hot and itchy rash, usually between the fingers. This is sometimes caused by contact with hairdressing chemicals and solutions.

Dermis The lower layers of newer skin below the outer epidermis.

Detergent A cleansing substance that dissolves dirt and oil.

Directional wind A technique of winding rods in, so that when finished, the hair will move in a particular direction.

Disulphide bonds The bonds within the hair that are permanently rearranged during perming, relaxing and neutralising.

Double booking An error in the appointment system where client's bookings overlap.

Effleurage A gentle stroking movement used in shampooing.

Epidermis The older, upper, protective layers of skin at the surface.

Evacuation procedures The arrangements made by the salon, i.e. exit route, assembly point etc., for emergency purposes.

Exfoliation To scrub skin with a gritty substance to remove the dead surface layer.

Fading A cutting term that refers to the blending of one area 'seamlessly' to another.

Features The aspects of a product or service that state its functions; i.e. what it does.

Follicle A tube-like indentation within the skin, from which the hair grows.

Freehand cutting A cutting technique carried out without holding the hair, usually to compensate for the natural fall of hair.

Friction (massage technique) A vigorous rubbing movement used when shampooing on the scalp areas.

Full head application of colour or bleach A colouring technique that requires a sequence of applications to the mid-lengths, ends and regrowth area.

Graduation A cutting technique that joins together longer hair that over falls shorter hair in one continuous cutting angle.

Guideline First or starting section of hair that is held and cut to the required length and then used as a template for the following sections.

Hair colour The resultant effect from two colour aspects: *depth*, the lightness or darkness of a colour and *tone*, the degree of red, gold, ash etc. within the hair.

Hair tendency The hair's straightness, wave, body, curl or frizziness.

Hair tests Pull test, elasticity test and skin test, used to determine contra-indications to hair extension services.

Hair texture Texture refers to the 'thickness or thinness' of individual hairs: coarse, medium or fine.

Harmonises Goes with, compliments.

Harmony Maintaining a good working relationship and atmosphere with your fellow staff.

Hazard Something with a potential to cause harm.

Henna From a shrub with leaves that yield the red dye henna.

HL or H/L Appointment abbreviation for highlighting.

HL T sect Appointment abbreviation for highlight, top and sides only.

Hygroscopic Readily absorbing moisture from the atmosphere.

ICC (International Colour Chart) system A tabular system for identifying hair colours made by different manufacturers by their depth and tone.

Incompatibility Refers to incompatible chemistry. When incompatibles are present within the hair – e.g. colour restorers, 'Just for Men' or compound henna – no organic chemicals can be used.

Incompatibility test A method of testing hair to see if previous chemical treatments are compatible with those used with professional salons.

Influencing factors Anything which could affect the hairdressing service.

Inverse clippering A way of holding the clippers to produce outlines necklines and detail within a design.

Layering (layered cut) A cutting technique carried out on either short or long hair to produce a multi-length effect.

Legal requirements This refers to laws affecting the way businesses are operated, how the salon or workplace is set up and maintained, people in employment and the systems of working which must be maintained.

Lighteners Lighteners are products that remove natural tone from hair such as bleach, or high lift colour.

Limits of your authority The extent of your responsibility at work.

Litmus paper paper strip treated with litmus, used to find out if something isan acid or an alkali.

Long hair graduation A cut when the inner/upper layers of a haircut are shorter than the lengths of the outline, perimeter hair.

Manufacturer's instructions Explicit guidance issued by manufacturers or suppliers of products or equipment, concerning their safe and efficient use.

Neutraliser The second chemical (rebonding) phase for perming or relaxing hair. See *permanent wave*.

Oblong facial shape An outline perimeter facial shape that has proportions that roughly resembles an oblong shape.

Occipital bone The saucer shaped bone at the rear of the skull that connects with the spinal column.

Oily scalp Condition caused by the over-production of-natural oils, i.e. sebum, which exudes from glands within the scalp on to the surface and eventually the hair – affects the handling, maintenance and style durability.

One-length hair cut A cutting technique where the hair is cut *with* the natural hair fall to produce a one-length effect.

Outlines The shapes created by the perimeter of nape and front hairlines.

Oval facial shape An outline perimeter facial shape that has proportions that roughly resemble an oval or elipsed shape.

Overbooking See double booking.

Oxidation The acidic chemical process which reforms the disulphide bridges within the polypeptide chains by introducing oxygen.

Para-phenylenediamine A dye compound found in many permanent colours.

Penetrating conditioner Deep acting conditioners working on the inside of the hair.

Perm (permanent wave) A two-part system for adding movement to hair by chemical means.

Perm solution The first part of a permanent wave system which chemically modifies the hair's inner structure.

Permanent tint (permanent colour) A penetrating colour product that adds synthetic pigments to natural hair until it grows out.

Personal development Recognising the opportunities that arise at work when you get the chance to learn new things.

Personal presentation This includes personal hygiene and the use of personal protective equipment, clothing and accessories suitable to the particular workplace.

Personal protective equipment (PPE) You are required to use and wear the appropriate protective equipment during perming, colouring and relaxing services or in any situation where personal harm may be encountered.

Petrissage (massage technique) A slower circulatory kneading movement generally used for scalp massage when applying conditioner.

pH The presence of positive hydrogen ions with a compound which denotes its levels of acidity or alkalinity.

Point cutting (pointing) A cutting technique where the cutting angle is changed to remove hair bulk from the ends of each cutting section.

Porous hair Hair that has lost surface protection, therefore having a greater absorption and less resistance to chemicals and products. This affects the hair's manageability, handling and ability to hold in a style.

Portfolio A system for recording experiences, case studies, personal accounts, results from tests/ assessments and the findings from projects and assignments.

Post-damping Application of perming lotion to previously wound curlers.

Pre-damping Application of perming lotion prior to winding in the curlers.

Pre-perm treatment A product applied to the hair before perming to balance out uneven porosity.

Prices Act (1974) The price of products has to be displayed in order to prevent a false impression to the buyer.

Professional advice Providing information based upon experience and knowledge.

Project Similar to an *assignment*.

PW Appointment abbreviation for permanent wave (perm).

Quasi-permanent colours Colour products which should be treated as permanent colours in terms of application, testing and future services.

Reduction The alkaline chemical process which breaks the disulphide bridges within the polypeptide chains by introducing hydrogen.

Referral The situations where you need to redirect clients to other sources of treatment or service, i.e. when there are adverse hair and skin conditions, or because of other services that your salon doesn't provide.

Relaxing A chemical process (usually in two parts) which removes natural movement/curl from hair.

Resale Prices Act (1964 and 1976) The manufacturers can supply a recommended retail price (MRRP), but the seller is not obliged to sell at the recommended price.

Reshape (reshaping) Cutting hair back into style (a six-weekly reshape cut will maintain a hairstyle).

Resources Anything used to enable the delivery and completion of service to the client (e.g. people, equipment stock).

Responsible persons A term used particularly in health and safety to mean the person(s) at work to whom you should report any issues, problems or hazards. This could be a supervisor, line manager or your employer.

Restyle Cutting hair into a new hairstyle.

Reverse graduation A cutting technique that joins together shorter hair down to longer hair in one continuous cutting angle.

Risk The likelihood of the hazard's potential actually occurring.

Role play A way of exploring different scenarios by simulation.

Rotary massage A quicker and firmer circular movement used in shampooing.

Round facial shape An outline perimeter facial shape that has proportions that roughly resemble a circular or round shape.

Sale and Supply of Goods Act (1994) The vendor must ensure that the goods they sell are of satisfactory quality (defined as the standard that would be regarded by a reasonable person as satisfactory having taken into account the description of the goods, the price and other relevant circumstances) and reasonably fit (ensuring as a vendor that the goods can meet the purpose they are claimed to do).

Salon policy Any hairdressing procedures or work rules issued by the salon management.

Salon services The extent and variety of all the services offered in your workplace.

Scalp The skin covering the top of the head.

Scalp plaits Also known as a French plait, a cane row or corn row.

Scissor over comb A technique of cutting hair with scissors, using the back of the comb as a guide, especially when the hair is at a length that cannot be held between the fingers.

Sebum A natural oil produced by the sebaceous gland.

Self-adhesive extensions Pre-coloured wefts of hair that have self-cling, peel-off strips that reveal a sticky tape that attaches the extension to the client's hair.

Semi-permanent colour A semi-permanent colour is not mixed with hydrogen peroxide. It only penetrates to the lower cuticle and therefore lasts for a few washes.

Shape, proportion and balance The physical and notional aspects that control hair design and hair styling.

Sharps A Health and Safety Executive term to describe sharp objects e.g. razors and razor blades, scissors.

Sharps box A sealed, safe storage for used sharp items awaiting disposal.

Short graduation cut A short graduation cut is when the inner/upper layers of a hair cut are longer than the lengths of the outline, perimeter hair.

Slice or slider cutting A technique used with very sharp scissors assimilating the action and effect produced by razoring to create a tapering effect.

Square facial shape An outline perimeter facial shape that has proportions that roughly resemble a square shape.

Sterilisation The eradication of all living organisms

Strand test A test carried out upon hair prior to chemical services to determine the effects of processing.

Strengths and weaknesses The difference between personal skill areas that you excel in and those that you need to work on.

Style line The directions in which the hair is positioned or appears to flow.

Surface conditioner A light conditioner that works on the outside of the hair to smooth and fill areas of damaged, missing or worn cuticle.

Tapered Necklines Tapered necklines have soft outlines that follow the natural hairline shape so that the nape outline appears to fade out with no harsh lines visible.

Temporary bonds The hydrogen bonds within the hair that are modified and fix the style into shape.

Temporary colour Colour added to hair that lasts until the next wash.

Texturising A variety of cutting techniques that are used to achieve different effects within the cutting scheme of a hairstyle.

'T' liner A type of clipper with a different blade type to standard clippers, enabling closer cut outlines around ears, necklines and facial hair shapes.

Tone The aspects of colouration of the hair, normally grouped into similar tints i.e. copper tones, red tones, ash tones.

Trades Descriptions Act (1968 and 1972) Products must not be falsely or misleadingly described in relation to their quality, fitness, price or purpose, by advertisements, orally, displays or descriptions. And since 1972 it is also a requirement to label a product clearly, so that the buyer can see where the product was made.

Tramliner A specialist clipper with a tapered, narrow blade for detailing designs on hair.

Trichologist A 'hair and scalp doctor' or qualified person who specialises in hair and scalp problems. A trichologist diagnoses hair and scalp dysfunctions or conditions and prescribes remedial treatments or suitable courses of action for them.

Trichology The study and treatment of hair and its disease.

Trim (trimming hair) See reshape.

Ultraviolet radiation A form of sterilization.

Uniform layer cut This type of haircut has sections that are equal i.e. the same length throughout.

Universal indicator A solution that undergoes several colour changes over a wide rage of pH values.

Valid and invalid payment The differences between the honest and dishonest attempts for payment.

Virgin hair Hair that has not been chemically treated.

Wefts Long continuous strands of pre-coloured, pre-bonded hair that create a 'curtain' of hair that can be used to add to, or extend a client's own natural hair.

Wetting agent A chemical agent that allows a liquid to spread more easily across or into a surface by lowering the liquid's surface tension.

Workplace practices Any activities, procedures, use of materials or equipment and working techniques used in carrying out your job.

W/C Appointment abbreviation for wet cutting.

9-section wind A classic technique for perming that starts by sectioning and securing the hair into 9 predefined workable areas.

Index